Electronic Semiconductors

Electronic Semiconductors

Eberhard Spenke

Translated with additions by
D. A. Jenny, H. Kroemer, E. G. Ramberg, and A. H. Sommer
RCA Laboratories, Radio Corporation of America
Princeton, New Jersey

McGraw-Hill Book Company, Inc.
New York   Toronto   London
1958

ELECTRONIC SEMICONDUCTORS

Library of Congress Catalog Card Number: 57-8020

The German edition of Dr. Spenke's book was published under the title *Elektronische Halbleiter* by Springer-Verlag, Berlin-Goettingen-Heidelberg.

III

60225

THE MAPLE PRESS COMPANY, YORK, PA.

Translators' Note

This translation of the second German edition of Eberhard Spenke's "Elektronische Halbleiter" has been augmented by a section on junction capacitance (Chap. IV, §10), and a series of problems inserted at the end of every chapter. The problems not only serve to test the reader's familiarity with the contents of the preceding chapter, but challenge him to carry his studies beyond the limits of the text, eventually with the help of references to readily accessible sources. The more difficult problems have been marked with an asterisk.

An effort has been made to preserve Dr. Spenke's original approach as far as possible. However, American practice has been followed with respect to nomenclature and symbols wherever this has been possible without doing undue violence to the original text.

D. A. Jenny

H. Kroemer

E. G. Ramberg

A. H. Sommer

To

WALTER SCHOTTKY AND MAX STEENBECK

in admiration and friendship
this book is dedicated

Foreword

This introduction to semiconductor theory is the result of a series of lectures on the fundamentals of semiconductor physics, particularly as related to rectifier and transistor problems, which my friend and coworker E. Spenke has given at physical meetings and to groups of younger colleagues in industry. The reception of these lectures demonstrated that a need existed in Germany for an able introduction to these fundamentals, even in the presence of the well-known book by Shockley. The derivation of the important relationships from precisely defined basic concepts and assumptions, in a manner which is clear even to the beginner, was recognized as a particular advantage of Spenke's representation. Spenke's audience is spared the unpleasant sensation of being suspended in mid-air.

The present arrangement of these lectures exhibits these advantages in enhanced measure. Care has been taken also that Chaps. I to V make good individual reading for the young technically trained person who has a special interest in the specific problem covered. The first three chapters deal with subjects of importance to semiconductor theory in general (and hence also to thermionics, luminescence, and photoconductivity):

I. The Conduction Mechanism in Electronic Semiconductors
II. The Nature, Models, and Reactions of Impurities and Imperfections
III. The Hole

Other chapters supply the fundamentals for two fields of application:

IV. The Mechanism of Crystal Rectifiers
V. The Physical Mechanism of Crystal Amplifiers (Transistors)

Spenke's own contributions to the basic publications for Chap. IV are well known.

Whereas the first part of this book constitutes reading matter which should provide a firm basis for the treatment of the semiconductor problems which are of greatest practical importance even to the beginner with some orientation in general physics, the second part is intended primarily for more advanced students who wish to have a thorough understanding of the fundamentals for the first part and to share in the clarification of the many unsolved problems. It covers the following chapters:

VI. Approximation Methods in the Quantum Mechanics of the Hydrogen Molecule

VII. The Band Model

VIII. Fermi Statistics of the Electrons in a Crystal

IX. The Dynamic Approach to Imperfection Equilibria and the Inertia of Impurity Reactions

X. Boundary Layers in Semiconductors and Metal-Semiconductor Contacts

Unquestionably, good reviews of all these fields are available in books, particularly books published abroad; however, apart from Shockley's book, which treats transistor physics in particular, the reader is obliged to collect the fundamentals from a whole series of monographs, among which Bethe and Sommerfeld's classical article in Geiger and Scheel's "Handbuch der Physik" (vol. XXIV, part 2) may well take first place. However, this representation, in particular, is aimed primarily at the physics of electrons in a metal and provides an introduction which may be understood in detail only in combination with other articles from Geiger and Scheel's book. Furthermore, it lacks, of course, the new emphases and ideas which have colored semiconductor theory since 1931.

The thoroughness and realism of the author are a guarantee that, in this more advanced portion of the book, the existing limits to our knowledge are never obscured and that, at the same time, within these limits meaningful considerations and conclusions are derived and proved in reliable manner. The careful treatment of the acceleration of electrons in Chap. VII, §6, of the Zener effect in Chap. VII, §7 and §9, and of the statistics and kinetics of electrons as modified by electrostatic potentials in Chap. VIII are worthy of special mention. The last treatment also points out the significance of the Fermi potential for the current problems of diffusion theory and indicates its relationship with the general electrochemical potential of charged particles, whose gradient in the concentration and potential distribution replaces as driving force the field strength of the theory of homogeneous media. These concepts permit, in Chap. X, an unusually clear representation of the basis and development of the diffusion theory of metal-semiconductor boundary layers.

If I am to define the circle of readers for whom the reading of the second part may be useful, I am inclined to include, in addition to those who are active in this field in industrial research, all the younger scientists who may wish to have a part, both benefiting and contributing, in the solution of the preeminent semiconductor problems of our time. The manifold relationships of semiconductor physics to other fields demand the cooperation of theoretical and experimental physicists, of physical and inorganic chemists, of crystallographers and electrical engineers. I believe that all these specialists will find, in the second part of Spenke's book, representations which will extend their general knowledge of the semiconductor field in certain directions. Hence I trust that this treatment may have a stimulating effect on the advancement of theory and practice in this field as well, even though this cannot be the objective of a publication of this type.

It should be mentioned, finally, that Spenke's nomenclature follows closely international usage, so that the book should be easily readable for interested foreign workers, without the dreaded fruitless effort of a general transformation of symbols.

My best wishes speed the book on its way.

Pretzfeld, February, 1954

W. Schottky

Preface*

It was my privilege to take my first steps in the labyrinth of semi-conductor physics under the guidance of Walter Schottky who, in the preceding foreword, has so kindly outlined the circle of readers to whom this introduction to the physics of electronic semiconductors may be of value. Thus, the book is not addressed to experienced semi-conductor specialists, but to the "beginners" and the "more advanced." Hence it may be proper to enumerate some of the subjects and problems which are not treated in the present book even though they also belong to the fundamentals of electronic semiconductor physics. Among others, these are the problems in the forefront of present developments in the semiconductor field:

The attempts to pass beyond the current one-electron approximations by treating a solid really as a many-electron problem.

The theory of the mean free path with the difficult problem of energy and momentum transfer between conduction electrons and lattice.

Excitons and polarons, plasma interactions, and multiple collisions.

Conduction processes in an impurity conduction band, which may appear in highly doped semiconductors or at very low temperatures because, under these conditions, they are no longer overshadowed by the usual processes in the normal conduction band.

Semiconductor optics, the physics of phosphors, and the photoeffect.

Titanates, spinels, and ferrites.

Limiting frequencies in rectifiers and transistors.

The omission of all these interesting subjects naturally raises the question to what objectives and intentions of the author the treatment of these important problems has been sacrificed. The answer lies in the purely pedagogic purpose of the present book. Semiconductor electronics requires for its foundation primarily wave mechanics and statistics. However, crystallography, thermodynamics, and chemistry also have a share in it and, quite generally, "it is incredible what miserable quantities of thought and mathematics are needed to provide even the simplest tools for daily use in semiconductor physics" (from a conversation of W. Schottky with the author).

*To the first German edition.

xiii

The present Introduction aims to be of some help in this respect. Hence the author was not interested in the treatment of the above-mentioned practical problems but in the most easily understood, and yet precise, treatment of fundamental concepts and fundamental equations. Customarily, these are passed over more quickly in proportion as the questions hidden under a simple external form are more involved. The objectives and methods employed may be clarified by an example.

A whole section is devoted to an equation as simple as Eq. (IX.1.01)

$$\frac{dN_S}{dt} = -\frac{1}{\tau_{\text{rel}}} N_S$$

In the usual presentations, this equation is introduced without further justification, with at most a note to the effect that τ_{rel} is the mean life of particles of type S. The statistical problems related to the concept of mean life are omitted altogether, and the concepts of mean life, mean life expectation, and relaxation time are commonly not distinguished. While in the present book such specialized problems are not treated in detail, the reader is at least made aware of the existence of the problem.

A whole series of kind helpers must be thanked for their valuable assistance. First of all, some associates at Pretzfeld are to be mentioned, namely, Dr. Arnulf Hoffmann, Dr. Adolf Herlet, and Hubert Patalong. Every newly written chapter was discussed with them in detail, and the author is indebted to all of them for innumerable suggestions for improvements in the text and the figures. Professor Helmut Volz and Dr. Hermann Haken (University of Erlangen) helped with a detailed "translation" of Heisenberg's original paper on the hole into the language of "ordinary" wave mechanics. Dr. Hermann Haken has also carried out a series of calculations on which §11 of Chap. VII is based. With the aid of Dr. Dieter Pfirsch (University of Frankfurt a. M.) a remark of Hintenberger regarding the effective mass of an electron in a crystal was confirmed quantitatively; the result is to be found in Chap. III, §2, and in Chap. VII, §6. For the author and subject index I am also indebted to Mr. Patalong, who also bore the chief burden of proofreading, along with Dr. Otfried Madelung, Dr. Bernhard Seraphin, and Claus Freitag. In the preparation of the manuscript, the untiring effort of Miss Aurelie Bathelt was invaluable. My thanks are extended once again to all these kind helpers. Finally, it must not remain unmentioned that I would not have arrived at a successful conclusion without the enduring patience and the continuous encouragement of my wife.

Pretzfeld, November, 1954

Eberhard Spenke

Contents

Fundamentals of Semiconductor Physics

Appendixes

List of Symbols

a = lattice constant

a_0 = Bohr radius

$\mathbf{a}_1, \mathbf{a}_2, \mathbf{a}_3$ = axis vectors in a translation lattice

A = cross-sectional area of n-p-n transistor

A = acceptor

$A^\times$ = neutral acceptor

A^- = negatively charged acceptor

A = integration constant

$b = \mu_n/\mu_p$ = ratio of electron to hole mobility

$\mathbf{b}_1, \mathbf{b}_2, \mathbf{b}_3$ = axis vectors in reciprocal lattice

B = integration constant

C = conduction band

C_{stor} = storage capacity

C_{tr} = transition capacity

$\mathbf{c}$ = collector

D = donor

$D^\times$ — neutral donor

D^+ = positively charged donor

D = diffusion constant

D_n = diffusion constant of electrons

D_p = diffusion constant of holes

$\mathbf{D}$ = dielectric displacement

$e = 1.6 \cdot 10^{-19}$ coulomb $= 4.803 \cdot 10^{-10}$ cm$^{3/2}$ g$^{1/2}$ sec^{-1} = elementary charge

$-e$ = charge of electron

e $= 2.718 \ldots$ = Napierian base

$\mathbf{e}$ = emitter

E = crystal energy of an electron in a crystal (see Chap. X, §1)

E_A = electron energy at acceptor level

E_{at} = atomic eigenvalue

$E_{AV} = E_A - E_V$ = association (activation) energy of acceptors

E_C = electron energy at lower edge of conduction band

$E_{CD} = E_C - E_D$ = dissociation (activation) energy of donors

$E_{CV} = E_C - E_V$ = width of forbidden band

E_D = electron energy at donor level

E_F = electron energy at Fermi level

E_n = electron energy

E_p = hole energy

E_{pot} = potential energy

E_V = electron energy at upper edge of valence band

$\mathbf{E}$ = total energy of electron in a crystal (see Chap. X, §1)

$E_F^{(n)}$ = electrochemical potential of electrons

$E_F^{(p)}$ = electrochemical potential of holes

$\mathbf{E} = \{E_x, E_y, E_z\}$ = electric field strength

$\mathbf{E}_B$ = boundary field strength in a Schottky barrier layer

E_0 = field strength in filamentary transistor without injection

E_1 = incremental field strength due to injection

$f(E)$ = Fermi distribution function

f = frequency

$\mathbf{F} = \{F_x, F_y, F_z\}$ = external force

F = external force

g = rate of pair production

g = acceleration due to gravity

$\mathbf{g}$ = acceleration

$g_{11}, g_{12}, g_{21}, g_{22}$ = differential conductance values of n-p-n transistor

$\left. \begin{array}{l} G, G_{ll}, G_{lr}, G_{rl}, G_{rr} \\ G_{ll_n}, G_{ll_p}, G_{lr_n}, G_{rl_n}, G_{rr_n}, G_{rr_p} \end{array} \right\}$ = "conductances" of n-p-n transistor

G = number of cells along edge of fundamental domain

$G_{\text{I II}}$ = Galvani voltage between solids I and II

h = Planck constant

$\hbar = \dfrac{1}{2\pi} h$ = Dirac constant

$\mathbf{h} = h_1\mathbf{b}_1 + h_2\mathbf{b}_2 + h_3\mathbf{b}_3$ = vector in reciprocal lattice

$\mathbf{H} = \{H_x, H_y, H_z\}$ = magnetic field strength

$\mathbf{i}$ = current density

i_b = base current increment

i_c = collector current increment

i_{c_n} = electron component of collector current increment

i_{diff} = density of diffusion current

i_e = emitter current increment

i_{e_n} = electron component of emitter current increment

i_{field} = density of field current

i_{forw} = current density in forward direction

i_n = density of current component carried by electrons

i_p = density of current component carried by holes

i_{rev} = current density in reverse direction

i_S = density of saturation current in rectifier theory

i_{sat} = density of saturation current in electron emission of solids

i_{tot} = density of total current

I = current

I_b = base current

I_c = collector current

I_{c_n} = electron component of collector current

I_{c_p} = hole component of collector current

I_e = emitter current

I_{e_n} = electron component of emitter current

I_{e_p} = hole component of emitter current

$j = \sqrt{-1}$ = imaginary unit

k = Boltzmann constant

k = wave number

$\mathbf{k} = \{k_x, k_y, k_z\}$ = wave number vector

K = mass-action constant

K_A = mass-action constant of acceptors

K_D = mass-action constant of donors

l = mean free path

l = thickness of barrier layer (Chap. IV, §4 and §5)

L_c = distance between collector and emitter in filamentary transistor

L_n = diffusion length of electrons

L_p = diffusion length of holes

m = electron mass

m_{eff} = effective mass

m_n = effective mass of electrons

m_p = effective mass of holes

M = mass

$\boldsymbol{M}$ = dipole moment

n = principal quantum number

n = electron concentration

n_A = total acceptor concentration

$n_{A\times}$ = concentration of neutral acceptors

n_{A^-} = concentration of negative acceptors

n_D = total donor concentration

$n_{D\times}$ = concentration of neutral donors

n_{D^+} = concentration of positive donors

n_S = neutrality concentration at the semiconductor end of Schottky barrier layer

n_i = intrinsic (inversion) density

n_n = electron concentration on n side of p-n junction

n_p = electron concentration on p side of p-n junction

n_B = concentration at metal boundary of Schottky barrier layer

$n_\ominus$ = electron concentration

$n_\oplus$ = hole concentration

n_0 = electron concentration in filamentary transistor *without* injection

n_1 = incremental electron density in filamentary transistor due to injection

N = band number

N = number of particles, number of particles of a selected group

N_C = effective density of states in conduction band

N_V = effective density of states in valence band

p = hole concentration

p_S = neutrality concentration of holes at Schottky barrier layer

p_n = hole concentration on n side of p-n junction

p_p = hole concentration on p side of p-n junction

p_B = concentration of holes at boundary of Schottky barrier layer

p_1 = incremental hole density in filamentary transistor due to injection

$\mathbf{p}$ = momentum

Q = cross section

r = recombination coefficient

r_b = differential base resistance

$r_c = \dfrac{L_c}{e\mu_n n_0 Q}$ = unmodulated collector resistance

r_e = differential emitter resistance

$r_{11}, r_{12}, r_{21}, r_{22}$ = differential resistance values of network or of transistor

R = radius

R_b = internal base resistance of point-contact transistor (see Figs. V.4.4 and V.4.5)

R_B = spreading resistance of rectifier

R_{diff} = differential resistance

R_K = external feedback resistance

R_L = load resistance

R_0 = zero-bias resistance of rectifier

s = density of particle current

S = distance between emitter and collector in point-contact transistor

t = time

t_{tr} = transit time

T = absolute temperature

T_{relax} = $\varepsilon/4\pi\sigma$ = dielectric relaxation time of solid

u_c = collector-voltage increment

u_e = emitter-voltage increment

u_L = voltage increment across load resistance R_L

U = terminal voltage

U_c = collector voltage

U_e = emitter voltage

U_{forw} = terminal voltage in forward direction

$U(\mathbf{r})$ = lattice potential

U_{rev} = terminal voltage in reverse direction

$U(x)$ = lattice potential (one-dimensional)

v = velocity

v_{drift} = drift velocity

v_{th} = thermal velocity

$\mathbf{v}$ = $\{v_x, v_y, v_z\}$ = velocity

V = volume

V = valence band

V = electrostatic potential

V_D – diffusion voltage

V_{fund} = fundamental domain of crystal

$\mathbf{V}$ = kT/e = volt equivalent of temperature

W = width of p layer in n-p-n transistor

x_b, x_e, x_c = space coordinates in Fig. V.3.4

Z = atomic number

Z_{eff} = effective atomic number

α = $\alpha_i\beta\gamma$ = current amplification factor

α_e = $(1 + b)\beta\gamma$ = equivalent current amplification

α_i = inherent (true) current amplification

β = transport factor

γ = injection efficiency

γ_c = collection efficiency

γ_e = emitter injection efficiency

∂ = partial derivative

ε = dielectric constant

$\zeta(n/\mathbf{N})$ = special function (see p. 384)

Θ_n = Hall angle of electrons

Θ_p = Hall angle of holes

λ = wavelength

μ_n = electron mobility

μ_p = hole mobility

ρ = space-charge density

σ = conductivity

σ_{coll} = collision cross section

σ_{D^+} = effective cross section of donors

σ_i = intrinsic conductivity

τ = mean free time

τ = lifetime

$\tau_{D^\times}$ = lifetime of neutral donors

τ_{D^+} = lifetime of positively charged donors

τ_n = electron lifetime in p-type conductor

τ_p = hole lifetime in n-type conductor

τ_{rel} = relaxation time of assembly of particles, of current, etc.

$\psi = \psi(\mathbf{r}; \mathbf{k})$ = eigenfunction

$\psi = \psi(\mathbf{r}, t)$ = time-dependent wave function

ψ_{at} = atomic eigenfunction

Ψ = work function

Ψ_{met} = work function of metal

Ψ_{sem} = work function of semiconductor

$\Psi_{\text{met sem}}$ = work function from metal to semiconductor

$\Psi_{\text{met vac}}$ = work function from metal to vacuum

$\Psi_{\text{met sem}}^{(n)}$ = electron work function (see p. 358)

$\Psi_{\text{met sem}}^{(p)}$ = hole work function (see p. 362)

Ψ_{I} or Ψ_{II} = work function of metal I or II

$\omega = 2\pi f$ = angular frequency

$\ominus$ = conduction electron

$\oplus$ = hole

$\bullet(\ \ )$ = substitutional imperfection (see Fig. II.4.2)

$\bigcirc$ = interstitial lattice position (see Fig. II.4.2)

$\square$ = vacancy (see Fig. II.4.2)

$\times$ = neutral

$\cdot$ = singly positively charged

$\cdot\cdot$ = doubly positively charged

$'$ = singly negatively charged

$''$ = doubly negatively charged

Electronic Semiconductors

The Conduction Mechanism
of Electronic Semiconductors
and the Physics
of Rectifiers and Transistors

CHAPTER I

The Conduction Mechanism in Electronic Semiconductors

§1. Introduction

The semiconductors, among the crystalline solids, conduct an electrical current better than insulators but not so well as metals. Accordingly, their conductivity range at room temperature extends from 10^{-12} ohm^{-1} cm^{-1} to 10^4 ohm^{-1} cm^{-1}. These limits are drawn somewhat arbitrarily, and it will be shown that there is no fundamental difference between insulators and semiconductors. It cannot be decided at the present stage of development whether there is a physically meaningful border line between metals and semiconductors.[1] The extreme sensitivity of the electrical resistivity to various factors, particularly the "chemical composition," is a characteristic property of semiconductors.

The significance of the chemical composition in semiconductor physics goes far beyond the previous usage of this term in chemistry. The chemical difference between two bodies means, to the unbiased reader, the difference, for instance, between cupric oxide (CuO) and cuprous oxide (Cu_2O). The semiconductor physicist, on the other hand, compares two samples by the magnitude of their electrical resistivity, whereby variations of a fraction of a per cent in the oxygen content can be of decisive significance. Minute deviations from the stoichiometric composition (of the order of 10^{-4}) may manifest themselves in the electrical resistivity by changes of several orders of mag-

---

[1] The negative temperature coefficient of the electrical resistivity, i.e., the fact that many semiconductors are better conductors at high temperatures than at low temperatures, is often used to define a semiconductor. The existence of substances such as niobium hydride and nitride, which are "low-temperature conductors," speaks against the validity of this definition, for they are superconductors with surprisingly high transition temperatures. On the other hand, they can hardly be called metals and must therefore be classified among the semiconductors, although they are not true "high-temperature conductors." A substantial number of substances fall in this group, such as CuS and the borides, carbides, and nitrides of zirconium, hafnium, titanium, vanadium, and tantalum.

nitude (possibly 10^4).[1] Similarly, a minute amount of a foreign substance, such as a chlorine content of the order of 10^{-4} in selenium (1 chlorine atom per 10^4 selenium atoms), can influence the electrical resistivity decisively. This is the reason why in semiconductor physics a difference between, for instance, selenium with an addition of 10^{-4} chlorine and 10^{-5} chlorine is called a "chemical difference," although both are essentially selenium and the only distinction lies in the minute amount of added foreign substance.

Other factors which can influence the resistivity appreciably shall be listed briefly; some of the meanings may be understood only by the reader who is already somewhat familiar with the semiconductor field: (1) The previous history of the material, particularly the thermal treatment in certain atmospheres. (2) The fine or coarse polycrystallinity or single crystallinity of the material, as well as possible predominant crystal directions and textures. (3) Possible deviations from the chemical homogeneity of the material, where "chemical" is to be understood in the foregoing sense as applied to semiconductor physics. This is particularly applicable to the neighborhood of crystal grain boundaries, where a certain lattice distortion can favor vacancies, interstitials, and precipitation of foreign atoms.[2] (4) Microscopic and colloidal precipitation of dissimilar phases (in the metallurgical sense), which can form metallic conductivity bridges or insulating layers. (5) The surface structure of the entire sample or the single crystallites can affect the resistance appreciably because of space-charge barriers with polarized characteristics. (6) The surrounding atmosphere can affect the properties, particularly at high temperatures. (7) The resistivity of a semiconductor is often highly temperature dependent. (8) The magnitude of the electrical field during measurements influences the semiconductor properties in many cases.

In view of the great number of effective parameters, it is not surprising that the field of semiconductor physics is characterized by a multitude of confusing phenomena and apparently contradictory observations. For many years one had to be satisfied with the observation and analysis of "order-of-magnitude effects" in the semiconductor field. Few physicists appreciate this type of research, which led to the bad reputation of semiconductor physics as the "physics of dirt effects." In spite of this reputation, an ever-increasing number of scientists have become interested in this field over the years. One

---

[1] The same sensitivity can be found in the optical absorption, so that the appearance of a substance may be changed drastically by, for instance, heating in the vapor of one of the components: for example, copper iodide, alkali halides.

[2] See Chap. II, The Nature, Models, and Reactions of Impurities and Imperfections.

reason was the application of the methods of wave mechanics to the giant crystal molecule in the late 1920s, which gave a great boost to solid-state physics and along with it to semiconductor physics. Furthermore, the continuously increasing technical importance of semiconductors as well as economic reasons demanded intensive research and development.[1] We shall name a few examples: thermistors, electrolytic capacitors, crystal rectifiers and detectors, transistors, oxide cathodes, overvoltage regulators and varistors of SiC, photovoltaic cells.

Even in technical problems apparently not related to electrical conduction, the principles of semiconductor physics are of decisive importance, as for instance: luminescent screens for cathode rays and X-rays, the photographic exposure and development process, the protection of metals against corrosion by various atmospheres, corrosion-resistant alloys.

Finally, after the Second World War, a prototype substance was found in the form of germanium, in which the complications do not seem to be insurmountable and it is possible to progress beyond order-of-magnitude relations toward a number of theoretically derived formulas which are accessible to quantitative verification by experiment. This is the reason why, in the following chapters, we shall always emphasize germanium and its properties rather than discuss the extensive research on other materials.

The entire field which might fall within the realm of this book has become so large that certain restrictions are unavoidable. We shall not deal with materials or mechanisms which involve primarily ionic conduction. Problems of cohesion and the magnetic semiconductors, the so-called ferrites, have to be left out. Nor shall we consider optical effects in detail; therefore we can eliminate the extensive subject of phosphors. But we shall treat the *conduction* mechanism of *electronic* semiconductors within the framework of the *band model* to which this first chapter is devoted.

§2. The Band Model

a. The One-electron Approximations of Solid-state Physics: The Atomistic Picture and the Band Model[2]

The formation of a crystal takes place when many atoms are arranged in a systematic manner to form a single giant molecule.

---

[1] However, one must not underestimate the driving force of scientific curiosity which does not tolerate the ever-increasing use of devices in practical applications without an understanding of the fundamental mechanisms involved.

[2] See also Chaps. VI and VII.

Hence the two models of solid-state theory, namely, the atomistic picture on one hand and the band model on the other, correspond to the two approximations of molecular physics which are the "method of atomic eigenfunctions" (Heitler-London) and the "collective treatment" or the "method of the molecular eigenfunctions" (Hund and Mulliken). The Heitler-London method uses the limiting case of widely spaced complete atoms as a starting point and considers the mutual interaction only as a perturbation. According to this concept, an electron belongs to a specific nucleus and its behavior is modified only by the presence of the surrounding atoms. In solid-state physics this approximation corresponds with the atomistic picture where the electrons are assigned to single lattice points—ions, atoms, or molecules (Fig. I.2.1). Their behavior differs from that in an isolated atom only inasmuch as it is modified by, for instance, a polarizable environment with a dielectric constant $\varepsilon \neq 1$. The atomistic picture is particularly useful in the treatment of problems where the electrons in the inner shells of the lattice atoms play an important part, such as in the emission and absorption of X-rays. The atomistic picture is indispensable for the theory of ferromagnetism and cohesion, and it is very valuable for the treatment of crystals with pronounced ionic character such as the

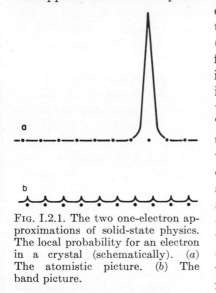

Fig. I.2.1. The two one-electron approximations of solid-state physics. The local probability for an electron in a crystal (schematically). (a) The atomistic picture. (b) The band picture.

alkali halides. Although it allows very plausible qualitative statements about the conductivity problem, the quantitative treatment must be left to the band model, which, as pointed out previously, is based on the approximation of Hund and Mulliken in molecular physics. The starting point in this case is the opposite extreme of the Heitler-London method, namely, very close-spaced nuclei. This limiting case does not allow the assignment of an electron to a single nucleus, for it is affected continuously by the force field of all the surrounding nuclei. In this method, the mutual interaction between the different electrons is treated as a small perturbation. Besides the obvious treatment by a perturbation calculation of higher order, it is possible to apply a first-order treatment by introducing screening factors for the field of the nuclei which act on the electron under consideration.

The screening factors are a consequence of the charge of the surrounding electrons. In solid-state physics, this procedure is represented by the band model where a particular electron is affected by the field of *all* lattice points rather than just one (Fig. I.2.1). In the band model, the interaction between the electron under consideration and the other electrons is taken into account in the form of a modification of the nuclear potential caused by the charge of the surrounding electrons.

As in the case of the atomistic picture, this is essentially a one-electron approximation because the energy levels of a single electron are determined in a given fixed force field. The transition to the many-electron problem lies not in the introduction of an interaction between electrons, but simply in filling the energy levels of the one-electron problem with all the electrons which must be accommodated in the crystal. The occupancy of the energy levels follows the principles of the Fermi statistics, whereby a certain rough consideration for electron-electron interaction is given in the form of the Pauli exclusion principle.

b. The Band Model

If one asks for the energy-level diagram which forms the basis for the band model, one recognizes that the name "band model" is in itself the answer to the question: The energy-level diagram of the stationary allowed energies shows a bandlike division into alternating "allowed" and "forbidden" energy ranges. This can be demonstrated satisfactorily with a purely conceptual approach without resorting to mathematical methods:

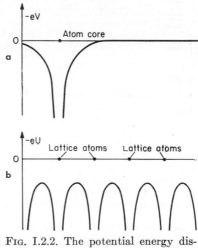

FIG. I.2.2. The potential energy distribution of an electron (a) in a single atom and (b) in the lattice of ordered atoms.

An electron in a crystal[1] is not in the force field of a single atom, but rather in the periodic[2] potential field of many uniformly distributed atoms (Fig. I.2.2). The discrete eigenvalues of the electron energy[3] in

[1] We speak of an "electron in a crystal" when we want to emphasize that an electron is not *free*, but is exposed to the strong lattice forces which lead to a more or less strong binding to the crystal.

[2] This is a hypothesis. See p. 163.

[3] As usual, this is the sum of kinetic energy and potential energy, the latter being

the single atom are multiply degenerate because of the spatial accumulation of many atoms in the crystal (Fig. I.2.3). Many different eigenfunctions are associated with one and the same atom eigenvalue; they are always grouped in the same manner around a different lattice point. Because of the exchange interaction, each atom eigenvalue is split into a multitude of quasi-continuous bandlike energy eigenvalues. The splitting becomes more pronounced as the atoms approach each other more closely, and therefore the exchange interaction increases.

Besides this method, quantitatively treated by Bloch[1] to obtain the band spectrum of a crystal, it is possible to start from the wave nature of the electron according to Brillouin.[1] In this case it is understandable that at certain wavelengths and propagation directions an electron

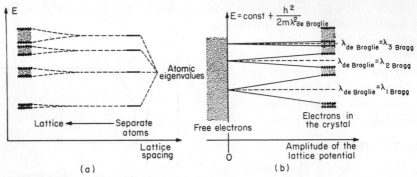

Fig. I.2.3. The band model of the energy terms. (a) The splitting of the *allowed* bands from the atomic eigenvalues upon spatial approximation of initially separated atoms (Bloch approximation). (b) The splitting of the *forbidden* bands from the continuous spectrum of free electrons upon increasing the amplitude of the periodic lattice potential (Brillouin approximation).

wave can encounter Bragg reflections similar to those of X-rays. This means that for certain electron waves a reflected wave is formed because of interference with the lattice, which has the same wavelength and therefore, according to de Broglie, the same electron energy and hence is degenerate with the incident wave. The degeneracy is canceled by splitting of the common energy eigenvalue because of the interaction with the periodic lattice potential in space. This splitting becomes more pronounced as the amplitude of the lattice potential increases. The Bloch treatment demonstrates the splitting of the discrete atomic levels into the *allowed* bands, whereas the Brillouin

caused by the force field of the nucleus. We avoid the expression "total energy," because we shall see in Chap. X that in some solid state problems an electrostatic energy contribution must be considered, which stems from an electrostatic macropotential, see p. 338.

[1] See Chap. VII, §2 and §3.

treatment shows the splitting of an originally continuous energy spectrum of free electron waves into the *forbidden bands*.

If an electron has a sharply defined energy which corresponds to one of the described levels of the strictly periodic ideal lattice, it is represented by a similar eigenfunction as that of a free electron, hence with a plane wave:

$$\psi(x; k) = A\,e^{jkx} \qquad k = \frac{2\pi}{\lambda} = \text{wave number} \qquad (I.2.01)$$

The eigenfunction of an electron in a crystal differs from that of a free electron by a modulation of the wave amplitude due to the periodic lattice potential:

$$\psi(x; k) = u(x; k) \cdot e^{jkx} \qquad\qquad (I.2.02)$$
$$u(x; k) = \text{periodic with the lattice period}$$

The absolute square $u(x; k)^2$ of the wave amplitude $u(x; k)$ gives the probability of the presence of the electron, so that in the case of a

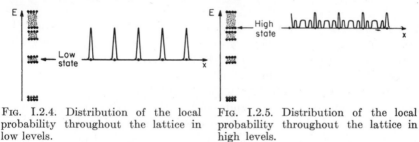

FIG. I.2.4. Distribution of the local probability throughout the lattice in low levels.

FIG. I.2.5. Distribution of the local probability throughout the lattice in high levels.

sharply defined energy the probability of the presence of the electron is the same for all lattice cells. If the sharply defined energy value of an electron lies in a *deep*[1] level (Fig. I.2.4), the probability of finding the electron near a lattice point[2] is appreciably higher than for locations between two lattice points, but these fluctuations are repeated from cell to cell throughout the entire lattice in a periodic manner, so that the electron cannot be assigned preferentially to a single lattice point. If the electron is in a *high*[3] level (Fig. I.2.5), the probability does not vary as much between lattice points and intermediate locations, and the electron is rather evenly "smeared out" throughout the entire lattice. Through formation of wave packets it is possible to attain a

---

[1] Such a level belongs to a band which results from the splitting of one of the deep atom eigenvalues and therefore belongs to one of the *inner* shells.

[2] "Lattice point" refers to the position of a lattice atom, ion, or molecule in the crystal.

[3] This level corresponds with the outer shell of a lattice point.

more or less sharp localization of the electron, but only by combining several neighboring levels so that an accurately defined energy value has to be abandoned. Even so, an important property of these eigenfunctions of the band model is not sacrificed: All these functions represent an electron which moves unhindered and uniformly through the lattice, so that one is tempted to call it a free electron. The Brillouin picture points even more strongly to the existence of free electrons; for only at certain energy values is the electron prevented by Bragg reflection from propagating through the lattice, so that avoiding these forbidden energy values ought to result in a free electron. The fact that this is not entirely true is best demonstrated by studying the behavior of an electron in a crystal under the influence of an external force such as an electric field.[1]

For this purpose an effective mass m_{eff} is defined by the following equation:

$$\mathbf{F} = m_{eff} \cdot \frac{d\mathbf{v}}{dt} \tag{I.2.03}$$

$\mathbf{v}$ = velocity of the crystal electron. It is not surprising that the values for m_{eff} derived from this defining equation are very peculiar because the interaction between electron and crystal has been completely ignored. m_{eff} values which are higher than the free electron mass m are acceptable for narrow bands with little splitting and appear even plausible, for narrow bands with little splitting indicate strong binding of the electrons to the lattice points, and it is entirely reasonable that this leads by way of a large effective mass to sluggish electrons. The dependence of the value of m_{eff} on the exact energetic location of the electron in its energy band is less understandable. The most surprising fact is at first that m_{eff} is negative in the upper part of a band.

How this comes about because of the neglected lattice forces in the defining equation (I.2.03) may be more easily understood from the following considerations. We start with the assumption that the velocity of the electron $\mathbf{v}$ and the external force $\mathbf{F}$ have the same direction, so that the external force $\mathbf{F}$ acts on the electron by increasing its energy. This raises the electron in the band diagram of Fig. I.2.3 so that it approaches finally the upper edge of the allowed band in which it was located at the beginning of the process. The more the electron approaches the band edge, the more the condition for Bragg reflection is fulfilled, and the lattice reflects more of the incident wave in the form of a reflected wave. At the upper band edge, the condition of

[1] See Chap. VII, §6.

equality of incident and reflected wave results in a standing electron wave, and the velocity **v** of the electron has become zero. During this entire process, the force **F** and the electron velocity **v** have had the same direction, so that the electron mass must be considered negative in order to explain zero velocity, if one ignores the actual cause, namely, the Bragg reflection of the lattice.

The foregoing may have aided the reader to gain a conceptual understanding for the negative values of the effective mass, and we can proceed to the deductions derived from this surprising result.

c. The Band Model and Conductivity Problems

In a solid, an electric current is carried by more than just one electron. Therefore, in order to treat conductivity problems, it is necessary to fill the band diagram of energy levels, which was developed in the previous section, with many electrons in a crystal, as was implied at the end of section *a*. The Pauli principle restricts the number of electrons which can occupy each single energy level to two electrons with opposite spin. The available electrons in a crystal can thus fill the energy diagram from the bottom up to a certain limit, above which the diagram remains empty according to the foregoing principles. The transition from the filled levels to the empty ones is very gradual at high temperatures and becomes more abrupt at lower temperatures until the limit of absolute zero is approached $(T \rightarrow 0)$, where the transition is discontinuous. This transition is governed by the Fermi statistics, from which the expression "Fermi level" for the dividing line between filled and empty levels originates.

Below the Fermi level, one or more bands are completely filled with electrons. It can be shown that these bands do not contribute to the current; for the electrons in the lower part of the band have a positive effective mass and are accelerated in the direction of the external force, whereas the effective electron mass in the upper part of the band is negative, which results in an acceleration in the opposite direction. Their respective contributions to the current cancel exactly as the accurate calculation shows:[1] *A filled band does not contribute to the conductivity*.

The deep lying bands, corresponding to the inner electron shells of the free atoms, are the ones which are filled and do not contribute to the conductivity. From this standpoint, the objectionable result of negative effective masses in the upper part of a band leads to a reasonable result: The electrons of the inner shells do not play a part in the conduction process. One can consider them as bound electrons which,

[1] See pp. 262 to 263, 264, and 267.

for the consideration of conductivity problems, form an "atom core" together with the nucleus itself. The internal structure of this atom core is, in *this* connection, as uninteresting as the structure of the nucleus itself. The conduction of the current and similar transport phenomena depend entirely on the outer electrons of the lattice atoms.

This leads to a natural classification of the solids into insulators and metals (Fig. I.2.6). If the number of electrons to be placed in the energy diagram is such that a series of deep bands are just filled and no electrons are left over for the higher bands, the crystal is an insulator; for all the completely filled bands do not contribute to the conductivity. A conductor, namely a metal, therefore must have a partially filled uppermost band, for instance, a half-filled band.[1]

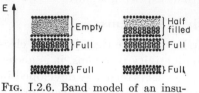

FIG. I.2.6. Band model of an insulator and a metal.

The behavior of the *conduction electrons* in such a partially filled *conduction band* of a metal is actually extremely complicated. The effective mass is not the same for all conduction electrons, but depends entirely on the particular location the electron occupies in the energy band at any one time. Besides, the effective mass is not isotropic, but is rather described by a tensor in any crystal system (even in symmetrical ones), so that force and acceleration of the electron are in general not in the same or exactly opposite directions but at an angle with each other. If the crystal system is not symmetrical, further complications set in. In the theoretical treatment of conductivity problems, these difficulties are removed through simplifying assumptions about the distribution of energy levels within the conduction band. This approach allows the treatment of the conduction electrons as if they formed a free Fermi gas with a potential energy which corresponds to the lower edge of the conduction band.[2]

The electrons in such a gas are never at rest. The kinetic theory of heat teaches that each electron is continuously moving in a zigzag path (Fig. I.2.7). The straight portions of such a zigzag path are called "free path l," and the time required to complete a free path is called "free time τ." The velocities of the electron during the free time, while on the free path, are distributed statistically around the "mean thermal velocity." At the end of the free path, the electron collides with a col-

[1] The actual application of these criteria, for instance, to the elements of the periodic table, meets considerable difficulties which are, at present, by no means solved. See Chap. VII, §11.

[2] See p. 299.

lision partner, which we shall now discuss in detail. The collision itself requires an extremely short time compared with the free time and can be considered a quasi-discontinuous change in the velocity of the electron. The collision partners are characteristically different from those in an ordinary gas of, for instance, H_2 molecules. In such a gas the H_2 molecules collide *with each other*, whereas in a Fermi gas the conduction electrons collide with *foreign* collision partners. These collision partners are of a peculiar nature. We saw in section *b* that in a lattice of ideal regularity an electron, because of its wave nature, does not in general[1] encounter any resistance and can therefore traverse paths of arbitrary length without any disturbance, scattering, or deflection. This ceases to be true as soon as the regularity of the lattice is disturbed in any way, which is unavoidable at finite temperatures because of the thermal motion of the lattice atoms.

FIG. I.2.7. The path of an electron with the assumption of a uniform mean free path *without* external force.

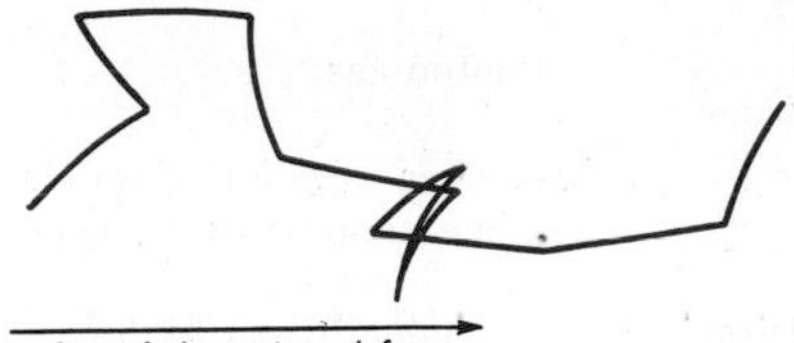

Direction of the external force

FIG. I.2.8. Same as Fig. I.2.7 but *with* external force.

At present, we can tentatively state that the conduction electrons are scattered by the thermal expansions and compressions of the lattice. In the theoretical treatment of the problem of interaction between the electron in the crystal and the self-oscillation of the lattice, these thermal density changes of the lattice are treated as a superposition of elastic and acoustical self-oscillations of the lattice.

However, this obvious picture of a "collision" requires a particle as a collision partner. According to the quantum laws, the interaction between electrons and the elastic and acoustical oscillations of a solid can be interpreted as collisions between electrons and "phonons." Most physicists, however, are more familiar with photons than with phonons, so that Fig. I.2.9 will be helpful as a schematic of notations where the concept of the phonon is compared with the corresponding well-known photon concept.

In this schematic, we see that the quantum expression $nh\nu$ for the energy of an oscillator leads to the Planck radiation equation, if the

[1] Unless its wavelength happens to correspond with a Bragg reflection.

oscillators represent the electromagnetic eigenoscillations of a cavity with perfectly reflecting walls.[1] For the phonon, the same quantum law results in the Einstein-Debye theory of the specific heat of solids,[2,3] if the oscillators represent the elastic self-oscillations of a solid. The next step on the "electromagnetic" side of the schematic is the interpretation of the cavity radiation as a photon gas.[4,5] The equivalent

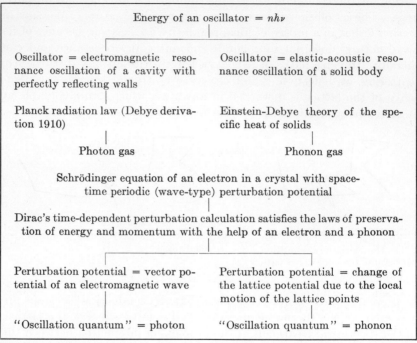

FIG. I.2.9. Schematic table of the chronological and the physical development of the "phonon" concept.

step on the "elastic" side of the schematic of notation interprets the thermal oscillations of the solid as a "phonon" gas[6] with Bose statistics.

If we calculate the interaction between an electron in the crystal and an electromagnetic wave,[7] we find that this electron is described by a Schrödinger equation with a periodic crystal potential of the lattice in

[1] P. Debye, *Ann. Physik*, **33**: 1427 (1910).

[2] A. Einstein, *Ann. Physik*, **22**: 180 (1907).

[3] P. Debye, *Ann. Physik*, **39**: 789 (1912).

[4] A. Einstein, *Ann. Physik*, **17**: 132 (1905).

[5] S. N. Bose, *Z. Physik*, **26**: 178 (1924).

[6] L. Nordheim, *Ann. Physik*, **9**: 607 (1931).   A. H. Wilson, *Proc. Roy. Soc. (London)*, **133**: 458 (1931).

[7] See, for instance, Chap. VII, §8.

which the classically introduced (vector) potential of the light wave occurs as perturbation. The result can be interpreted as a collision between the electron in a crystal and a light quantum, although only the electron is introduced in the quantized form (Schrödinger equation), whereas the electromagnetic wave is used with its classical vector potential in the Schrödinger equation.

Similarly, the mathematical treatment of the interaction of an electron in a crystal and an elastic lattice wave leads also to a Schrödinger equation with a space periodic lattice potential and a space and time periodic perturbation potential of the lattice wave.[1] Although the expression for the lattice wave does not represent the quantized properties, the result can be interpreted as a collision between lattice electron and phonon. This pure particle interpretation is, in both cases, only possible on a historical basis, which is indicated by the first few lines of the schematic.

Besides these thermally determined phonons, a real lattice contains other deviations from strictly ideal periodicity, because of deviations from the ideal structure. For instance, atoms may be missing at certain lattice points (vacancies), or atoms can be misplaced in the wrong lattice points or be placed interstitially, or foreign atoms can be incorporated which are not part of the ideal lattice. All these atomic "imperfections" act as scattering centers or collision partners like the phonons.

Up to this point, we have treated the behavior of the Fermi gas of the conduction electrons in thermal equilibrium. Finally, we want to treat the Fermi gas under the influence of an externally applied electric field, so that a current is flowing. The previously straight paths between two collision processes are now bent into parabolas because of the continuous action of the external force field (Fig. I.2.8). All the electrons receive during each free path an additional velocity in the direction of the external force, so that the entire thermally agitated electron cloud is drifting slowly in this direction. Thus an electric current is created. As long as the drift velocities due to the external force are small compared to the mean thermal velocity, the drift velocity $\mathbf{v}$ is proportional[2] to the field strength $\mathbf{E}$:

$$\mathbf{v} = \mu_n \mathbf{E} \tag{I.2.04}$$

The factor μ_n is called the *mobility* of the negative electrons.[3]   Ohm's

---

[1] F. Bloch, Z. Physik, **52**: 555 (1929), particularly pp. 578ff.

[2] See, for instance pp. 244 to 246.

[3] In contrast to the corresponding mobility μ_p of the positive holes (defect electrons or missing electrons) which will be introduced later (see pp. 16 to 19 and 27).

law applies in this case

$$i = \sigma E \qquad (I.2.05)$$

where the conductivity is given by

$$\sigma = e\mu_n n \qquad (I.2.06)$$

n = concentration of the negative electrons.

An example of the opposite case is that of the cathode-to-anode current in a vacuum diode, where the electrons do not find collision partners because of the vacuum and therefore fall down the potential slope in one single free path, so that the motion of all electrons is essentially the same. There is obviously no linear, i.e., ohmic, relation between anode voltage and anode current; instead the laws of the thermal, space-charge limited, and saturation regions are valid.

§3. The Band Model of a Semiconductor

We have seen in §2, section c, that a completely filled band does not contribute to the conductivity and that a crystal with only filled bands is an insulator. The band model of an insulator shows that the uppermost filled band is followed by a forbidden band, which in turn is

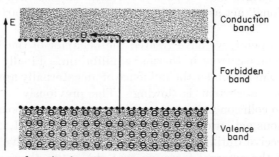

Fig. I.3.1. Thermal excitation of a valence electron into the conduction band.

followed by an allowed but empty band. Such a distribution of the electrons in the band diagram is, strictly speaking, possible only at the temperature $T = 0°K$, even if exactly the right number of electrons are present just to fill completely the last occupied band. At any finite temperature $T > 0$, a fraction of the electrons from the last "filled" band are thermally excited or raised into the next higher "empty" band above the intermediate forbidden band (Fig. I.3.1). The electrons which are raised into the empty band represent, according to the principles of section c of §2, the gas[1] of the conduction electrons and

[1] See pp. 299 and 306.

cause a certain amount of conductivity. Whether this effect is real and experimentally observable depends on one hand on the temperature and on the other on the width of the forbidden band. The smaller the width of the forbidden band, the smaller the energy for thermal excitation and therefore the lower the temperature at which the effect is observed. Wilson[1] has pointed out in his work that the thermal excitation of a fraction of the electrons from the band below the conduction band leaves this originally filled band only partially occupied, so that its contribution to the current is no longer zero. Therefore the electrons of this band carry a certain current which is added to the current of the conduction electrons. It is found that this current of the nearly filled band is of the same magnitude as if one assumed, in place of the holes in the filled band, positive electrons with positive effective mass but no other current carriers. The fact that this concept has proved valid in the interpretation of the sign of the Hall effect and the thermoelectric effect and in the rectification direction of metal semiconductor contacts has led to the introduction of the term "hole" (or defect-electron) conduction.

Many years after the work of Wilson, it was still uncertain whether the described conduction mechanism of a semiconductor is actually realized in one of the known semiconductors. It was shown only toward the end of the Second World War, almost simultaneously in Germany[2] and the United States,[3] that the current transport in germanium above 150°C is of the type just described. It is now necessary to supplement the somewhat abstract description of the "last completely filled band" and the "conduction band" with more concrete concepts, for which we elect germanium as the example. The germanium lattice has a diamond-type structure, where each atom is surrounded by four neighbors (Fig. I.3.2). The binding of these four neighbors consists of four electron-pair bonds as we know them for the homopolar binding of the hydrogen molecule. The bonds consist of the four valence electrons of the germanium atom under consideration together with one of the valence electrons from each of the four neighboring atoms to which the bond leads. We see that the diamond lattice points are occupied by Ge^{+4} ions and that the four valence electrons per atom are located in the pair bond between the Ge^{+4} ions (Fig. I.3.3). The localized particle representation is the atomistic parallel to the band model, in which the four valence electrons of the germanium just fill a band, which is therefore called the "valence

[1] A. H. Wilson, *Proc. Roy. Soc. (London)*, **133**: 458 (1931).
[2] J. Stuke, Dissertation, Göttingen.
[3] K. Lark-Horovitz and V. A. Johnson, *Phys. Rev.*, **69**: 258 (1946).

band." The fact that the next higher band, the conduction band, is entirely empty to begin with corresponds in the atomistic picture accurately to the fact that all valence electrons are fixed in the pair bonds and therefore will not be available for the conduction process. In the case of thermal excitation, one or the other valence electron is separated from one of the pair bridges and becomes quasi-free to move through the lattice (Fig. I.3.4, upper left).[1] This corresponds in the band model to the thermal excitation of a valence electron from the upper edge of the valence band to the lower edge of the conduction band (Fig. I.3.4, upper right). Here we see again how the atomistic picture and the band model complement each other; that is, the band model teaches that the empty place among the valence electrons acts

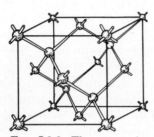

Fig. I.3.2. The germanium lattice.

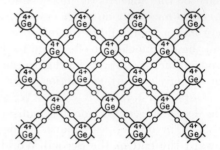

Fig. I.3.3. Two-dimensional representation of the germanium lattice.

as a hole $(+m, +e)$ if one considers the wave nature of the electrons, which means that the hole can migrate through the unperturbed lattice without encountering any resistance and therefore contributes an essentially equal part to the conductivity as the freed electron $(+m, -e)$ in the conduction band. The migration without resistance of a hole in the band model corresponds to the motion of the valence electrons into neighboring empty places without energy expenditure in the atomistic picture (see Fig. I.3.4, left side).

This conduction mechanism is called intrinsic conduction in contrast to extrinsic or impurity conduction. The existence of the latter conduction type has, for a long time, overshadowed the intrinsic conduction; this is still the case in most germanium samples below 150°C. In the previous paragraph we became briefly acquainted with the

---

[1] The presentation of the migration of the conduction electron on the right-hand side of Fig. I.3.4 assigns to the abscissa the significance of a spatial coordinate within the solid, whereas no significance was attributed to the abscissa in Figs. I.2.6 and I.3.1. See also pp. 21 and 22 in connection with Fig. I.3.6.

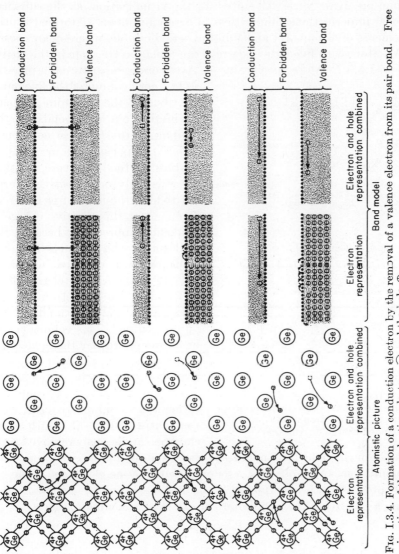

Fig. I.3.4. Formation of a conduction electron by the removal of a valence electron from its pair bond. Free migration of the conduction electron $\ominus$ and the hole $\oplus$.

imperfection as a collision partner of the conduction electrons. Now we shall treat an even more important function of these narrowly localized disorder points in the crystal lattices. The conditions in germanium are again very well suited for the visualization, as the substitutional imperfections (impurities) in germanium can be formed by the elements of Groups III and V in the periodic table, whereby an arsenic (As) atom with five outer electrons can replace a Ge atom in the lattice (Fig. I.3.5). More specifically an As^{5+} core is substituted in place of a Ge^{4+} core. Four of the five outer electrons of the As atom are used up in the four pair bonds for the binding to the four Ge neighbors, which compensates four positive charges of the As^{5+} core, so that there is only one positive charge left to bind the fifth outer electron. The field of this positive charge is weakened appreciably because the medium in which it acts is polarizable, with a dielectric constant $\varepsilon = 16$. Therefore the charge cloud of the fifth outer electron extends over a large volume around the impurity center. This condition can be approximated by the model of a single electron in the field of a positive charge, namely, a hydrogen atom, which is not in a vacuum but rather in a medium with a dielectric constant $\varepsilon = 16$. This fifth outer electron can be easily removed from the impurity and thus migrates away as a conduction electron: The impurity acts as a source or "donor" of conduction electrons. The entire process can be interpreted as the dissociation of a neutral donor $D^{\times}$ into a positively charged donor core D^{+} and a conduction electron $\ominus$:

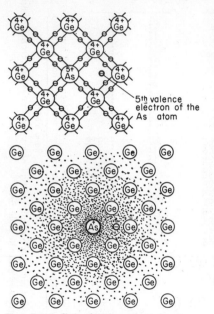

FIG. I.3.5. Substitution of an As atom for a Ge atom. Weak binding of the fifth valence electron in the form of an extended charge distribution.

$$D^{\times} \rightarrow D^{+} + \ominus \qquad (I.3.01)$$

The presence of such an impurity manifests itself in the band model through the lowering of one of the conduction-band levels of the unperturbed lattice into the forbidden band, so that the energy difference between the "impurity level" and the lower edge of the conduction band equals the dissociation energy of the donor. The donor is neutral if an electron is present in the impurity level; if the donor is ionized by, for instance, thermal excitation, the electron is raised from the impurity level to the conduction band. There is a fundamental difference concerning the character of the eigenfunction between the electrons in the impurity level and in the conduction band, besides the quantitative difference concerning the energy. The eigenfunctions of the conduction band are of the type of propagating waves, and the probability of finding the electron in a certain location is distributed evenly over all lattice cells, whereas the eigenfunction of the impurity level is concentrated around the donor in a hydrogen-like way. Even if the energy is sharply defined, the donor electron is strongly localized, whereas an electron in the conduction band can be localized only if the sharp energy fixation is sacrificed. In order to express this difference in the energy-level diagram, we shall introduce the abscissa in Fig.

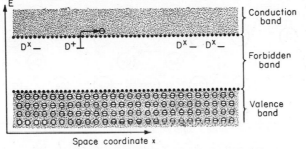

Fig. I.3.6. Band model with neutral and ionized donors.

I.3.6 as a spatial coordinate within the semiconductor under consideration. The levels of the unperturbed lattice are thus drawn throughout the entire body, which signifies that the probability of finding an electron in a certain place is evenly distributed over all lattice cells. The impurity levels of the donor, however, are drawn as short dashes near the particular impurity in order to signify the localized character of an electron in this energy level.

So much for the substitutional incorporation of elements of Group V and the corresponding donors. As mentioned previously, the elements of Group III of the periodic table can also be incorporated in germanium. If a Ge atom is replaced by an In atom (Fig. I.3.7), only three valence electrons are introduced, so that one valence electron is missing in the four pair bonds to the four Ge neighbors. This vacancy can easily be filled by a valence electron from one of the neighboring bonds. The process of completing an incomplete pair bond from a neighboring complete pair bond by the motion of a valence electron allows the vacancy, or what we now call the hole, to move in the lattice.[1]   The In atom remains in its original place and has now acquired an electron in addition to its original three valence electrons so that it is negatively charged.   This is an example of an impurity which accepts an additional electron and is therefore called an "acceptor."   This

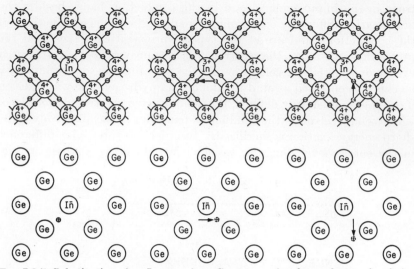

FIG. I.3.7. Substitution of an In atom for a Ge atom.   A valence electron is missing so that neighboring valence electrons can move in (above).   Thus the valence electron vacancy or the "hole" migrates (below).

process includes the liberation of a hole and the charging of the impurity by one negative charge:

$$A^\times \rightleftarrows A^- + \oplus \tag{I.3.02}$$

The acceptor can be represented by a "hydrogen" model, in the form of a positive "defect" electron in the field of a negative point charge, in a medium with the dielectric constant of germanium $\varepsilon = 16$ as in the case of the donor (Fig. I.3.8).   Such an impurity introduces in

---

[1] This interpretation of the migration of a hole, namely, the successive motion of neighboring valence electrons into neighboring incomplete pair bonds in order to fill the holes, represents the atomistic or localized-particle standpoint.   This should not lead one to ignore the wave nature of all electrons, including the valence electrons, which allows an unhindered migration of the valence electrons throughout the crystal on one hand and represents on the other hand the valence electrons as evenly "smeared out" over all pair bonds.   The motion of one valence electron into the hole of an incomplete neighboring bond does not require any energy expenditure because it is not necessary to break a pair bond.   An actual breaking of a pair bond occurs only if the valence electron is converted into a conduction electron, which obviously requires energy, rather than just changing place as a valence electron into another pair bond (see also pp. 18 to 20 and Fig. I.3.4).

the band model a localized impurity level above the valence band. Thermal excitation lifts an electron from the upper edge of the valence band to the impurity level of the neutral acceptor. Expressed in terms of holes, this is the ionization process $A^\times \rightarrow A^- + \oplus$, in which a hole is pushed down from the impurity level into the valence band.

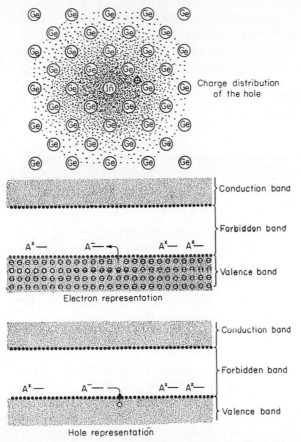

FIG. I.3.8. The charge distribution of a hole around a substitutional In atom. A band model with neutral and ionized acceptors in the electron and the hole representation.

Electrons fall by themselves into lower levels, but energy must be supplied—for instance, by thermal or photon collisions—to raise an electron into a higher level. In contrast to this, holes spontaneously move upward in the band-level scheme like air bubbles in water, but energy is necessary to push them down into deeper levels.[1] Every

[1] See also pp. 375 and 377.

process in the band model can be expressed either in electron or hole language.   The valence band may thus be regarded either as almost filled with electrons or as nearly devoid of holes.   The choice between these two ways of expressing the same thing is a matter of convenience.[1]

A semiconductor which contains only donors as impurities, for instance, is naturally described with the help of the electron representation; for the conductivity is in this case determined only by the negative electrons in the conduction band.   Such a semiconductor is called an n-type or excess semiconductor (Fig. I.3.9).   If, on the other hand, the semiconductor contains only acceptor impurities, the current is

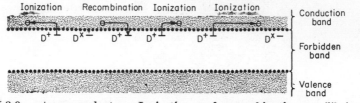

FIG. I.3.9. n-type conductor. Ionization and recombination equilibrium of donors: $D^\times \leftrightarrows D^+ + \ominus$.

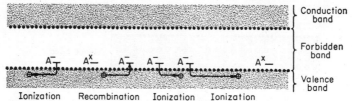

FIG. I.3.10. p-type conductor. Ionization and recombination equilibrium of acceptors: $A^\times \leftrightarrows A^- + \oplus$.

carried only by the positive holes in the valence band, and one speaks of p-type or defect conduction (Fig. I.3.10).

According to the preceding explanations, it appears as if the first described intrinsic conduction and the later introduced impurity conduction constitute two mutually exclusive opposites.   This is, however, true only to a certain degree.   We can understand this by considering a semiconductor with donors and analyzing its behavior with increasing temperature, starting out from a low enough temperature so that the thermal energy is barely sufficient to ionize an occasional donor.   The conductivity is, in this case, only very small because of the low concentration of conduction electrons; however, one can increase the conductivity by raising the temperature, because a large number of not yet ionized donors is available (case of partial ionization).   If the temperature is increased further, we approach the case

[1] See also pp. 65 to 66.

where all donors have given off their electrons to the conduction band. A further increase of temperature will not raise the conductivity as there are no neutral donors left (saturation case). A continuing temperature increase will, after a constant conductivity range, result in a further very steep conductivity increase caused by the mechanism of intrinsic conduction. This is the result of thermal excitation of electrons from the upper edge of the valence band to the lower edge of the conduction band. Since each such process produces an electron-hole pair, it is often called "pair formation." Impurity conduction and intrinsic conduction are thus not mutually exclusive, but can coexist. Impurity conduction predominates at low temperatures. The temperature at which the intrinsic conductivity overtakes the impurity conductivity depends only on the impurities. It is, of course, possible that in the case of very large forbidden bands and/or at very high

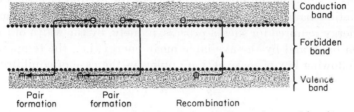

Fig. I.3.11. Intrinsic semiconductor. Pair formation and recombination equilibrium of the intrinsic semiconductor lattice: $0 \leftrightarrows \ominus + \oplus$.

impurity concentrations this temperature may be beyond the melting point of the crystal lattice.

We already mentioned the process of pair formation, namely, the simultaneous creation of an electron-hole pair by raising a valence electron from the upper edge of the valence band to the lower edge of the conduction band in the unperturbed lattice (Fig. I.3.11). There must be a complementary process to such a microscopic elementary process which occurs under equilibrium conditions as often as the elementary process. The recombination of an electron with a hole is the counterpart to the pair formation. Here a conduction electron in random thermal motion within the conduction band encounters a hole, namely, an electron vacancy in the otherwise full valence band, and falls back into the valence band. Such a process occurs more frequently the more frequently a conduction electron $\ominus$ meets a hole $\oplus$, in other words, the larger the number of holes. The number of recombinations per unit time and per unit volume is therefore proportional to the concentration of the positive holes p.[1] The fact that it is also

[1] Higher terms involving p^2, p^3, p^4, etc., can be neglected if the dilution is high enough.

proportional to the concentration of the negative electrons n follows from a similar consideration in which attention is fixed on a particular hole instead of an electron. Thus the same principles apply to the holes $\oplus$ as were previously applied to the electrons $\ominus$. We find that the number of recombinations per unit time and per unit volume is

$$r \cdot n \cdot p$$

where the factor r is called the recombination coefficient. The pair formation g, namely, the number of pair-formation processes per unit time and per unit volume, is, however, independent of the concentration. This means that whether a certain valence electron is raised from the valence band to the conduction band cannot depend on the concentration of electrons already present in the conduction band nor on the concentration of holes in the valence band—at least as long as there is a sufficient number of free places for excited electrons in the conduction band. The pair formation g is therefore determined by the energy required for such a process, namely, by the width of the forbidden band and by the available mean energy, i.e., the temperature. The following law of mass action applies in the case of equilibrium:

$$g = r \cdot n \cdot p$$

or[1] $$p \cdot n = n_i^2 = \frac{g}{r} \qquad (\text{I.3.03})$$

The so-called intrinsic density n_i is accordingly that concentration below which neither n nor p can fall without causing, at equilibrium, the other quantity p or n to rise above the concentration n_i. n_i could also be called the inversion density, because the transition from $n \gg n_i$, $p \ll n_i$ to $p \gg n_i$, $n \ll n_i$ is connected with the transition from n-type conductivity to p-type conductivity, which represents an inversion of the conductivity type of the semiconductor.

The name "intrinsic density" stems from the fact that in an intrinsic semiconductor the following neutrality requirement must be fulfilled:

$$n = p = n_i \qquad (\text{I.3.04})$$

In order to render a semiconductor intrinsic at room temperature, it is necessary to reduce appreciably the generally present impurity concentration by purification[2] of the semiconductor. Hence it is plausible

---

[1] See also p. 305.

[2] The degree of extreme purity necessary for this purpose, in contrast to the meaning of the term purity in chemistry, can be demonstrated by the following numerical example. The intrinsic density n_i at room temperature is about 2.5×10^{13} cm^{-3}. In order to attain the intrinsic condition $n = p = n_i$, it is

that the condition of intrinsic conduction corresponds to the minimum conductivity attainable at a certain temperature in a particular semiconductor.

This is not entirely true, however. An extension of Eq. (I.2.06) gives for the conductivity

$$\sigma = e(\mu_n n + \mu_p p) \qquad (I.3.05)$$

and with the law of mass action (I.3.03) this becomes

$$\sigma = e\left(\mu_n n + \mu_p \frac{n_i^2}{n}\right) \qquad (I.3.06)$$

It is easy to see that the minimum of the conductivity is

$$\sigma = 2e \sqrt{\mu_n \mu_p}\, n_i \qquad (I.3.07)$$

and that it is obtained for

$$n = n_i \sqrt{\frac{\mu_p}{\mu_n}} \qquad p = n_i \sqrt{\frac{\mu_n}{\mu_p}} \qquad (I.3.08)$$

Since μ_n and μ_p are of the same order of magnitude (for instance,[1] in Ge $\mu_n = 3,600$ cm^2/volt-sec, $\mu_p = 1,700$ cm^2/volt-sec), this condition for minimum conductivity lies not too far from the condition for intrinsic conduction.

$$\sigma_i = e(\mu_n + \mu_p)n_i \qquad (I.3.09)$$
$$n = n_i \qquad p = n_i \qquad (I.3.04)$$

The described processes of pair formation and recombination can be represented by a reaction

$$0 \rightleftarrows \ominus + \oplus \qquad (I.3.10)$$

in which the zero on the left side represents the fully periodic lattice which is unperturbed even with respect to the electron distribution. The law of mass action (I.3.03) which we formulated for this reaction equation (I.3.10) could similarly be established for the reaction equa-

necessary to reduce the impurity concentrations below $n \approx 2.5 \times 10^{13}$ cm^{-3}, for each impurity contributes an electron or a hole. The concentration of the germanium atoms is 4.52×10^{22} cm^{-3}. Therefore there cannot be more than *one* impurity atom per $4.52 \times 10^{22}/2.5 \times 10^{13} = 1.8 \times 10^9$ germanium atoms. This signifies a purity in the chemical sense of between "9 and 10 nines"! On a straight line through the germanium lattice, one would encounter $\sqrt[3]{1.8 \times 10^9} = 1.2 \times 10^3$ germanium atoms between two impurity atoms. The numerical values are taken from E. M. Conwell, *Proc. IRE*, **40**: 1327 (1952).

[1] E. M. Conwell, *Proc. IRE*, **40**: 1330 (1952). P. P. Debye and E. M. Conwell, *Phys. Rev.*, **93**: 693 (1954).

tions (I.3.01) and (I.3.02) of the donor and the acceptor ionization, respectively; for the counterparts of donor and acceptor recombination exist here also, a fact which we have already taken into consideration in Figs. I.3.9 and I.3.10.

However, we shall leave this to the next chapter on impurity reactions and impurity equilibria, where we shall treat these conditions in more detail.

§4. Problems

1. Verify Eqs. (I.3.07) and (I.3.08). Give numerical values for the intrinsic conductivity and the minimal conductivity in germanium, assuming the values for n_i, μ_n, and μ_p given in §3. Give the corresponding resistivities.

2. Transform Eq. (I.3.06) into expressions for the electron and hole density as a function of the conductivity. For each conductivity value, two sets of electron and hole density values are possible. What are these values for a Ge crystal with a resistivity of 30 ohm-cm?

3. If μ_n and μ_p are not equal, the conductivity minimum corresponds to the type of conduction with the lower mobility, for $\mu_p < \mu_n$ to p-type conduction. For what hole density, then, will the conductivity again be equal to the intrinsic conductivity, and what would be the conductivity of a crystal whose electron concentration has that value? Give numerical values for germanium.

4.* (Cyclotron resonance.) The free carriers in a semiconductor move in circular orbits if the semiconductor is brought into a magnetic field. An electromagnetic wave passing through the semiconductor will be strongly absorbed if its frequency is equal to the rotational frequency of the carriers. Since the rotational frequency depends upon the mass of the carriers, one can in this way determine the effective mass of the electrons and holes.

Determine the mutual relationships between the following quantities: effective mass, rotational frequency, magnetic field strength, velocity of the carriers, radius of the orbit. Show that the rotational frequency does not depend on the velocity of the carrier. What does this mean for the sharpness of the resonance?

5.* In order to get a sharp cyclotron resonance, it is necessary that the mean free path l be long compared to the circumference of the cyclotron orbit. What magnetic field is necessary to satisfy this condition under the following two conditions: (1) $l = 10^{-5}$ cm, $T = 300°$ abs and (2) $l = 10^{-4}$ cm, $T = 10°$ abs, and an effective mass equal to the free mass in both cases?

Note Concerning Cyclotron Resonance. The effective masses, actually, are not constant but depend upon the direction within the crystal in which the electron (or hole) is accelerated. For our more illustrative purposes, we can neglect this directional dependence which goes far beyond the scope of this book. The interested reader is referred to Herman[1] or to Dresselhaus, Kip, and Kittel[2] for more details and references.

[1] F. Herman, *Proc. IRE.*, **43**: 1703 (1955).
[2] G. Dresselhaus, A. F. Kip, and C. Kittel, *Phys. Rev.*, **78**: 368 (1955).

CHAPTER II

The Nature, Models, and Reactions of Impurities and Imperfections

The band model, as described in the previous chapter, was formulated in the course of the development of the theory of metals and was taken over by semiconductor physics. The idea of the atomic lattice defect—the imperfection or impurity confined to a lattice point and its immediate vicinity—is, in contrast, typical of semiconductor physics, and its conception can, in a way, be considered as the beginning of modern semiconductor physics in general. It may be desirable to defer general considerations to the end of this chapter and to begin immediately with the discussion of specific concrete examples.

§1. Substitutional Impurities in Valence Crystals

Few types of imperfections are as easily understood with respect to their nature and characteristics as the substitutional impurities in the valence crystals of Group IV of the periodic table. In these lattices of the diamond type (Fig. II.1.1), such as the germanium lattice, each Ge atom is bound to four tetrahedrally arranged identical Ge neighbors by four electron-pair bonds. Any one germanium atom contributes four valence electrons, one to each pair bond, whereas the remaining electron of each pair bond, with opposite spin, is provided by the Ge neighbor to which the pair bond leads.

If one admixes or alloys a small amount of an element from Group III or V of the periodic table to a Ge sample, these atoms replace Ge atoms in their regular lattice positions, i.e., they are *substituted* for a Ge atom (Fig. II.1.2). For instance, an As atom introduces five valence electrons into the Ge lattice, but only four of these can be absorbed by the four pair bonds to the four Ge neighbors. The fifth valence electron is bound only very weakly to the As core if it remains at all attached to it.

The strength of this bond can be estimated, according to Bethe,[1] as follows:

The charge cloud of the fifth valence electron extends over a relatively large volume as a consequence of the weak binding and therefore encompasses many of the Ge neighbors of the arsenic core. This fact can be taken into consideration by the following approximation: The

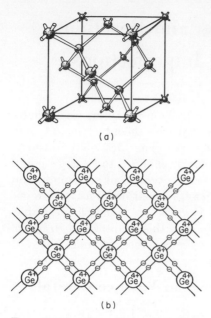

(a)

(b)

Fig. II.1.1. The diamond lattice. (a) The spatial arrangement. (b) Two-dimensional representation.

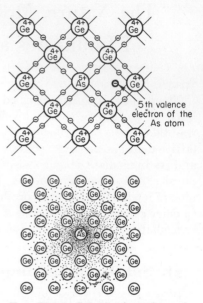

5th valence electron of the As atom

Fig. II.1.2. Substitution of an As atom for a Ge atom. Weak binding of the fifth valence electron in the form of an extended charge distribution.

coulomb field of the positively charged arsenic core which carries a single positive charge, because of the absence of the fifth valence electron, is reduced by a factor $1/\varepsilon_{Ge}$, where $\varepsilon_{Ge} = 16.1$ is the macroscopic dielectric constant of Ge. Thus we have the well-known hydrogen problem in a medium with the dielectric constant ε_{Ge}. Formally,

[1] H. A. Bethe, R. L. Report No. 43–12, 1942. See also H. C. Torrey and C. A. Whitmer, "Crystal Rectifiers," pp. 65 and 66, McGraw-Hill Book Company, Inc., New York, 1948. The corresponding approximation for imperfections in ionic crystals can be found already in N. F. Mott and R. W. Gurney, "Electronic Processes in Ionic Crystals," pp. 80–86, Clarendon Press, Oxford, 1940 and 1948. Finally, the corresponding result for an electron in the field of a defect electron (hole), namely, for an "exciton," has been derived by G. H. Wannier, *Phys. Rev.*, **52:** 191 (1937).

this is equivalent to the vacuum problem with an effective atomic number $Z_{eff} = 1/\varepsilon_{Ge}$. The reduction of the coulomb field causes an increase of the first Bohr radius[1] $a_0 = \hbar^2/Z_{eff}me^2$ by the factor $1/Z_{eff} = \varepsilon_{Ge} = 16.1$, so that $a_0 = 16.1 \cdot 0.53 \cdot 10^{-8}$ cm $= 8.5 \cdot 10^{-8}$ cm.

Further we obtain from the $1s$ eigenfunction $(1/\sqrt{a_0^3\pi})e^{-\frac{r}{a_0}}$ the radius $2a_0 = 17 \cdot 10^{-8}$ cm of a sphere which contains three quarters of the charge cloud of a $1s$ electron. The unit cell of the Ge lattice is a cube with a side dimension of $5.62 \cdot 10^{-8}$ cm containing eight Ge atoms, so that the previously mentioned spherical charge cloud includes $4(\pi/3)(17 \cdot 10^{-8}/5.62 \cdot 10^{-8})^3$ unit cells and $4 (\pi/3) (3.02)^3 \cdot 8 \approx 925$ Ge atoms. This surprisingly large extension of the charge cloud in space justifies the calculation with the macroscopic dielectric constant. The ionization energy for the fifth valence electron can be calculated by multiplying the product of the ionization potential $2\pi^2me^4Z_{eff}^2/h^2$ of hydrogen with e by the factor $Z_{eff}^2 = 1/(\varepsilon_{Ge})^2 = 1/(16.1)^2 = 1/259.2$, which gives finally $13.59/259.2$ ev $= 0.052$ ev.

The binding of the fifth valence electron of a substitutional As atom to its As^+ core is very weak in comparison with that of the valence electron of hydrogen.

Hence even slight perturbations of thermal or other nature can remove the fifth valence electron, leaving the positively charged As^+ core. The substitutional impurity, just described, acts as a neutral electron "source" or "donor" $D^\times$ which is dissociated into a positive donor residue D^+ and a negative electron $\ominus$: $D^\times \rightarrow D^+ + \ominus$.

The picture is somewhat different if a Ge atom is replaced by an atom of Group III of the periodic table such as an indium atom (Fig. II.1.3), which introduces only three valence electrons into the Ge lattice. One of the four pair bonds leading from the lattice point of the indium atom to the four germanium neighbors is initially incomplete. This bond can be completed at the expense of another pair bond, if a valence electron of this other pair bond changes over to the originally incomplete pair bond of the substituted In atom.[2] The initially neutral indium atom becomes thus negatively charged, and the vacancy in a pair bond, the "hole" in the totality of the valence electrons, moves[2]

---

[1] See, for instance, H. Geiger and K. Scheel, "Handbuch der Physik," vol. XXIV, part 1, pp. 273 and 274, Springer-Verlag OHG, Berlin, 1933. The quadratic dependence of the ionization energy on the nuclear charge number Z can be explained as follows: A reduction in nuclear charge obviously causes a dilation of the charge cloud of the electron. Any mean orbital radius is therefore proportional to Z^{-1}. In order to obtain the ionization energy, one must introduce the value of the orbital radius into the denominator of the expression for the potential Ze/r. This is the reason for the proportionality of the ionization energy to Z^{+2}.

[2] See footnote 1, p. 22.

therefore in the force field of the negatively charged In atom. We recognize again a hydrogen problem, where, in contrast to the well-known vacuum case, the difference lies not only in the changed dielectric constant of the medium but also in an exchange of sign of the charges of nucleus and electron.

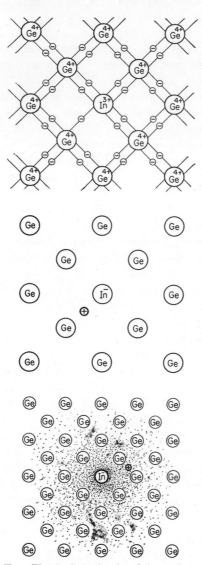

Previously we found that the fifth valence electron of a substitutional As atom is bound only lightly to the As atom which acts as a donor. This result can now be applied to the case of the substitution of indium, and it can be said that a hole $\oplus$ is only weakly bound to an indium atom. This positive particle $\oplus$ is easily removed or given up, leaving a negatively charged indium atom or rather an ion In^-. The description of this process in the hole language is only a figure of speech, and the real process consists in the *acceptance* or capture of an electron in the force field of the In^-, which is the origin of the name *acceptor A* for such an impurity. Without regard to the origin of this name, we prefer, in this connection, the hole representation,[1] where we speak of the dissociation of a neutral acceptor $A^\times$ into a negative acceptor "residue" A^- and a positive hole $\oplus$

$$A^\times \rightarrow A^- + \oplus$$

FIG. II.1.3. Substitutional impurity: replacing a Ge atom by an In atom.

We can summarize the preceding explanations in the following generalizations:

[1] See, however, p. 36, where, in ZnO, acceptors take electrons from the *conduction* band rather than from the *valence* band and thus reduce the initially present excess conductivity.

In the diamond-type valence lattice of the elements of Group IV of the periodic table, the chemical additions of elements from Groups III and V are built in *substitutionally,* which means that the foreign atoms occupy lattice points in the host lattice.   This leads to donor formation from the elements of Group V, which give off negative electrons, and acceptor formation from the elements of Group III, which take up electrons or, in other words, give off holes.

In the following it is convenient to use an abbreviated symbolism for the various types of impurities and imperfections.   In common with K. Hauffe, O. Stasiw, and J. Teltow (Fig. II.4.2), we adopt the system recently suggested by W. Schottky.   The previously discussed substitutional impurities in valence lattices can be represented by

$$P \bullet^{\cdot} (Ge) \qquad As \bullet^{\cdot} (Ge) \qquad Sb \bullet^{\cdot} (Ge)$$
$$Al \bullet' (Ge) \qquad Ga \bullet' (Ge) \qquad In \bullet' (Ge)$$

where, for instance, the first symbol $P \bullet^{\cdot} (Ge)$ refers to the substitution of the substituent phosphor P for the substituted germanium (Ge) and $\bullet$ indicates the substitutional character of the impurity in contrast to the vacancies and interstitials to be described later.   "$\cdot$" and "$''$" indicate the effective state of charge[1] of the entire impurity, namely, the difference compared to the normally occupied lattice, so that "$\cdot$" stands for a single positive charge, "$\cdot\cdot$" a double positive charge, and "$''$" signifies a single negative charge, "$''''$" a double negative charge, etc.

The foregoing symbols represent the substitutional impurities in the condition where they have given off their electron $\ominus$ or hole $\oplus$, respectively.   If this is not the case and the electron $\ominus$, for instance, is located around the substituent P, on a hydrogenic orbit enlarged by ε_{Ge}, the impurity as a whole is neutral.   This shall be indicated by the symbol "$\times$".   In this associated condition, the foregoing impurities are represented by

$$P \bullet^{\times} (Ge) \qquad As \bullet^{\times} (Ge) \qquad Sb \bullet^{\times} (Ge)$$
$$Al \bullet^{\times} (Ge) \qquad Ga \bullet^{\times} (Ge) \qquad In \bullet^{\times} (Ge)$$

The dissociation-association equilibria between a donor and an electron and between an acceptor and a hole, respectively, are given by the following reaction equations:

$$As \bullet^{\times} (Ge) \rightleftarrows As \bullet^{\cdot} (Ge) + \ominus$$
$$In \bullet^{\times} (Ge) \rightleftarrows In \bullet' (Ge) + \oplus$$

[1] Here the history of this actual state of charge is completely ignored.   This remark will be of special importance in ionic crystals.   See p. ,40 particularly footnote [1].

§2. Substitutional Impurities in Ionic Crystals[1]

Substitutional impurities have also been investigated in ionic crystals, such as metal oxides, sulfides, selenides, and tellurides, by C. Wagner[2] and coworkers, K. Hauffe[3] and his students, and finally by E. J. W. Verwey, P. W. Haaymann, and F. C. Romeyn.[4] For instance, K. Hauffe and A. L. Vierk[5] replace Zn^{++} ions by Al^{+++} ions in a ZnO lattice, which consists of Zn^{++} and O^{--} ions, by adding Al_2O_3. In contrast to the unperturbed lattice, the substituted impurity is positively charged with a single charge and must therefore be represented with the Schottky symbol Al •· (Zn). A negative electron can again be freed or captured in the coulomb field of this positive charge, so that this impurity acts as a donor:

$$\text{Al } \bullet^{\times} \text{ (Zn)} \rightleftarrows \text{Al } \bullet \cdot \text{ (Zn)} + \ominus$$

Several complications enter in the calculation of the dissociation energy compared with the corresponding problem in valence crystals. One is the difference between the dielectric constant of the crystal for slowly varying electric fields and that for rapidly varying ones. An appreciable part of the dielectric screening of an electric field in an ionic crystal stems from the polarization of the crystal, because the positive and negative ions yield somewhat to the external field and are therefore displaced in space compared with their normal field-free position. This contribution of dielectric screening of an electric field

---

[1] We restrict ourselves to electronic conduction in ionic crystals, although the systematic substitution of ions of the host crystal was accomplished in crystals with predominantly ionic conduction earlier than in those with predominantly electronic conduction. In the case of the silver halides, we refer to E. Koch and C. Wagner, *Z. physik. Chem.*, **B38**: 295 (1937). O. Stasiw and J. Teltow, *Ann. Physik*, 5/40: 181 (1941), and 6/1: 261 (1947). O. Stasiw, *Ann. Physik*, 6/5: 151 (1949). J. Teltow, *Ann. Physik*, 6/5: 63, 71 (1949). J. Teltow, *Z. physik. Chem.*, 195: 197, 213 (1950). The substitution of polyvalent ions in alkali halides was especially discussed by H. Pick, *Ann. Physik*, 5/35: 73 (1939); and G. Heiland and H. Kelting, *Z. Physik*, 126: 689 (1949).

[2] C. Wagner, *J. Chem. Phys.*, 18: 62 (1950).

[3] K. Hauffe, *Ann. Physik*, 6/8: 201 (1950). K. Hauffe and A. L. Vierk, *Z. physik. Chem.*, 196: 160 (1950). K. Hauffe and J. Block, *Z. physik. Chem.*, 196: 438 (1950). K. Hauffe and J. Block, *Z. physik. Chem.*, 198: 232 (1951). K. Hauffe and H. Grunewald, *Z. physik. Chem.*, 198: 248 (1951).

[4] E. J. W. Verwey, P. W. Haaymann, and F. C. Romeyn, *Chem. Weekblad*, 44: 705 (1948). See also E. J. W. Verwey, P. W. Haaymann, F. C. Romeyn, and F. W. van Oosterhout, *Philips Research Repts.*, 5: 173 (1950).

[5] K. Hauffe and A. L. Vierk, Über die elektrische Leitfähigkeit von Zinkoxyd mit Fremdoxydzusätzen, *Z. physik. Chem.*, 196: 160 (1950).

disappears for rapidly changing electric fields, because the large and heavy ions are not capable of following the rapid field changes. The only remaining electrical screening is due to the polarization of the lattice ions themselves. NaCl, for instance, exhibits for static fields $\varepsilon = 5.62$, whereas for alternating fields above 5.10^{12} cycles, namely, for optical fields, $\varepsilon_{opt} = 2.25$. Based on the Franck-Condon principle, one can say that the separation of an electron from the charged perturbation center is such a sudden process that the ions must be considered as stationary or immobile. Therefore one introduces ε_{opt} instead of ε_{stat} into the equation $E = -13.59/n^2\varepsilon^2$ ev. The resulting values are considerably higher than in the case of Ge ($\varepsilon = 16.1$) and Si ($\varepsilon = 11.2$), since $\varepsilon_{opt} = 2.25$ for NaCl. We find that the ground state with $n = 1$ lies below the continuum of the conduction band by about $13.59/1^2(2.25)^2$ ev ≈ 2.67 ev. This separation energy, which is enormous compared to that for valence crystals, has further consequences.

Besides the ground state we must now consider the excited states since the state with the quantum number 2 is still $13.59/2^2(2.25)^2$ ev $= 0.67$ ev below the conduction band. In the "dissociation" of a donor, for instance, an electron may first be raised by optical excitation from the ground state to the first excited state, for which only $(2.67 - 0.67)$ ev $= 2.00$ ev are necessary. The remaining step to the conduction band can, under certain circumstances, be effected thermally.

Thermal excitation for an energy step of 0.67 ev seems improbable, at least at room temperature. Here, another complication enters the picture. After the first optical excitation of the electron, we find that the ions in the vicinity of the impurity are not in equilibrium any more. They rearrange themselves in a slow and inertia-retarded process into a new equilibrium configuration of lower energy. The remaining excitation of the electron can now be effected by less than 0.67 ev, if it is thermal. In the case of the rapid single processes, one must consider the energies of the initial state and the end state without any ionic rearrangement, namely, for stationary ions, whereas the thermal-excitation energies are determined as differences between real equilibrium conditions arising in the statistics of collective systems with large numbers of participants.

Unfortunately, we must restrict ourselves to this short discussion and refer for further details to the well-known book by Mott and Gurney.[1] However, it appeared appropriate to indicate the reasons why the conditions in ionic crystals are fundamentally more complicated than in valence crystals.

[1] N. F. Mott and R. W. Gurney, "Electronic Processes in Ionic Crystals," Clarendon Press, Oxford, 1948. See, for instance, pp. 85, 115, and 160.

Up to now, we have mentioned only the formation of donors by introducing ions of higher valence.   One can also build in lower-valence ions in order to form acceptors.   ZnO is inherently an excess conductor, and we indicated previously in footnote [1] on page 32 that, in such a case, an acceptor A receives an electron from the conduction band with the liberation of energy and does not require energy to raise an electron from the valence band:

$$A^\times \rightarrow A^- - \ominus$$

The number of current carriers is thus reduced by 1, and the conductivity of the ZnO is lower as a consequence of the "trapping" of the previously freely migrating electron.   Schottky speaks, in these cases, very descriptively of the "poisoning" of excess conduction through introduction of additional acceptors.   We summarize once more as follows:

Addition of Al_2O_3 to ZnO produces[1] donors

$$Al \bullet^\times (Zn) \rightleftarrows Al \bullet^\cdot (Zn) + \ominus$$

Addition of Li_2O to ZnO produces acceptors

$$Li \bullet^\times (Zn) \rightleftarrows Li \bullet' (Zn) - \ominus$$

Shortly before the experiments of K. Hauffe and A. L. Vierk,[2] E. J. Verwey, P. W. Haaymann, and F. C. Romeyn[3] obtained the following results with another host lattice, namely, NiO:

Addition of Cr_2O_3 to NiO produces donors

$$Cr \bullet^\times (Ni) \rightleftarrows Cr \bullet^\cdot (Ni) - \oplus$$

Addition of Li_2O to NiO produces acceptors

$$Li \bullet^\times (Ni) \rightleftarrows Li \bullet' (Ni) + \oplus$$

The action on the conductivity of the p-type NiO is exactly opposite to that on the n-type ZnO, so that the introduction of low-valence ions increases the conductivity by the addition of acceptors.   The introduction of higher-valence ions poisons, however, the p-type conduction of NiO by the addition of donors.

In order to understand the difference in behavior between ZnO and

---

[1] The oxygen balance is established through exchange with a surrounding gas phase (see p. 45).

[2] K. Hauffe and A. L. Vierk, Über die elektrische Leitfähigkeit von Zinkoxyd mit Fremdoxydzusätzen, *Z. physik. Chem.*, **196:** 169 (1950).

[3] E. J. W. Verwey, P. W. Haaymann, and F. C. Romeyn, *Chem. Weekblad*, **44:** 705 (1948).   See also E. J. W. Verwey, P. W. Haaymann, F. C. Romeyn, and F. W. van Oosterhout, *Philips Research Repts*, **5:** 173 (1950).

NiO, we must know why ZnO is in itself an n-type conductor and why NiO is p-type. For this purpose we have to introduce a new concept, namely, that these two lattices contain atomic imperfections other than foreign impurities and that two different types of imperfections are effective in NiO and ZnO, respectively. Since we are not yet familiar with these types of imperfections, we shall first study them in valence crystals.

§3. Vacancies and Interstitials in Valence Crystals

If we ask about the possible types of *atomic* imperfections which can occur in a Ge crystal without any addition of foreign atoms, we find two possibilities for a deviation from the ideal lattice occupancy:

1. A Ge atom can be missing from a regularly occupied lattice point. A "lattice vacancy" is thus formed.

2. A lattice atom is in a so-called "interstitial position," which means that a Ge atom is placed in a suitable location between the atoms of an already complete diamond lattice. The diamond lattice, especially, offers a relatively large amount of space for these interstitials.

Like the substitutional impurities, the interstitials and the vacancies act as donors and acceptors, respectively. This is relatively easy to understand in the case of a Ge atom in an interstitial position.[1] The ionization energy of a Ge atom in vacuum is 8.13 ev. The Ge atom in an interstitial position acts roughly in the same manner as a Ge atom with a dielectric constant $\varepsilon_{germanium} = 16.1$. Its ionization energy is therefore reduced by the factor $1/(\varepsilon_{germanium})^2 = \frac{1}{259}$ compared with the vacuum value, yielding only 8.13/259 ev = 0.0314 ev. We see that a Ge atom in an interstitial position can give off an electron with an excitation energy of only 0.0314 ev, thus acquiring a positive charge:

$$\text{Ge } \bigcirc^\times \rightleftarrows \text{Ge } \bigcirc^\cdot + \ominus$$

The second ionization energy of germanium in vacuum is 16.0 ev. If the calculation with the macroscopic dielectric constant $\varepsilon = 16.1$ were applicable to the case of double ionization of the Ge atom in the interstitial position, we would find the still very small value of 16.0/259 ev = 0.0618 ev. It is, however, questionable whether this ε calculation is permissible, for the second electron to be removed from the Ge core moves in the force field of a doubly positive charge of the remaining core, so that its orbit radius must be considerably smaller

---

[1] Schottky symbol: Ge $\bigcirc^\times$ or Ge $\bigcirc^\cdot$, depending on the charge condition (see Fig. II.4.2).

than that of the first electron.   James and Lark-Horowitz[1] favor the interpretation of the interstitial Ge atom as a doubly ionizable donor. The higher ionization energies beyond the second one are then assumed to be larger than the width of the forbidden band, which eliminates further imperfection levels in the forbidden band.   These higher ionization levels would fall in the valence band and would hence be of no importance for the conduction processes.

The action of a lattice vacancy as an acceptor is more difficult to understand.   One may give the following explanation: The Ge^{++++} ions are connected by the valence electron bonds in a perfect lattice, as we have described previously (Fig. II.1.1).   The common point of the four valence bonds to the four nearest neighbors is largely screened from the outside by the Ge^{++++} under consideration, so that it is much less likely for a conduction electron to approach the Ge^{++++} ion than for a valence electron.   In addition, there is a certain repulsion of the conduction electron by the valence electrons.   The energy of a conduction electron, in order to approach the Ge^{++++} ion, must be appreciably higher than that of a valence electron, which manifests itself in the higher energy of the levels in the conduction band compared with those in the valence band, as indicated by the width of the forbidden band. If at one lattice point a Ge^{++++} including its valence electrons, namely, a whole Ge atom, is missing, there seems to be no reason for a conduction electron either to seek or to avoid this point in view of charge neutrality.   However, there is an appreciable amount of empty space at this vacancy location.   An electron approaching this point is not attracted by a positive Ge^{++++} ion, but it will move as far as possible from the surrounding valence electrons in view of their repulsion, so that the vacancy location becomes an energetically more favorable position for the electron than the normal level in the conduction band. Nevertheless, valence electrons are still favored energetically over conduction electrons in view of the absence of an attracting Ge^{++++} ion. Thus a localized electron energy level below the conduction band but above the valence band in the forbidden band is formed by the Ge vacancy, which becomes charged negatively if it is occupied by an electron.   This means that the lattice vacancy acts as an acceptor, for an acceptor is an imperfection which provides electrons with an energy level below the conduction-band levels and becomes negatively charged in the energy-liberating process of capture.

Lark-Horowitz and his coworkers[2] produced vacancies and inter-

---

[1] H. M. James and K. Lark-Horowitz, *Z. physik. Chem.*, **198**: 107 (1951).

[2] K. Lark-Horowitz, in "Semiconducting Materials" (Reading Report), p. 47, Butterworths Scientific Publications, Ltd., London, 1951.

stitials in Ge and Si by bombardment with high-energy particles of various types, which led to a better understanding of the role of these imperfection types.[1]

The annealing effects found by Scaff and Theuerer[2] are not due to vacancies but rather a consequence of diffusion and precipitation processes of metallic impurities (mainly Cu).[3] If these effects are eliminated by working with extreme cleanliness and other precautions, p conductivity is observed which was previously overshadowed by the much larger Scaff-Theuerer effects. These acceptors are beyond doubt caused by thermally created imperfections.[4]

§4. Vacancies and Interstitials in Ionic Crystals

Vacancies acting as acceptors are easier to understand in ionic crystals than in valence crystals. Let us consider the heretofore practically important and intensively investigated cuprous oxide (Cu_2O). During the preparation of the samples to be investigated, an excess of oxygen was introduced by the proper choice of conditions. This oxygen excess should rather be called a defect in the stoichiometric metal content, for the deviation from stoichiometry is caused by vacancies in the lattice of the Cu^+ ions. There is no doubt that such a vacancy acts electrostatically like an additional negative charge; for one positive charge is missing at the vacated lattice point. The coulomb field of the additional negative charge can thus capture or give off a positive hole. The imperfection as a whole is neutral if the hole is captured; otherwise it is negatively charged. The vacancy in

[1] It remains to be seen whether the detailed interpretations of Lark-Horowitz will prove valid in the long run. James and Lark-Horowitz themselves point out in Z. physik. Chem., **198**: 112 (1951), that their interpretation does not take into consideration an accumulation and cloud formation of vacancies and interstitials. Such accumulations at the periphery of the trajectories of fast particles appear more probable than a homogeneous distribution over the entire Ge lattice.

[2] J. H. Scaff and H. C. Theuerer, Trans. Am. Inst. Mining Met. Engrs., **189**: 59 (1951).

[3] C. S. Fuller, H. C. Theuerer, and W. van Roosbroeck, Phys. Rev., **85**: 678 (1952). C. S. Fuller and J. D. Struthers, Phys. Rev., **87**: 526 (1952). W. P. Slichter and E. D. Kolb, Phys. Rev., **87**: 527 (1952). C. Goldberg, Phys. Rev., **88**: 921 (1952). L. Esaki, Phys. Rev., **89**: 1026 (1953). K. Seiler, D. Geist, K. Keller, and K. Blank, Naturwiss., **40**: 56 (1953). F. van der Maesen, P. Penning, and A. van Wieringer, Philips Research Repts., **8**: 241 (1953). G. Finn, Phys. Rev., **91**: 754 (1953). F. van der Maesen and J. A. Brenkman, Philips Research Repts., **9**: 225 (1954).

[4] R. A. Logan, Phys. Rev., **91**: 757 (1953). S. Mayburg and L. Rotondi, Phys. Rev., **91**: 1015 (1953).

the lattice of the positive Cu^+ ions acts as an acceptor according to the reaction equation with the Schottky symbol Cu $\square'$.[1]

$$Cu\ \square' + \oplus \rightleftarrows Cu\ \square^\times$$

While the effective imperfections in Cu_2O are vacancies in the *cation* lattice, we recognize the well-known F centers, introduced by Pohl,[2] as vacancies in the anion lattice of the alkali halides (Fig. II.4.1). A vacancy in the lattice of the Cl^- ions in KCl acts as an attraction center for negative excess electrons:

$$Cl\ \square^\cdot + \ominus \rightleftarrows Cl\ \square^\times$$

The F center is equivalent to such a donor in the *associated* state (namely, the imperfection $Cl\ \square^\times$). In order to obtain a model for this imperfection,[3] it is important to introduce the low infrared value of the dielectric constant, which lies between 1.74 and 3.80, into the hydrogen analog of Mott and Gurney.[4] The vacuum value of the Bohr radius of $0.53 \cdot 10^{-8}$ cm is thereby increased only very little to 0.92 to $2.01 \cdot 10^{-8}$ cm. Even if, as in §1 (page 31), we take again twice the Bohr radius to define a sphere which contains 76.2 per cent of the charge cloud of the electron, we arrive at only 1.84 to $4.02 \cdot 10^{-8}$ cm. The lattice constants of the alkali halides are, however, between 2.07 and $3.66 \cdot 10^{-8}$ cm. Although the hydrogen model still has a limited conceptual significance in the alkali halides, it is not nearly so meaningful as in Ge ($\varepsilon = 16.1$), Si ($\varepsilon = 11.9$), and also in Cu_2O ($\varepsilon = 12$); for the charge cloud of the outermost electron is concentrated in the immediate vicinity of the halogen vacancy, so that we are inclined to distribute the electron in a statistical manner among the six neighboring metal ions. The resulting model of a color center becomes thus a halogen vacancy with a neutral metal atom $K^\times$ (Fig. II.4.1) as neighbor.[5]

---

[1] Cu $\square'$ represents, by definition, an imperfection in the form of the absence of a Cu^+ ion as compared with the unperturbed lattice. Whether the neutral atom is removed first with the subsequent removal of a hole or the vacancy is formed by the removal of a Cu^+ ion is quite irrelevant. The symbol "'" describes the actual charge condition of the imperfection without regard to the previous history.

[2] R. W. Pohl, *Physik. Z.*, **39**: 36 (1938).

[3] W. Schottky, *Z. physik. Chem.*, **29/B**: 335 (1935), particularly p. 342; and *Wiss. Veröffentl. Siemens-Werken*, **14** (2): 1 (1935), particularly middle of p. 4. J. H. de Boer, *Trav. chim. Pays-Bas*, **56**: 301 (1937).

[4] Mott and Gurney, *op. cit.*, p. 12, Table 5.

[5] Even the experiments on the spin resonance of the F-center electron do not appear to lead to a decision between the two models. See in connection with this, A. F. Kip, C. Kittel, R. A. Levy, and A. M. Portis, *Phys. Rev.*, **91**: 1066 (1954); and D. L. Dexter, *Phys. Rev.*, **93**: 244 (1954).

The high dissociation energies of F centers, of the order of 2 to 3 ev, are a further consequence of the low effective values of the dielectric constant for fast processes.   Thermal dissociation of the electron and the Cl vacancy is therefore for all practical purposes out of question. The raising of the electron to an excited state by light, with the subsequent thermal transition into the conduction band, is the process which led to the name of this type of imperfection (F center = color center).[1]

The action mechanism of ions in interstitial positions in the lattice is even more obvious.   For instance, ZnO contains probably Zn^{++} ions in interstitial positions[2] which are plentiful in the wurtzite lattice[3] of ZnO.   The positively charged Zn^{++} act of course as attraction centers

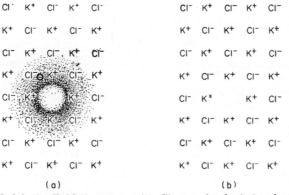

(a)   (b)

FIG. II.4.1. Model of a Pohl F center.   (a) Charge cloud of the electron around the Cl^- vacancy.   (b) Neutral K atom adjacent to the Cl^- vacancy.   The charge cloud of the electron around the Cl^- vacancy is not very far-reaching.   Thus representation b is possible.

for negative excess electrons.   A zinc atom in an interstitial position acts therefore as a donor:

$$\text{Zn} \bigcirc^\times \rightleftarrows \text{Zn} \bigcirc^\cdot + \ominus$$

We mention merely in passing that the halogen vacancies in the alkali halides can also capture two electrons (formation of F' centers):

$$\text{Cl} \,\square^\cdot + 2 \ominus = \text{Cl} \,\square^\times + \ominus = \text{F center} + \text{electron} = \text{Cl} \,\square'$$
$$= \text{F' center}$$

---

[1] See Mott and Gurney, *op. cit.*, p. 135.   See further the discussion on pp. 34 to 35.

[2] F. Stöckmann, *Z. Physik*, **127**: 563 (1950).   Another type of imperfection in ZnO is probably the anion vacancy $O \,\square^\cdot$ or $O \,\square^{\cdot\cdot}$, which acts like $ZnO^\times$ as donor:

$$O \,\square^\times \rightleftarrows O \,\square^\cdot + \ominus$$

[3] The wurtzite lattice is closely related to the diamond lattice, for which the interstitial positions were shown in Fig. II.3.1.

Furthermore, we shall not enter into a discussion of the effects which occur when several imperfections form closely associated clusters.[1]

We turn now to the question of the laws which govern the concentration of the various impurity and imperfection types in a crystal.   We

---

● ( ) = Substitutional Impurity
Example: Arsenic atom in a germanium position in the germanium lattice

$$\text{As} \bullet^\times (\text{Ge}) \rightleftarrows \text{As} \bullet^{\cdot} (\text{Ge}) + \ominus$$

○ = *Interstitial Occupancy*
Example: Zinc atom in an interstitial position in the zinc oxide lattice

$$\text{Zn} \bigcirc^\times \rightleftarrows \text{Zn} \bigcirc^{\cdot} + \ominus$$

□ = *Vacancy*
Example: Nickel vacancy in the nickel oxide lattice

$$\text{Ni} \square^\times \rightleftarrows \text{Ni} \square' + \oplus$$

Charge condition of the impurity or imperfection in the undisturbed lattice:
   $^\times$ = neutral
   $^{\cdot}$ = singly positively charged
   $^{\cdot\cdot}$ = doubly positively charged
   $'$ = singly negatively charged
   $''$ = doubly negatively charged

FIG. II.4.2. The Schottky impurity and imperfection symbols.

assume, a priori, that these concentrations may be temperature dependent and that changes in temperature cause impurity and imperfection reactions, which lead to changes in the respective concentrations.

§5. Impurity and Imperfection Reactions

To permit dissociation or association processes during a chemical reaction, at least one of the reaction partners must be mobile, since spatial separations or combinations are involved.   We are by now fully acquainted with the mobility of electrons $\ominus$ and holes $\oplus$, respectively, so that the impurity and imperfection reactions mentioned so far do not require a new concept.   They constitute an analogy to the dissociation-association equilibrium of a donor

$$D^\times \rightleftarrows D^+ + \ominus$$

or an acceptor

$$A^\times \rightleftarrows A^- + \oplus$$

---

[1] See, for instance, the comprehensive summary of H. Pick, *Naturwiss.*, **38:** 323 (1951), particularly pp. 328 and 329; and F. Seitz, *Phys. Rev.*, **83:** 134, (1951), particularly pp. 136 and 137.

The occurrence of diffusion, electrolysis, and in general the processes of chemical reactions in solids shows that the migration of matter is, after all, possible in solids which seem to be so compact and impenetrable. Although macroscopic imperfections such as cracks and large dislocations can play a role (e.g., diffusion at grain boundaries), it has become increasingly clear during the last twenty years that migration of matter can take place even within a single crystallite. This is possible only if the lattice atoms are not irremovably fixed in their prescribed lattice positions, so that deviations from the ideal lattice structure can occur. The presence of atomic disorder, i.e., the existence of atomic imperfections, allows migration processes through the transport of matter within a crystallite. Similar to the mobility of

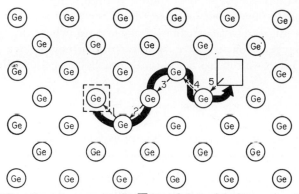

FIG. II.5.1. Migration of a vacancy Ge □ from left to right by means of the steps 1, 2, 3, 4, and 5 of the neighbor atoms from right to left.

electrons $\ominus$ and holes $\oplus$ in the crystal lattice, a lattice vacancy Ge □, for instance, possesses a certain mobility in a Ge lattice which is, however, orders of magnitude smaller than the electronic mobilities $\mu_\ominus$ and $\mu_\oplus$. This mobility is particularly easy to comprehend in the case of a vacancy. If a neighboring atom oscillates momentarily with an unusually large amplitude of its thermal vibration, it can jump over into the new equilibrium position, provided that the amplitude is in the direction of the vacancy (Fig. II.5.1). Thus the Ge atom has moved the distance between two adjacent atoms to the left, whereas the vacancy has moved the same distance to the right. If this process is repeated, one can speak of a migration of the vacancy rather than an atom, for a different Ge atom is involved in the move in each case. The migration of a vacancy is, in effect, nothing else than the transport of the charge and mass of an atom through the crystal in the opposite direction.

A Ge atom which is located in an interstitial position can also migrate by jumping from one interstitial position to the next adjacent one, for there is plenty of space in the Ge lattice for this process. Furthermore, experimental observations leave no doubt that substitutional impurities and, in general, all types of imperfections have a certain mobility in the valence as well as in the ionic crystals.

Thus with the introduction of the Schottky symbols for the various imperfection and impurity types, the number of possible reactions to be investigated has increased enormously compared with the few just mentioned. Although the Schottky symbols and the introduction of reaction equations may initially have appeared to be trivial, they now become indispensable aids in visualizing the many phenomena.

We shall mention, as a first example, the reaction between zinc oxide and a surrounding oxygen atmosphere at high temperatures $> 500°C$. The previously mentioned (see page 41) interstitial zinc ions $Zn\, \bigcirc\cdot$ or $Zn\, \bigcirc^{\times}$ can migrate to the surface of the crystal, where they recombine with the oxygen from the atmosphere to form new lattice molecules. Such a reaction establishes an equilibrium between the following two conditions:

Original crystal + zinc imperfection + oxygen atmosphere

$$\leftrightarrows$$

Original crystal + additional lattice molecules + oxygen atmosphere
$$- \text{ oxygen molecules}$$

The actual "medium" in which this process takes place, namely, the original crystal, together with the oxygen atmosphere, can be left out on both sides of the reaction symbol $\rightleftarrows$. We obtain in a more quantitative form:

$$2Zn\, \bigcirc^{\times} \rightleftarrows 2ZnO - O_2^{(gas)}$$

The neutral interstitials $Zn\, \bigcirc^{\times}$ give off at least one electron $\ominus$ at these high temperatures

$$Zn\, \bigcirc^{\times} \to Zn\, \bigcirc\cdot + \ominus$$

so that the final equation can be written

$$2Zn\, \bigcirc\cdot + 2 \ominus + O_2^{(gas)} \rightleftarrows 2ZnO \qquad \text{(II.5.01)}$$

A further example is the reaction between an NiO crystal and a surrounding O_2 atmosphere. In analogy to the preceding ZnO example, crystal molecules are formed at the crystal surface and Ni is transported from the interior of the crystal to the surface by the migration of the imperfections in NiO. These imperfections, in contrast to the interstitial metal ions of ZnO, are negatively charged or neutral nickel vacancies[1] Ni $\square''$ or Ni $\square'$ or Ni $\square^\times$. In order to effect a nickel transport from the interior to the surface, the nickel vacancies Ni $\square^\times$ must migrate from the surface into the interior, so that the reaction equation has the following form:

Original crystal + oxygen atmosphere

$$\leftrightarrows$$

Original crystal + additional lattice molecules + nickel vacancies
+ oxygen atmosphere − oxygen molecules

or in the more quantitative form:

$$0 \rightleftarrows 2NiO + 2Ni\ \square^\times - O_2^{(gas)}$$

The probable liberation of a hole $\oplus$ from the neutral nickel vacancy Ni $\square^\times$ at these high temperatures leads to the following reaction equation:

$$O_2^{(gas)} \rightleftarrows 2NiO + 2Ni\ \square' + 2\ \oplus$$

Further examples for reaction equations are the following four, which describe the introduction of ions of higher and lower valence into the two host lattices ZnO and NiO, as discussed on page 36:

$$Al_2O_3 \rightleftarrows 2Al\ \bullet\ (Zn) + 2 \ominus + 2ZnO + \tfrac{1}{2}O_2^{(gas)}$$
$$Li_2O \rightleftarrows 2Li\ \bullet'\ (Zn) - 2 \ominus + 2ZnO - \tfrac{1}{2}O_2^{(gas)}$$
$$Li_2O \rightleftarrows 2Li\ \bullet'\ (Ni) + 2 \oplus + 2NiO - \tfrac{1}{2}O_2^{(gas)}$$
$$Cr_2O_3 \rightleftarrows 2Cr\ \bullet\ (Ni) - 2 \oplus + 2NiO + \tfrac{1}{2}O_2^{(gas)}$$

These equations describe the conductivity-increasing or decreasing effect of the foreign ions and the oxygen exchange with the surrounding atmosphere. The conductivity can be calculated as a function of the partial oxygen pressure of the surrounding atmosphere, as will be shown on page 51 with the help of simple examples.

§6. Calculation of Equilibrium Concentrations with the Aid of the Laws of Mass Action

The significance of these reaction equations, some of which we have encountered previously, goes far beyond a means of general orientation.

[1] The energy necessary for the creation of a certain type of imperfection determines whether a lattice contains predominantly interstitials or vacancies or both, namely, cations or anions. Concerning the calculation of such activation energies, see W. Jost, *Trans. Faraday Soc.*, **34** II: 860 (1938). W. Jost, "Diffusion und chemische Reaktion in festen Stoffen," T. Steinkopf, Leipzig, 1937. N. V. Mott and M. J. Littleton, *Trans. Faraday Soc.*, **34:** 485 (1938). E. S. Rittner, R. A. Hutner, and F. K. Du Pré, *J. chem. Phys.*, **17**, 198, 204 (1949); **18:** 379 (1950). P. Brauer, *Z. Naturforsch.*, **7a:** 372 (1952).

They are rather the basis for the computation of equilibrium concentrations of the reaction partners.   We shall demonstrate this with the help of one of the simplest reactions, namely, the dissociation and association of a donor:

$$D^{\times} \rightleftarrows D^{+} + \ominus$$

The concentrations of the participating partners in such a reaction follow the so-called law of mass action[1]

$$K_D \cdot n_{D^{\times}} = n_{D^{+}} \cdot n_{\ominus}$$

This law is best explained with the help of the following reasoning.[2] The number of dissociation processes per unit time and volume is proportional to the concentration $n_{D^{\times}}$ and inversely proportional to the mean lifetime $\tau_{D^{\times}}$ of the undissociated donors:

$$\frac{\text{Dissociation processes}}{\text{cm}^3 \text{ sec}} = \frac{1}{\tau_{D^{\times}}} \cdot n_{D^{\times}} \qquad (\text{II.6.01})$$

The number of association processes per unit time and volume is proportional to the concentrations of the two reaction partners, for association can take place only when two reaction partners D^{+} and $\ominus$ meet in space, which occurs more often the more representatives of the two types are present:[3]

$$\frac{\text{Association processes}}{\text{cm}^3 \text{ sec}} = r_D n_{D^{+}} \cdot n_{\ominus} \qquad (\text{II.6.02})$$

r_D is the recombination coefficient for the recombination D^{+} and $\ominus$. The number of dissociation and association processes must be the same at equilibrium:

$$\frac{1}{\tau_{D^{\times}}} n_{D^{\times}} = r_D n_{D^{+}} \cdot n_{\ominus} \qquad (\text{II.6.03})$$

The law of mass action is thus

$$K_D n_{D^{\times}} = n_{D^{+}} \cdot n_{\ominus} \qquad (\text{II.6.04})$$

[1] In the following, we shall encounter the concentrations of many other "particles" such as positively charged sodium vacancies Na $\square^{\cdot}$. We choose the symbol n for these values with the Schottky symbol as subscript, so that the above example is described by $n_{\text{Na } \square^{\cdot}}$.   Correspondingly, we shall write $n_{\oplus}$ and $n_{\ominus}$ for the concentrations of electrons and holes instead of n and p in this chapter as well as in Chap. IX.

[2] The kinetic foundation of the law of mass action, as previously sketched, is treated in more detail on pp. 329 to 330.   For the foundation on a statistical basis, see pp. 317 to 320.

[3] The fact that no further sum terms are added, such as $n_{D^{+}}^{2} n_{\ominus}^{1}$, $n_{D^{+}}^{3} n_{\ominus}^{1}$, . . . , $n_{D^{+}}^{1} n_{\ominus}^{2}$, $n_{D^{+}}^{1} n_{\ominus}^{3}$, . . . , etc., is based on the assumption of "sufficient" dilution of the reaction partners to which we restrict this discussion.

with the mass-action constant

$$K_D = \frac{1}{r_D \tau_{D^\times}} \tag{II.6.05}$$

If the temperature of the crystal is high enough, a thermal collision often has enough energy to dissociate an associated donor. In this case, the lifetime $\tau_{D^\times}$ is small and the mass-action constant $K_D = 1/r_D \tau_{D^\times}$ large. Statistics teaches in detail[1] that

$$K_D = \tfrac{1}{2} N_C \, e^{-\frac{E_{CD}}{kT}} \tag{II.6.06}$$

where N_C is the so-called effective density of states in the conduction band[2] $2.5 \cdot 10^{19}$ cm$^{-3} (m_{\text{eff}}/m)^{3/2} (T/300°\text{K})^{3/2}$ and E_{CD} is the dissociation energy of a donor.

The concentrations $n_{D^\times}$, n_{D^+}, and $n_\ominus$ are not determined by the law of mass action alone. We must resort to additional equations which depend on the conditions of the experiment. In experiments far enough below the melting point, the total number n_D of donors per unit volume of the crystal is in general independent of temperature:[3]

$$n_{D^\times} + n_{D^+} = n_D \tag{II.6.07}$$

From this total balance (II.6.07) of the donors and from the law of mass action (II.6.04), we obtain

$$n_{D^\times} = n_D \, \frac{1}{1 + \dfrac{K_D}{n_\ominus}} \tag{II.6.08}$$

$$n_{D^+} = n_D \, \frac{1}{1 + \dfrac{n_\ominus}{K_D}} \tag{11.6.09}$$

and we see that the charge condition of the donors is dependent on the electron concentration $n_\ominus$ which can be adjusted by experimental conditions that are independently variable. We shall leave this until later and start with the discussion of Eqs. (II.6.08) and (II.6.09). Two cases can be distinguished:

The case of unsaturated donors:

$$n_\ominus \gg K_D \qquad n_{D^\times} \approx n_D \qquad n_{D^+} \approx n_D \cdot \frac{K_D}{n_\ominus} \ll n_D \tag{II.6.10}$$

[1] See Eq. (VIII.5.20).

[2] See Eqs. (VIII.4.04) and (VIII.4.17).

[3] At temperatures far below the melting point of the crystal, the atoms and ions change places very seldom. A certain degree of disorder established at higher temperatures is frozen in at the lower temperatures. For further details, see p. 53.

The case of saturated donors:

$$n_\ominus \ll K_D \qquad n_{D^\times} \approx n_D \cdot \frac{n_\ominus}{K_D} \ll n_D \qquad n_{D^+} \approx n_D \qquad (\text{II.6.11})$$

If there are many electrons ($n_\ominus \gg K_D$), many recombination partners $\ominus$ are available to the donors. Therefore most donors are in the associated state, which is the case of unsaturated donors ($n_{D^+} \ll n_D$). If there are only a few electrons ($n_\ominus \ll K_D$), however, most donors do not find recombination partners and are in the dissociated state $D^+(n_{D^+} \approx n_D)$.

What are then the experimental means by which one can influence the electron concentration $n_\ominus$? If no further impurities or imperfections are present in the semiconductor besides the donors already considered, the electron concentration $n_\ominus$ appears to be fully determined by the neutrality requirement[1] for a crystal. For the number of positive donors D^+ must be equal to the number of negative electrons $\ominus$:

$$n_{D^+} = n_\ominus \qquad (\text{II.6.12})$$

from which follows with (II.6.09)

$$n_{D^+} = n_\ominus = K_D \left[-\frac{1}{2} + \sqrt{\frac{1}{4} + \frac{n_D}{K_D}} \right] \qquad (\text{II.6.13})$$

In spite of this it is possible, at least in principle, to establish either the unsaturated or saturated condition by varying the temperature. At low temperatures

$$T \ll \frac{1}{k} E_{CD} \cdot \frac{1}{\ln \dfrac{N_C}{2n_D}} \qquad (\text{II.6.14})$$

we find
$$\tfrac{1}{2} N_C \, e^{-\frac{E_{CD}}{kT}} = K_D \ll n_D$$

and from (II.6.13) one obtains the limiting relation

$$n_{D^+} = n_\ominus \approx K_D \sqrt{\frac{n_D}{K_D}} \gg K_D$$

which corresponds, according to (II.6.10), to the unsaturated impurity case. This leads finally to

$$n_\ominus \approx \sqrt{n_D K_D} \approx \sqrt{n_D N_C} \, e^{-\frac{\frac{1}{2} E_{CD}}{kT}} \qquad (\text{II.6.15})$$

The temperature dependence of the electron concentration, and thereby essentially also that of the conductivity, is, in this case, deter-

[1] Apart from surface or boundary-layer effects.

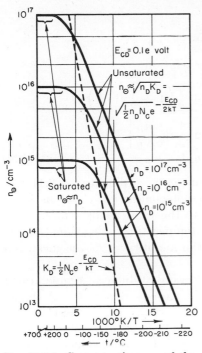

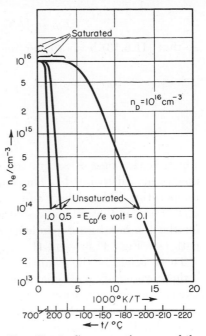

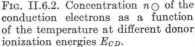

Fig. II.6.1. Concentration $n_\ominus$ of the conduction electrons as a function of the temperature at different donor concentrations n_D.

Fig. II.6.2. Concentration $n_\bigcirc$ of the conduction electrons as a function of the temperature at different donor ionization energies E_{CD}.

mined by *half* the activation energy E_{CD} of the donors (see Figs. II.6.1 and II.6.2). We find, however, that at high temperatures[1]

$$T \gg \frac{1}{k} E_{CD} \cdot \frac{1}{\ln \dfrac{N_c}{2n_D}} \qquad (II.6.16)$$

[1] One might easily be misled to the erroneous conclusion that dissociation of the great majority of donors is possible only if the mean energy content kT of a thermal collision is large compared to the dissociation energy E_{CD} of the donors. The condition for donor saturation would then be

$$T \gg \frac{1}{k} E_{CD}$$

The comparison with (II.6.16) shows, however, that the condition is in reality attenuated by a factor $(1/\ln N_C/2n_D)$. The mistake in this reasoning lies in the fact that the number of the dissociating collisions is not compared with the number of the recombination processes, which would be correct, but rather with the number of *all* collisions, which is quite irrelevant for the final equilibrium condition.

the mass-action constant is

$$K_D = \tfrac{1}{2}N_C\, e^{-\frac{E_{CD}}{kT}} \gg n_D$$

so that (II.6.13) leads to the limiting relation

$$n_{D^+} = n_\ominus = K_D\left[-\frac{1}{2} + \frac{1}{2}\left(1 + \frac{1}{2}\, 4\, \frac{n_D}{K_D}\right)\right]$$

$$= K_D\left[-\frac{1}{2} + \frac{1}{2} + \frac{n_D}{K_D}\right]$$

$$n_{D^+} = n_\ominus = n_D (\ll K_D) \tag{II.6.17}$$

which is the case of saturated impurities according to (II.6.11); all donors are dissociated. The number of conduction electrons $n_\ominus$ is temperature independent and equal to the total donor concentration n_D. The conductivity is essentially temperature independent except for the temperature dependence of the mobility or of the mean free path (see Figs. II.6.1 and II.6.2).

These would be the conditions in a crystal at different temperatures, if there were only one type of impurity, namely, donors D. A change in electron concentration in the neutral crystal such as the transition from saturation to the unsaturated condition can, in this case, be effected only by a change in temperature. If one introduces a second type of impurity into the crystal, however, the dissociation-association conditions of the original impurity type can be influenced by means of the concentration of the second impurity type. This second type of impurity can be represented by donors with a different activation energy or by acceptors which become negatively charged when capturing an electron. A detailed discussion of this problem would consume too much space. We see, a priori, that a second type of impurity introduces two new unknown concentrations into the problem, namely, those of the associated and of the dissociated impurities. The dissociation-association equilibrium of this second type of impurity is also governed by a law of mass action, and the sum of the associated and dissociated impurity concentrations is equal to the total number of the introduced impurities. Thus two new equations are added, and the problem is again fully determined.

The reaction equations

$$2\text{Zn}\, \bigcirc^\cdot + 2\ominus + O_2^{(\text{gas})} \rightleftarrows 2\text{ZnO} \tag{II.5.01}$$

are also governed by a law of mass action in the case of sufficient "dilution" of the reaction partners. In this case, we can interpret the reaction process from left to right as *association* of two Zn ions in interstitial Zn positions $\text{Zn}_\bigcirc{}^\cdot$, two quasi-free electrons $\ominus$, and an oxygen molecule O_2 (gas) of the gas atmosphere. The frequency of such an association is again equal to the product of the concentrations of each single reaction partner. If *two* reaction partners are of the same type, the concentration of this type occurs *twice* as a factor. The coefficients of the reaction equation appear, therefore, as exponents of the concentrations in the law of mass action

$$n_{Zn\,O\cdot}^2 \cdot n_{\ominus}^2 \cdot n_{O_2} \text{ (gas)} = K_1\, n_{ZnO}^2$$

The concentration of the lattice molecules ZnO is incomparably larger than the concentration of all reaction partners, so that it remains practically unchanged during any conceivable reaction process. Therefore, the ZnO concentration is included in the constant, and the law of mass action assumes the form

$$n_{Zn\,O\cdot}^2 \cdot n_{\ominus}^2 = K_2 \cdot n_{O_2}^{-1} \text{ (gas)} = K_3 p_{O_2}^{-1} \text{ (gas)} \qquad \text{(II.6.18)}$$

where instead of the concentration n_{O_2} (gas) of the oxygen molecules in the gas phase the partial oxygen pressure is introduced because it can be obtained directly by experiment.

If the $ZnO\cdot$ are the only imperfection in the ZnO, the quasi-neutrality condition requires

$$n_{\ominus} = n_{Zn\,O\cdot}$$

and from (II.6.18) follows

$$n_{\ominus} = K_3^{\frac{1}{4}} \cdot p_{O_2}^{-\frac{1}{4}} \text{ (gas)}$$

The experiment[1] gives a conductivity proportional to $p_{O_2}^{-\frac{1}{4.3}\,\text{(gas)}}$.

Hence, the number of electrons and with it the conductivity decrease with increasing partial oxygen pressure in the adjacent gas phase: ZnO is a "reduction semiconductor."

If the corresponding reasoning is applied to the previously discussed equilibrium between a NiO crystal and an adjacent oxygen gas phase at elevated temperatures, we find[2]

$$n_{\oplus} = K_3^{\frac{1}{4}} \cdot p_{O_2}^{+\frac{1}{4}} \text{ (gas)}$$

This law has also been reasonably well verified by experiment.[3] NiO behaves as an "oxidation semiconductor" whose conductivity increases with increasing partial oxygen pressure.

[1] H. H. Baumbach and C. Wagner, Z. physik. Chem., **B22**: 199 (1933).

[2] Concerning the symbol $n_{\oplus}$ in place of p for hole concentration as used elsewhere in this book, see footnote 1, p. 46.

[3] H. H. Baumbach and C. Wagner, Z. physik. Chem., **B24**: 59 (1934).

The two examples show that this difference is causally connected with the electron conduction in ZnO on one hand and with the hole conduction in NiO on the other hand. Thus we obtain the rule:

Electron conductors are reduction semiconductors.

Hole conductors are oxidation semiconductors.

§7. Fundamentals of Atomic Disorder

An unbiased reader who is confronted for the first time with the atomic-disorder phenomena described in this chapter is apt to assume an attitude which can be expressed as follows: "These disorder phenomena cause certainly very interesting effects. However, they are all 'dirt effects.' It would be important to seek a solution to the problem of making crystals with a perfect lattice structure which will then allow the study of ideal crystals."

It may be well to point out that such an escape from the confusion of the disorder phenomena into the simplicity of the perfect lattice is *fundamentally* impossible. A certain degree of atomic disorder is basically unavoidable except at absolute zero, and at finite temperatures the perfect lattice is an improbable and anomalous exception just as a gas in which all molecules have exactly the same velocity.

An exact proof of this fact requires the extensive use of general statistics. We must restrict ourselves to plausibility considerations, which we shall demonstrate with the example of NaCl and AgBr. Both substances shall be of absolute chemical purity. Using this assumption, which is in principle, though not in practice, feasible, we exclude substitutional imperfections (impurities), so that the only possible imperfections are lattice vacancies or interstitials.[1] The following reactions can take place between these imperfections:

$$\text{Na } \bigcirc^{\cdot} + \text{Na } \square' \rightleftarrows 0 \qquad (\text{II.7.01})$$
$$\text{Cl } \bigcirc' + \text{Cl } \square^{\cdot} \rightleftarrows 0 \qquad (\text{II.7.02})$$
$$\text{Na } \bigcirc^{\cdot} + \text{Cl } \bigcirc' \rightleftarrows \text{NaCl} \qquad (\text{II.7.03})$$

Further reactions such as

$$\text{NaCl} + \text{Na } \square' + \text{Cl } \square^{\cdot} \rightleftarrows 0$$

can be constructed from Eqs. (II.7.01) to (II.7.03) by subtracting the first two equations (II.7.01) and (II.7.02) from the third equation (II.7.03).

---

[1] It is extremely improbable to find in the NaCl lattice a Cl atom or ion in an Na place, or vice versa. so that we need not consider this type of disorder.

The laws of mass action corresponding to Eqs. (II.7.01) to (II.7.03)

$$n_{\text{Na } \bigcirc} \cdot n_{\text{Na } \square'} = a \qquad \text{(II.7.04)}$$

$$n_{\text{Cl } \bigcirc'} \cdot n_{\text{Cl } \square} = b \qquad \text{(II.7.05)}$$

$$n_{\text{Na } \bigcirc} \cdot n_{\text{Cl } \bigcirc'} = c \qquad \text{(II.7.06)[1]}$$

show that all three mass-action constants a, b, and c must be zero, if all imperfection concentrations are to be zero. This, however, is possible only at the temperature $T = 0$; for the constants in the laws of mass action are generally governed by relations of the following type:[2]

$$a = N^2 \, e^{-\frac{E_a}{kT}}$$

N = total number of Na$^+$ and Cl$^-$ lattice positions per unit volume[1]
$= 2n_{\text{NaCl}}$.

We summarize: The perfect lattice can exist only at the temperature $T = 0$, where alone all disorder concentrations can vanish. At any temperature $T > 0$, a certain atomic disorder is present at thermal *equilibrium* and the ideal lattice occupancy assumes the character of a special case, which can be realized only in one way and therefore is so extremely rare during the fluctuation processes around the equilibrium condition that it can be ignored for all practical purposes.

The above-mentioned fluctuation processes can take place only if lattice atoms change their position. Such position changes require that lattice atoms overcome energy thresholds using the energy derived from thermal collisions. At low temperatures, the number of thermal collisions of sufficient intensity is very rare. The processes of position change and the fluctuations therefore freeze in at low temperatures. As a result, the degree of disorder corresponding to the equilibrium condition is established only at higher temperatures and a state of excessive disorder is frozen in by cooling to lower temperatures; this is, of course, only a different way of saying that the time required to establish the equilibrium condition corresponding to the lower temperature would be unrealistically long.

We see now that the fundamentally unavoidable degree of disorder associated with the study of thermal equilibrium can in practice be realized only if considerable precautions, such as slow cooling, etc., are taken. While this degree of disorder can be more or less attained through the skill of the experimental scientist, it is fundamentally impossible to reduce it further or even to attain ideal lattice occupancy.

---

[1] The concentration n_{NaCl} of the lattice molecules is again included in the constant c of the law of mass action.

[2] See, for instance, W. Jost, *op. cit.*, particularly p. 61, Eqs. (33) to (35). Concerning the definition of the lattice concentrations, see Jost, pp. 53 and 58.

§8. Problems

1. The calculation in §1 of the ionization energy of a donor does not take into account the fact that the effective mass of an electron is generally different from its free mass. Explain why a smaller effective mass increases the first Bohr orbit, and by what factor. How does this alter the ionization energy? Give numerical values for germanium, assuming[1] $m_{eff} = \frac{1}{4}m_0$.

2. (Geometry of the diamond lattice.) In Fig. II.1.1a the geometry of the diamond lattice is shown. How many atoms does every cell contain, if one counts atoms that are shared by several cells only as fractional atoms?

Consider all the atoms shown in Fig. II.1.1a as perfect spheres, just touching each other. If the length of the cube shown in the drawing is $2d$, what is the radius of the atomic spheres? Give the numerical value for the germanium atom.

3. (Interstitial positions.) Show that the radius of the largest atom that would fit into an interstitial position in the diamond lattice is equal to the radius of the host atom itself. Which lattice atoms would just touch an interstitial atom of the maximal size if that interstitial atom were put into the center of the cube shown in Fig. II.1.1a? Show all the other possible interstitial positions in that cube, including the ones that are shared with adjoining cubes. What is their number and what is the ratio of lattice positions to interstitial positions? What kind of a lattice structure do the interstitial positions themselves have?

4. At what acceptor density does germanium have its highest resistivity, assuming that all acceptors are negatively ionized? At what acceptor density would, under this condition, the conductivity again pass through the intrinsic value? What are the donor or acceptor densities in germanium with a resistivity of 30 ohm-cm? (See Probs. 1 to 3 of Chap. I.)

[1] $m_{eff} = \frac{1}{4}m_0$ is an average value given by E. M. Conwell, *Proc. IRE*, **40**: 1330 (1952). For a detailed treatment taking into account the directional dependence of m_{eff} we refer to M. A. Lampert, *Phys. Rev.*, **97**: 352 (1955).

CHAPTER III

The Hole

§1. Introduction

The measurement of the Hall effect is an important source of information in the investigation of the conduction mechanism of a particular solid; for one can derive from it the mobility and the sign (negative or positive) of the charge carriers. The experiment consists of making a current of density **i** flow in the x direction through a block of the material to be investigated while a magnetic field **H** is applied in the z direction. Figure III.1.1 shows that at the beginning of the

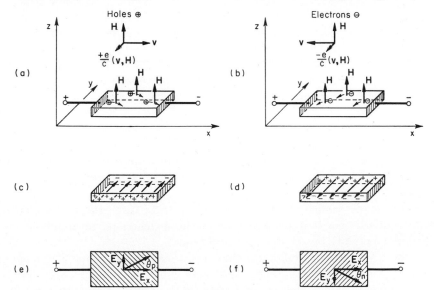

Fig. III.1.1. The Hall effect. (a) *Beginning of the process:* Deflection of the ⊕ in the negative y direction by the Lorentz force. (b) *Beginning of the process:* Deflection of the ⊖ in the negative y direction by the Lorentz force. (c) *Stationary condition:* The charging of the sample sides and the electrical cross field E_y. (d) *Stationary condition:* The charging of the sample sides and the electrical cross field E_y. (e) *Stationary condition:* The rotation of the field strength by the Hall angle. (f) *Stationary condition:* The rotation of the field strength by the Hall angle.

process the Lorentz force $\pm e/c[\mathbf{v}, \mathbf{H}] = \pm e/c[\mathbf{i}/\pm en, \mathbf{H}] = [\mathbf{i}/nc, \mathbf{H}]$ deflects the charge carriers in the negative y direction independently of the positive or negative charge of the particles. The front side of the sample is thus charged positively or negatively with respect to the back side, depending on the sign of the charge carriers, until the transverse electric field E_y just compensates the transverse force $[\pm (e/c)\mathbf{v}, \mathbf{H}]$ of the magnetic field. In the steady-state condition the field strength $\mathbf{E}$ is rotated out of the x axis by an angle which can be calculated with the help of Eq. (I.2.04) for holes

$$\tan \Theta_p = \frac{E_y}{E_x} = \frac{+\dfrac{1}{c} v \cdot H}{+\dfrac{1}{\mu_p} \cdot v} = \frac{1}{c} \mu_p \cdot H$$

or for electrons

$$\tan \Theta_n = \frac{E_y}{E_x} = \frac{-\dfrac{1}{c} v \cdot H}{+\dfrac{1}{\mu_n} v} = -\frac{1}{c} \mu_n \cdot H$$

The angle is therefore positive for holes and negative for electrons. The sign of the charge carriers can now be derived from the sign of the rotation of the field strength $\mathbf{E}$. In metals, the current is carried by the negative electrons. The resulting negative sign of the Hall angle Θ_n is called the normal Hall effect.

If in a particular case the Hall effect is anomalous and hence indicates positive-charge carriers, one might think at first of ion conduction by positive ions. In this case the current transport would be accompanied by the migration of matter, quite apart from the fact that ionic conduction in solids produces only very low conductivities of at most 10^{-7} ohm^{-1} cm^{-1}. In a number of metals—Mo, Zn, Cd, Pb, Ni— and in many semiconductors—such as Se and Cu_2O—the Hall effect is anomalous, which indicates positive-charge carriers, although there cannot possibly be any ionic conduction.

It is, a priori, beyond doubt that positrons cannot be made responsible for this observation, for the positrons which are found in cosmic-ray experiments have a very short lifetime in the presence of electrons. In the presence of the high electron concentration in a solid, a large positron concentration could be maintained only if positrons were continually created at a high rate. However, the creation of an electron-positron pair requires an energy of at least 10^6 ev; for, according to the Einstein relation, even the rest energy of two particles with the electron mass $m = 9 \cdot 10^{-28}$ g is $2mc^2 = 1.6 \cdot 10^{-6}$ erg $= 1 \cdot 10^6$ ev. On the other hand, the energy available in a solid is only the thermal energy $kT \approx 2.5 \cdot 10^{-2}$ ev (at room temperature), which is not nearly sufficient for the creation of an electron-positron pair.

Hence there is no doubt that the current transport in Se, Cu_2O, etc., is only *apparently* carried by relatively few positively charged electrons and that this can only be the relatively *simple* result of a *complicated* superposition of the contributions of many ordinary negative electrons.

In order to gain insight into this interaction of many negative electrons, we recall a few statements[1] concerning the behavior of a crystal electron in the periodic potential field of the lattice:

1. The energy spectrum of a crystal exhibits the well-known band structure (Figs. I.2.3, I.2.6, I.3.6, and I.3.8).[2] In a semiconducting crystal, the so-called valence band is almost entirely filled and the so-called conduction band is almost entirely empty and contains only the "free" conduction electrons[3] near its lower edge.

2. The Pauli principle must be applied to all electrons of a crystal. Each electron is, therefore, in a quantum state which can at most be occupied by one other electron with the opposite spin.

3. If, besides the lattice forces, an additional force—e.g., an electric field applied to the entire crystal—acts on the crystal electron, the reaction of the crystal electron is strongly dependent on the quantum state within the band spectrum in which it happens to be. The acceleration of a crystal electron by an external additional force is determined by an "effective mass" which has positive values for an electron in the lower part of a band and negative[4] values in the upper part of a band.

The current in a crystal is, therefore, not composed of many equal contributions, but rather, the contributions of the single electrons are, in general, very different. In particular, it is understandable that the electrons of the upper half of the valence band ($m_{eff} < 0$) compensate the contributions of the electrons of the lower half of the valence band ($m_{eff} > 0$). It can be shown that perfect compensation is obtained in a completely filled band. A filled band, therefore, does not contribute to the conductivity.

In a band where a few electrons are missing from full occupancy the compensation is not complete, and such an *almost* filled band does, in

---

[1] See also Chap. I.
[2] See also Chap. VII, §2 and §4.
[3] See also Chap. VIII, §4 and §5.
[4] See also Chap. VII, §6.

fact, furnish a contribution to the current.   Heisenberg[1] has demonstrated that this current contribution is the same as if the few empty states of the almost filled band were occupied by electrons with positive charge.   The mass of these fictitious particles must be chosen, according to their contribution, equal to the effective mass of an ordinary electron in the corresponding empty crystal state but with opposite sign.   As the holes are concentrated at the upper edge of the valence band (see page 22) where the effective electron masses are negative, the effective mass of the holes must be chosen positive, according to the stated rule.

It has been found that the equivalence between the few holes and the incomplete totality of the numerous valence electrons can be demonstrated without calculation.   We shall follow this course below. Since the concept of the effective mass and particularly its negative values in the upper half of an energy band are of decisive importance, the behavior of an electron in a crystal under the influence of an external force will be considered in §2 as a starting point.   In §3 we shall prove the postulated equivalence between an incomplete band, which is occupied by $N - M$ electrons, and M holes.   Then §4 will show clearly that this entire concept of holes and hole conduction is only a symbolic description of a really very complicated situation. We shall show that the validity of this equivalence ceases as soon as interaction between electrons is considered.

§2. The Negative Values of the Effective Mass in the Upper Part of an Energy Band

If an electron moves in a force field, its energy usually changes.   If, for instance, the force field **F** and the electron velocity **v** have the same direction, the force does work on the electron and increases its energy. If the force **F** and the electron velocity have opposite directions, the electron is slowed down and its kinetic energy is reduced.   An electron in a crystal, in contrast to a free electron, is almost exclusively subject to the forces of the lattice potential, the effect of which is much larger than that of any conceivable externally applied force.   Even field strengths of the order of the breakdown field, namely, about 10^5 volts cm^{-1}, do work equal to only about $3 \cdot 10^{-3}$ ev in the displacement of an electron over the distance of one lattice constant, $3 \cdot 10^{-8}$ cm, whereas the lattice potential itself changes by several volts within a lattice constant.   This allows us to utilize the force-free

[1] W. Heisenberg, *Ann. Physik*, **10**: 388 (1931).

band spectrum in the treatment of the behavior of an electron in a crystal under the influence of an external force. The following is the resulting detailed picture:

Let us assume that the electron is, for instance, in a quantum state in the middle of a band. Its eigenfunction is then essentially a *running* wave, and the electron transports a charge which constitutes a current. If a force acts in the direction of propagation of the wave, the energy of the electron is increased and it must change into a higher quantum state. After a while it occupies the highest quantum state in the particular band, namely, the upper band edge. In this state, the wavelength corresponds to the Bragg reflection condition for a certain group of lattice planes. The in-phase superposition of the spherical waves diffracted by the lattice points results in a wave propagated in the opposite direction with the same intensity, so that the electron in this quantum state is represented by a *standing* wave. The electron does not transport any charge in this state and, therefore, does not constitute a current. In spite of the energy increase, the electron has, as a result of the participation of the lattice, lost its transport action and its velocity. The electron has been slowed down to zero velocity, although the force and propagation direction of the wave, i.e., the force and electron velocity, were in the same direction.

The behavior of an electron in a crystal under the influence of the lattice is compared with a "quasi-free" electron, which is not affected by lattice forces, by describing the process on one hand by the equation

$$\mathbf{F} + \text{lattice forces} - m \cdot \frac{d\mathbf{v}}{dt} \tag{III.2.01}$$

and on the other hand by the equation

$$\mathbf{F} = m_{\text{eff}} \cdot \frac{d\mathbf{v}}{dt} \tag{III.2.02}$$

According to (III.2.02) one obtains the correct value for the acceleration $d\mathbf{v}/dt$ only if the effective mass m_{eff} of the quasi-free electron has a value[1] m_n which is different from the real mass m. In the case just considered, m_n must even be negative.

In general we find the following value[2] for m_n

$$m_n = \frac{\hbar^2}{E_n''(k, N)} \tag{III.2.03}$$

[1] To distinguish it from the effective mass m_p of holes to be introduced later.
[2] See in this connection Chap. VII, §5 and §6, particularly Eq. (VII.6.28), and D. Pfirsch and E. Spenke, Z. *Physik*, **137**: 309–312 (1954).

where E_n is the energy of the *negative* electron. E_n depends on the quantum state of the electron and is, therefore, a function of the wave number $k = 2\pi/\lambda$ of the electron (λ = de Broglie wavelength). In view of the band structure, E_n is a multivalued function of k (see Fig. III.2.1). The various branches, or more specifically "bands," are characterized by the band number N. " $'$ " indicates differentiation with respect to the wave number k.

It is now evident that in the upper part of the band the electron behaves like a free electron with a negative mass. Experience has shown that this statement is at first somewhat difficult to comprehend.

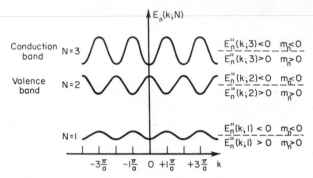

Fɪɢ. III.2.1. Electron energy E_n as a function of the wave number k. In the lower parts of the bands m_n is positive and in the upper parts it is negative.

$$[E_n'' \ (k; \ N) \ = \ \frac{\partial^2}{\partial k^2} E_n \ (k; \ N)]$$

I hope that I have helped to overcome this obstacle by pointing out as clearly as possible that the definition of the "effective" mass considers only the external force **F** and neglects entirely the strong influence of the lattice on the electron. It is not surprising that, with this approach, the proportionality factor between force and acceleration assumes most peculiar, e.g., negative, values.

However, for many considerations it is convenient to treat the totality of the electrons as a *free* electron gas. If this can be accomplished by a simple substitution of an effective mass for the real value of the electron mass, it is worth while to accept the modified mass values which can even become negative in the upper part of a band. In order to remember that the electrons are not really free but are subject to exceedingly strong lattice influences which are only apparently eliminated by an artifice, one often speaks of *quasi-free* electrons.

§3. The Equivalence of an Almost Filled Valence Band with a Fermi Gas of Quasi-free Holes

We shall now undertake the proof of the equivalence between an incompletely filled valence band and a Fermi gas of quasi-free holes. A logical step is the comparison of the following two particle ensembles:

1. $N - M$ electrons which leave M states of the N possible valence-band states unoccupied. We shall call this quantity of particles the "real almost filled valence band."

2. M fictitious positive charges $(+e)$ together with N ordinary negative electrons $(-e)$ which just fill the N available states of a valence band.[1] We shall call this quantity of particles the "filled valence band with fictitious positive additional charges."

First we shall consider the action of an external electric field on the two particle ensembles to be compared. The current thus produced is the same in both cases, provided that we can assign such properties to the M *fictitious* charges $+e$ that they move under the influence of the external electric field (and the lattice forces) in the same manner as those M electrons of the filled band which are in the M quantum states that are left unoccupied in the real valence band. This identical course in space and time of the M electrons and M fictitious positive charges can be attained simply by assigning a mass $-m$ to the positive charges. The external field as well as the lattice potential exert exactly opposite forces on the positive additional charges as on the electrons since the signs of the charges are opposite. Exactly the same motion results, however, if the sign of the mass is changed too.

From the standpoint of wave mechanics, the identical motion of the accompanied electron $(-e, +m)$ and the accompanying additional positive charge $(+e, -m)$ may be established as follows. The probability amplitude ψ_n of the *n*egative electron satisfies the Schrödinger equation

$$-\frac{\hbar^2}{2m}\Delta\psi_n - eU(\mathbf{r})\psi_n = +j\hbar\frac{\partial\psi_n}{\partial t}; \qquad U(\mathbf{r}) = \text{lattice potential}$$

(III.3.01)

The probability amplitude ψ_p of the fictitious *p*ositive additional charge satisfies the Schrödinger equation

---

[1] In this book e is always the absolute value $+1.6 \cdot 10^{-19}$ coulomb of the elementary charge, so that the charge of the negative electron is $-e$ and that of the positive hole $+e$.

$$+ \frac{\hbar^2}{2m} \Delta\psi_p + eU(\mathbf{r})\psi_p = + j\hbar \frac{\partial\psi_p}{\partial t} \qquad \text{(III.3.02)}$$

Comparison shows that the probability amplitudes ψ_n and ψ_p are not directly equal, but that they are complex conjugates.

$$\psi_n(x;\ k,\ N) = \psi_p^*(x;\ k,\ N) \qquad \text{(III.3.03)}$$

k = wave number; N = band number.

This is sufficient for the exact agreement of the space-time distribution of the probabilities $\psi_n\psi_n^*$ and $\psi_p\psi_p^*$, respectively, so that the positive charge accompanies the electron continually. If one converts to the stationary Schrödinger equations

$$- \frac{\hbar^2}{2m} \Delta\psi_n - eU(\mathbf{r})\psi_n = E_n\psi_n \qquad \text{(III.3.04)}$$

$$+ \frac{\hbar^2}{2m} \Delta\psi_p + eU(\mathbf{r})\psi_p = E_p\psi_p \qquad \text{(III.3.05)}$$

or $\qquad\qquad +\dfrac{\hbar^2}{2m} \Delta\psi_p^* + eU(\mathbf{r})\psi_p^* = E_p\psi_p^* \qquad \text{(III.3.06)}$

it can be seen that

$$E_n(k,\ N) = -E_p(k,\ N) \qquad \text{(III.3.07)}$$

This relation will be useful later.

The field thus creates the same current, on one hand, in the real almost filled valence band and, on the other hand, in the filled valence band with the fictitious positive charges of mass $-m$. If we calculate the current for the latter particles alone, the contribution of the filled valence band is eliminated; for we have already pointed out in the introduction that in a filled valence band the current contribution of the electrons in the lower part of the band with the positive effective masses and the current contribution of the upper part of the band with the negative effective masses compensate each other exactly. Therefore, the only remaining current is the original contribution of the M positive charges, namely, the "holes" with the charge $+e$ and the mass $-m$.

Similar to the case of the electrons in §2, we can now change over from the holes which are subject to the lattice forces (holes in a crystal) to the *quasi-free* holes by introducing an effective mass value m_p in place of $-m$, thus taking into account the effect of the lattice forces. In analogy to Eq. (III.2.03), we find

$$m_p = \frac{\hbar^2}{E_p''(k;\ N)} \qquad \text{(III.3.08)}$$

and with the help of (III.3.07) we obtain

$$m_p(k;\, N) \;=\; -m_n(k;\, N) \qquad\qquad \text{(III.3.09)}$$

The properties of electrons and holes are summarized once more in Fig. III.3.1.

The distribution of the M holes among the quantum states of the valence band is governed in the foregoing considerations by the following rule: Each quantum state which is not occupied in the real almost filled valence band can accommodate one hole in the filled valence band with a fictitious positive additional charge.   This rule can now be

	Electrons	Holes
Charge	$-e$	$+e$
Mass	$+m$	$-m$
Effective mass at the *upper* edge of the *valence* band	$m_n = \dfrac{\hbar^2}{E''(k,\ \text{valence})} < 0$	$m_p = -\dfrac{\hbar^2}{E''(k,\ \text{valence})} > 0$
Effective mass at the *lower* edge of the *conduction band*	$m_n = \dfrac{\hbar^2}{E''(k,\ \text{conduction})} > 0$	$m_p = -\dfrac{\hbar^2}{E''(k,\ \text{conduction})} < 0$

Fig. III.3.1. Properties of electrons and holes.
$E(k,\ \text{number of band}) = E_n(k,\ \ldots) = $ energy of the *electrons*.

replaced by one in which only holes are considered without reference to the distribution of electrons.   This comes about in the following manner:

The probability that a quantum state with the electron energy E_n is occupied by an electron is given by the Fermi distribution function

$$f(E_n) \;=\; \frac{1}{e^{\frac{E_n - E_F}{kT}} + 1}$$

The probability that this state is *not* occupied with an electron is therefore

$$1 - f(E_n) = \frac{e^{\frac{E_n - E_F}{kT}} + 1 - 1}{e^{\frac{E_n - E_F}{kT}} + 1} = \frac{e^{\frac{E_n - E_F}{kT}}}{e^{\frac{E_n - E_F}{kT}} + 1} = \frac{1}{1 + e^{-\frac{E_n - E_F}{kT}}}$$

$$= \frac{1}{e^{\frac{(-E_n) - (-E_F)}{kT}} + 1} = \frac{1}{e^{\frac{E_p - (-E_F)}{kT}} + 1} = f(E_p)$$

At the end we have put $-E_n = E_p$.   Besides, the energy of the Fermi level changes sign *as well*, like all energy values. E_p is then the energy of the positive hole; for in the potential or electrostatic part of the energy we find the charge as a factor, and in the kinetic part the mass. Both factors change their sign when we change over from electron to hole.[1]

The original rule yields the probability $1 - f(E_n)$ for the occupancy of a quantum state by a hole.   Without reference to electrons, we find the same probability of occupancy if we postulate Fermi statistics for the holes because then we have to introduce $f(E_p)$ as the probability of occupancy of a quantum state.   This is equal to $1 - f(E_n)$, according to the foregoing derivation.

In summary we see that the current contribution of the real valence band which is almost filled with $(N - M)$ electrons has exactly the same magnitude as that of a Fermi gas of M quasi-free holes with the charge $+e$ and the effective mass $m_p = -\hbar^2/E''(k, \text{valence}) > 0$.

The preceding argument can certainly be extended to the transport phenomena where magnetic fields $\mathbf{H}$ act upon the electrons.   The Lorentz force $-(e/c)\mathbf{v} \times \mathbf{H}$ which acts upon an electron moving with the velocity $\mathbf{v}$ contains also the charge as proportionality factor. Hence here, too, we must assign the mass $-m$ to the fictitious positive additional charges in order to compensate for the change of sign of the charge; the subsequent conclusions are the same as in the case of the electric fields.

Transport phenomena are not necessarily always a consequence of electric or magnetic fields; they can also be caused by concentration or temperature gradients.   The pertinent relations follow from the statistics of the participating current carriers.   We have just shown that the statistics of negative electrons lead to the same results as the Fermi statistics of positive holes, so that we are justified in applying the hole representation also to transport phenomena which are caused by concentration and temperature gradients.

Finally, if the conductor is accelerated or decelerated, the electrons in a conductor are set in motion by forces of inertia, similarly to soup which spills over in a carelessly moved plate.

If a coordinate system is, for instance, accelerated in the positive x direction, a mass M which is not acted upon by any forces will remain unmoved and stay behind with respect to the coordinate system.   To the observer, moving with the acceleration, the mass M appears to encounter a force in the direction of the negative x axis.   If the mass

---

[1] $-E_n = E_p$ also followed from the comparison of the two Schrödinger equations for electrons and holes.   See Eq. (III.3.07).

M encounters other additional forces (such as springs under tension) and the mass M performs certain motions due to these spring forces in the reference system, the observer in the accelerated reference system sees a change of these motions as if the mass M encountered an inertial force in the direction of the negative x axis in addition to the spring forces.

We shall apply these generally known relations to the accelerated solid and its electrons in the Tolman experiment: If a conductor encounters an acceleration $+\mathbf{g}$, a force $\mathbf{F} = -m\mathbf{g}$ seems to act on its electrons. This inertial force can be replaced by an electric field $\mathbf{E} = +(m/e)\mathbf{g}$; for this field would exert a force $\mathbf{F} = -e\mathbf{E} = -m\mathbf{g}$ on the electrons with their negative charges $-e$. The equivalent field $\mathbf{E}$ would, however, cause a current $\mathbf{i} = \sigma\mathbf{E}$. Therefore the acceleration $+\mathbf{g}$ of the conductor must cause a current arising from the inertial force $-m\mathbf{g}$ with a current density $\mathbf{i} = +(m/e)\sigma\mathbf{g}$, as was observed in experiments carried out by Tolman and others.

Even for such transport phenomena effected by inertial forces, we can choose either the electron or the hole representation. We have just seen that the acceleration or deceleration of a conductor acts on the observer, who is carried along, as an additional gravitational field $-\mathbf{g}$. In the same manner as one calculates the force exerted on an electron by an electric field $\mathbf{E}$, namely, by multiplication with the charge $(-e)$ one obtains the inertial force of the gravitational field $-\mathbf{g}$, namely, by multiplying with the real mass $(+m)$; for the lattice forces do not enter the picture in the calculation of the inertial force. Hence there is no possibility of overlooking them, and m_{eff} does not play any part. Accordingly, one derives the inertial force on the holes from the gravitational field $-\mathbf{g}$ by multiplication with the "true" mass $-m$. The gravitational field exerts, therefore, the inertial force $(+m) \cdot (-\mathbf{g}) = -m\mathbf{g}$ on the electrons and $(-m) \cdot (-\mathbf{g}) = +m\mathbf{g}$ on the holes.

If we calculate now the acceleration from the force, we must consider the lattice forces; this is accomplished by using the effective masses as proportionality factors between force and acceleration instead of the true masses (page 10). These have opposite signs for an electron and a hole in the same quantum state (see Fig. III.3.1). The resulting acceleration is again the same for both particles because the inertial force as well as the effective mass change their sign. This assures the permanent identity of the location in space of electron and hole. The hole representation must therefore be also applicable for the action of gravitational and inertial forces.

We have shown that the electron as well as the hole representation is applicable to transport phenomena which are caused by electric or magnetic fields, by temperature or concentration gradients, and by inertial or gravitational forces. In any specific case it is desirable to choose the representation which yields the lower carrier number because this will tend to allow the use of the Maxwell-Boltzmann limiting case of the Fermi-Dirac statistics.

For the case of a sparsely occupied conduction band, one prefers the electron representation which leads to a Maxwell-Boltzmann gas of quasi-free negative electrons with positive effective mass m_{eff}, for $m_{\ominus \text{ eff}} = \hbar^2/E''$ (k, lower edge of conduction band) $= m_n > 0$ is positive in the lower part of the conduction band.

In the case of an almost filled valence band, however, one will choose the hole representation with which one obtains a Maxwell-Boltzmann gas of quasi-free positive holes with positive effective mass

$$m_{\oplus \text{ eff}} = - \frac{\hbar^2}{E''(k, \text{ upper edge of valence band})} = m_p > 0$$

for E'' (k, valence) is negative at the upper edge of the valence band (see Fig. III.2.1).

Before concluding this §3, we shall briefly discuss another question. Sometimes the argument arises as to whether it is possible to distinguish between electron and hole conduction in a certain experiment. We can point out a relatively simple method to answer this question. The final equation for the result of the experiment in question should be, as far as possible, expressed in terms[1] of e, m, m_n, and m_p. Then we pass over from the hole conduction case p to the electron conduction case n by the following substitution[2]

$$p \to n$$
$$+e \to -e$$
$$-m \to +m$$
$$+m_p \to +m_n$$

[1] Here we often utilize the equation $\mu = (e/m_{\text{eff}})\tau$ for the carrier mobility μ. See Eq. (VII.9.25).

[2] The validity of the first three substitutions is beyond doubt. With respect to the fourth substitution, we must realize that we are *not* dealing with optional descriptions of one and the same case—such as electrons at the lower edge of the conduction band—in the electron or hole language. The following *equation* would be applicable if this were so:

$$m_{\oplus \text{ eff}} = -m_{\ominus \text{ eff}}$$

It is rather a transition between two different cases, namely, the transition from holes at the upper edge of the valence band to electrons at the lower edge of the conduction band. The correct *substitution* for this is

$$m_{\oplus \text{ eff}} = m_p \to m_{\ominus \text{ eff}} = m_n$$

In this transition $p \to n$, the result of the experiment either changes its sign or it does not. Accordingly, the experiment either allows a differentiation between hole and electron conduction or it does not. A few examples will clarify this procedure.

1. *Electric current due to an electric field.*

Experimental result:

$$\mathbf{i} = \sigma \mathbf{E}$$

Expressed in terms of e, m, m_n, m_p:

$$\mathbf{i} = e\mu_p p\mathbf{E} = \frac{e^2}{m_p} p\tau\mathbf{E}$$

Transition $p \to n$:

$$\mathbf{i} = \frac{(-e)^2}{(+m_n)} n\tau\mathbf{E} = \frac{e^2}{m_n} n\tau\mathbf{E}$$

There is no change of sign; therefore, it is not possible to distinguish between p-type and n-type.

2. *Hall effect.*

Experimental result:

$$\Theta_p \approx \frac{1}{c}\mu_p H$$

Expressed in terms of e, m, m_n, m_p:

$$\Theta_p \approx \frac{1}{c}\frac{e}{m_p}\tau H$$

Transition $p \to n$:

$$\Theta_n \approx \frac{1}{c}\frac{(-e)}{(+m_n)}\tau H = -\frac{1}{c}\frac{e}{m_n}\tau H$$

There is a change of sign; therefore, it is possible to distinguish between p-type and n-type.

3. *Tolman experiment.*

Experimental result:

$$\mathbf{i} - \frac{m}{e}\upsilon\mathbf{g}$$

Expressed in terms of e, m, m_n, m_p:

$$\mathbf{i} = \frac{m}{e}e\mu_p p\mathbf{g} = mp\frac{e}{m_p}\tau\mathbf{g}$$

Transition $p \to n$:

$$\mathbf{i} = (-m)n\frac{(-e)}{(+m_n)}\tau\mathbf{g}$$

$$= mn\frac{e}{m_n}\tau\mathbf{g}$$

There is no change of sign; therefore, it is not possible to distinguish between p-type and n-type.

Although C. G. Darwin[1] has pointed out that one cannot learn anything concerning the effective mass of the electrons from the Tolman experiment, the opposite has been assumed on occasions.[2] In order to clarify this situation, we pass beyond the somewhat formal substitu-

---

[1] C. G. Darwin, *Proc. Roy. Soc.* (*London*), **A154**: 61 (1936).
[2] Sheldon Brown and S. J. Barnett, *Phys. Rev.*, **87**: 601 (1952).

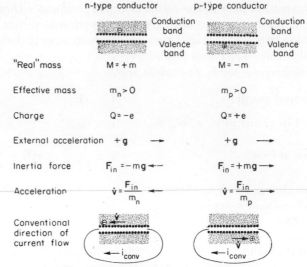

<figure>FIG. III.3.2. The Tolman experiment.</figure>

tion method of page 67 and represent the experiment with an electron and hole conductor by Fig. III.3.2.

§4. The Failure of the Hole Concept in Problems Involving Electron Interaction

The statements in §3 might give the impression that the hole concept is not only particularly useful in the case of almost filled bands, but also possible and completely permissible in all cases. Concerning the correctness of the last statement we find, upon critical examination of the derivations in §3, that this is not true because of the interaction between electrons. The first step in §3 consisted of the substitution of a filled band with N electrons and of M fictitious positive charges with negative masses for the band with $(N - M)$ electrons and M empty states. The statement, which was made in the course of this first step, that $N - M$ original electrons move in the same manner in both cases is probably correct even if we consider the interaction between the electrons.[1]

In the second step of the foregoing discussion it is stated that in

---

[1] Incidentally, a closer inspection of the interaction will give an opportunity to clarify the word "fictitious" further. It was chosen to indicate that each of these positive charges does not interact with the "accompanied" electron; for if it existed the interaction would be infinitely large.

transport problems the filled band plus the M additional holes are equivalent to the M fictitious positive charges *alone*, i.e., that the contributions of the N electrons cancel each other.   This statement cannot be maintained if interaction between electrons is taken into consideration.   In the *presence* of the M fictitious positive charges, the motion of the N electrons of the filled band differs from that in the absence of the M fictitious positive charges.   It is, however, only in the latter case that their contributions cancel exactly in transport problems, and we see that the second step in the foregoing discussion, namely, the omission of the electron contribution, is not permissible if interaction is considered.

The band model, however, considers the interaction of electrons only very inadequately, namely, only as a contribution to the fixed lattice potential which is independent of the position of the electron under consideration.   The hole representation is equivalent to the electron representation only if the action of the other electrons on the electron under consideration can be represented by such a fixed contribution to the potential.   This equivalence was demonstrated in §3 for fixed electric and magnetic fields which are *in*dependent of the electron under consideration.   One can state in summary: In so far as an adequate electron representation of processes in solids is possible within the scope of the band model, the hole representation is fully equivalent and in many cases more convenient.   Where the interaction between electrons breaks down the validity of the band model, the hole representation also loses its validity.   It remains to be seen whether this situation is final, or whether more comprehensive investigations are able to reestablish the hole representation in interaction cases.[1]

§5. Problems (Hall Effect)

1. Give numerical values for the Hall angle for n-type and p-type germanium for H = 1,000 oersteds.   What is the transverse voltage across a germanium bar of 1 cm width for a current density of 1 amp/cm^2 and for an impurity density of 10^{15} donors or acceptors/cm^3?

2.* When both electrons and holes are present in a semiconductor traversed by a current, a magnetic field will deflect them to the same side of the crystal, as shown in Fig. III.1.1.   If the initial deflection currents were equally large for both types of carriers, no electric charge and therefore no transverse electric field would build up.   Generally, however, the initial deflection currents will be different from each other.   An electric field will then build up such that the stronger one of the two deflection currents will be retarded while the weaker one, which consists of the opposite charge carriers, will be accelerated.   The final field is determined by the

---

[1] In this connection, see the experiments of K. G. McKay and K. B. McAfee, *Phys. Rev.*, **91**: 1079 (1954); and possibly also E. Spenke, "Hamburger Vorträge," 1954, published by E. Bagge and H. Brüche, Physikverlag Mosbach; in preparation.

condition that the net *electrical* current is zero; this means that the electron and hole *particle* currents are finite and equal.

Show that the Hall-angle Θ for the composite Hall effect is given by

$$\tan \Theta = \frac{p\mu_p^2 - n\mu_n^2}{p\mu_p + n\mu_n} \frac{H}{c} \qquad (III.5.01)$$

3. What is the value of $\tan \Theta$ according to Eq. (III.5.01) for (*a*) an intrinsic semiconductor, (*b*) a semiconductor with minimal conductivity [see Eqs. (I.3.07) and (I.3.08)]? Give numerical values for germanium for $H = 1,000$ oersteds. At what conductivity is the Hall angle equal to zero?

Make a qualitative plot of both σ and $\tan \Theta$ as a function of $\log n/n_i$ and show the relationships of the significant points on these curves (assuming $\mu_p < \mu_n$).

4. Calculate the density of the transverse particle current of electron-hole pairs. For what carrier density and what conductivity does this current have a maximum? What is the ratio of the maximal transverse current density to the longitudinal particle current density in germanium for $H = 1,000$ oersteds?

CHAPTER IV

The Mechanism of Crystal Rectifiers

§1. Introduction

Our ideas about the structure and the mechanism of commercial crystal rectifiers have changed during recent years. The introduction of a radically new type of rectifier is partially responsible for this change: This is the so-called *p-n* junction. It was developed by W. Shockley[1] and a large staff of coworkers at the Bell Telephone Laboratories in the United States. One realization[2] of this new rectifier type consists of a single-crystal germanium wafer (see Fig. IV.1.1). One electrical connection is made by soldering antimony (Sb) to one side and the other by soldering indium (In) to the opposite side. The crystal is subsequently heated to an elevated temperature for some time, so that the antimony and the indium diffuse[3] from their respective sides into the wafer. The transition region, thus introduced, between antimony-containing and indium-containing germanium or *n*-type and *p*-type germanium[4] exhibits pronounced rectifying properties. The voltage-current characteristics (see Fig. IV.1.2) show that large currents with small voltage drops can flow from the indium to the antimony side, whereas in the opposite direction there is only a small residual current even for large voltages.

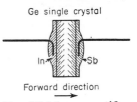

Ge single crystal

In — Sb

Forward direction

Fig. IV.1.1. *p-n* rectifier. In-Ge-Sb type.

[1] W. Shockley, *Bell System Tech. J.*, **28**: 435 (1949); "Electrons and Holes in Semiconductors," D. Van Nostrand Company, Inc., Princeton, N.J., 1950.

[2] R. N. Hall and W. C. Dunlap, *Phys. Rev.*, **80**: 467 (1950). R. N. Hall, *Proc. IRE*, **40**: 1512 (1952).

[3] It was recently found that alloying processes and subsequent recrystallization, rather than diffusion processes, are responsible for the formation of *p-n* junctions by the method just described. In this connection, see R. R. Law, C. W. Mueller, J. I. Pankove, and L. D. Armstrong, *Proc. IRE*, **40**: 1352 (1952). Similar principles apply to the process of preparing Si *p-n* rectifiers. See G. L. Pearson and B. Sawyer, *Proc. IRE*, **40**: 1348 (1952).

[4] See in this connection pp. 18 to 24.

How did the earlier rectifier types compare? The selenium rectifier of E. Presser,[1] which still dominates the high-current field, consists of a base electrode of iron (Fe) or aluminum (Al) (see Fig. IV.1.3). A crystalline selenium (Se) layer is deposited on this base which, in turn,

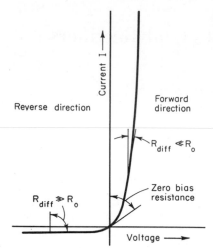

FIG. IV.1.2. Rectification characteristics.

is covered with an electrode of tin-cadmium alloy (Sn-Cd). The forward current direction is from the base to the cover electrode.

The predecessor of the selenium rectifier is the cuprous oxide rectifier of L. O. Grondahl[2] which consists of an oxidized copper (Cu) plate (see Fig. IV.1.4). The cuprous oxide layer is covered with a graphite or silver electrode. The forward current direction is from the graphite or silver electrode to the copper metal.

The crystal detector discovered by the Strasbourg physics professor Ferdinand Braun[3] in 1874 was widely used in the radio field between 1920 and 1930. It was then almost entirely replaced by the vacuum tube until about ten years later, when it made a sensational comeback in the form of the germanium and silicon diodes for microwave work. In these rectifiers (see Fig. IV.1.5), a metal point makes contact with a germanium (Ge) or silicon (Si) crystal under slight spring pressure.

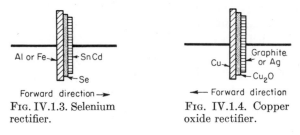

FIG. IV.1.3. Selenium rectifier.

FIG. IV.1.4. Copper oxide rectifier.

The crystal is attached through a nonrectifying large-area contact to its metal holder. In germanium diodes the forward current flows when

[1] E. Presser, *Funkbastler*, p. 558 (1925); *Elektrotech Z.*, **53**: 339 (1932).

[2] L. O. Grondahl, *Science*, **36**: 306 (1926); *J. Am. Inst. Elec. Engrs.*, **46**: 215 (1927).

[3] F. Braun, *Pogg. Ann.*, **153**: 556 (1874); *Wied. Ann.*, **1**: 95 (1877); **4**: 476 (1878); **19**: 340 (1883).

the metal point is positive, in silicon diodes, conversely, when it is negative.

The physical processes which effect the rectification are not distributed over the entire volume of the crystalline semiconductor material. It is known that these processes take place entirely within a "barrier layer" of 10^{-4} to 10^{-5} cm thickness.[1] The barrier layer in selenium rectifiers is at the surface of the selenium near the tin-cadmium alloy; in cuprous oxide rectifiers it is at the boundary of the copper base and in the detectors next to the metal boundary at the point contact.

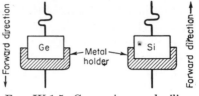

FIG. IV.1.5. Germanium and silicon detectors.

Thus it seemed that the unipolarity of these rectifiers was a consequence of an interaction of *metal and semiconductor* and that the *p-n* junction, with its rectifier effect between antimony and indium-containing germanium, constituted something entirely new. However, B. Davydov[2] pointed out as early as 1938 that strong unipolar effects are to be expected at the junction between *p*-type and *n*-type semiconductors. As a matter of fact, it was shown in recent years that in the selenium rectifier just described the barrier layer does not, in reality, occur at the boundary between the tin-cadmium alloy and the selenium. A chemical reaction between the tin-cadmium electrode and the selenium during the preparation of these rectifiers leads to the formation of a cadmium selenide layer[3] (see Fig. IV.1.6). Poganski[4] as well as Hoffmann and Rose[5] were able to demonstrate beyond doubt that the barrier layer is located at the boundary between the two semiconductors cadmium selenide and selenium, rather than at the boundary between the metal tin-cadmium, and the semiconductor cadmium selenide. A similar situation is most probably realized in germa-

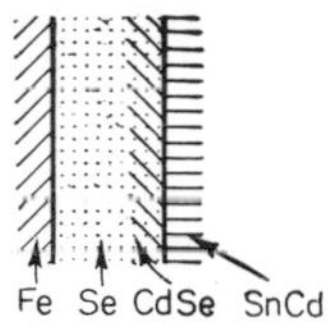

Fe Se CdSe SnCd

FIG. IV.1.6. CdSe layer in the selenium rectifier. The CdSe layer is deliberately shown too thick for illustrative purposes.

[1] W. Schottky and W. Deutschmann, *Physik. Z.*, **30**: 839 (1929).

[2] B. Davydov, *Tech. Phys. U.S.S.R.*, **5**: 87–95 (1938).

[3] See for instance, Uno Lamm, *ASEA Journal*, **16**: 114 (1939). W. Koch and S. Poganski, *FIAT Rev. Ger. Sci., Final Report* 706, p. 18 (1946). M. Tomura, *Bull. Chem. Soc. Japan*, **22**: 82 (1949); *J. Phys. Soc. Japan*, **5**: 349 (1950). S. Poganski, Dissertation, Technical University Berlin, 1949; *Elektrotech Z.*, **72**: 533 (1951); *Z. Elektrochem.*, **56**: 193 (1952).

[4] S. Poganski, *Z. Physik*, **134**: 469 (1953).

[5] A. Hoffmann and F. Rose, *Z. Physik*, **136**: 152 (1953).

nium and silicon point-contact detectors as well. In any case, special surface treatments and "forming processes"[1] are necessary to obtain good rectifier characteristics, which shows clearly that point-contact detectors do not consist of simple metal-semiconductor contacts.[2]

Nevertheless, rectification effects can occur in metal-semiconductor contacts.[3] We shall discuss the physics of the metal-semiconductor contact in the first part of this chapter, namely, in §1 to §4, principally because the context allows the discussion in simple terms of the space-charge boundary layer, the extension of the carrier density, the Boltzmann equilibrium between diffusion and field current, and other topics.

In the second part of this chapter, namely, in §5 to §8, we shall encounter the same phenomena in the rectification effects at a semiconductor-semiconductor boundary, though in more complex form. This underlines the present-day importance of the original boundary-layer theory of Schottky.[3]

PART 1. THE METAL-SEMICONDUCTOR CONTACT

§2. The Zero-current Condition of a Metal-Semiconductor Contact

The decisive advance of Schottky's boundary-layer theory for crystal rectifiers over all previous theories lies in the realization that special concentration and potential conditions prevail in the boundary region—in the "boundary layer" of the semiconductor—and that these conditions depend on the current through the rectifier.

Let us visualize, for instance, an n-type semiconductor with a uniform donor concentration n_D throughout (see Figs. IV.2.1 and IV.2.2). The concentration n_D of these donors and their dissociation energy E_{CD} shall be so small[4] that all donors have given up their electron $\ominus$ (saturated impurities) at normal temperatures. The concentration n_{D^+} of the positively charged donors is then a constant independent

---

[1] These are electrical overloads with forward or reverse currents or also alternating current. In spite of certain hypotheses, the forming processes as well as the surface treatments are still essentially an empirical art, for the physics of the point contact is not at all understood.

[2] R. Thedieck, *Physik. Verhandl.*, **3:** 31 (1952); **3:** 212 (1952); *Z. angew. Phys.*, **5:** 165 (1953). L. B. Valdes, *Proc. IRE*, **40:** 445 (1952).

[3] W. Schottky, *Naturwiss.*, **26:** 843 (1938); *Z. Physik*, **113:** 367 (1939); and **118:** 539 (1942). The experimental investigation of rectification effects in metal-semiconductor contacts without an intermediate layer is due to S. Poganski, *Z. Physik*, **134:** 469 (1953).

[4] Concerning the condition for saturated impurities, see pp. 47 to 50.

of location in space

$$n_{D^+} = n_D = \text{const} \qquad \text{(IV.2.01)}$$

and in the interior of the semiconductor the neutrality condition for the electron concentration n requires

$$n = n_S = n_{D^+} \qquad \text{(IV.2.02)}$$

However, at the boundary between semiconductor and metal the electron concentration n is determined by an entirely different requirement than the neutrality condition, namely, by the requirement of thermal equilibrium with the metal. For the time being we consider the condition of zero current, so that the number of electrons passing from left

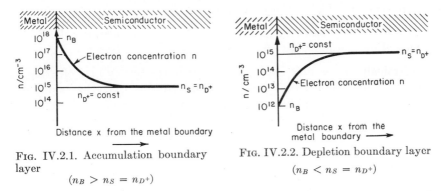

FIG. IV.2.1. Accumulation boundary layer

$$(n_B > n_S = n_{D^+})$$

FIG. IV.2.2. Depletion boundary layer

$$(n_B < n_S = n_{D^+})$$

to right through the metal-semiconductor boundary per unit time and area, because of their random thermal motion, must be equal to the number of electrons passing in the opposite direction. This requirement demands a very specific electron concentration n_B at the semiconductor boundary at a given temperature, and we shall state without further proof[1]

$$n_B = N_C \cdot e^{-\frac{\Psi_{\text{met sem}}}{kT}} \qquad \text{(IV.2.03)}$$

where

$$N_C = 2 \cdot \left(\frac{2\pi m_{\text{eff}} kT}{h^2}\right)^{3/2} = 2.5 \cdot 10^{19} \left(\frac{m_{\text{eff}}}{m}\right)^{3/2} \left(\frac{T}{300°\text{K}}\right)^{3/2} \text{cm}^{-3} \qquad \text{(IV.2.04)}$$

is an effective density of states in the conduction band. $\Psi_{\text{met sem}}$ is a type of work function of the metal electrons, but refers to electrons passing from the metal into a semiconductor rather than into vacuum as in the usual work function definition.

[1] The reader will find a proof in Eq. (X.7.01). N_C is introduced in Chap. VIII, §1 and §4, see Eqs. (VIII.1.04) and (VIII.4.04).

The most interesting feature of Eq. (IV.2.03) is, for the present, that n_B is determined by the work function $\Psi_{\text{met sem}}$, whereas the concentration n_S in the interior of the semiconductor is determined by the concentration n_{D^+} [see Eq. (IV.2.02)]. The work function $\Psi_{\text{met sem}}$ and the donor density $n_D = n_{D^+}$ are, however, entirely independent of each other, hence also the quantities n_B and n_S.

This fact is not surprising; for the density n_S deep in the interior of the semiconductor must be independent of the composition of the remote metal electrode—Cu or Sn for instance. The boundary density n_B, however, is very strongly affected by the neighboring metal. Thus we see that, in general, n_B and n_S have different values and that $n_B = n_S$ would be a most improbable coincidence.

Thus we can distinguish two cases:

Accumulation boundary layer: $n_B > n_S = n_D$ (see Fig. IV.2.1)
Depletion boundary layer: $n_B < n_S = n_D$ (see Fig. IV.2.2)

Physically observable effects will occur in the second case of a depletion boundary layer (see Fig. IV.2.2). In this case the boundary layer represents a high resistance as a result of carrier depletion. If the effect is sufficiently pronounced, a relatively thin high-resistance layer can dominate the electrical behavior of metal, boundary layer, and semiconductor connected in series. The *reduction* of the resistance of a thin layer, in the opposite case of the accumulation boundary layer, has a negligible effect on the total resistance in view of the constant and much larger resistance of the entire semiconductor body. Accumulation layers are, therefore, of interest only with reference to *nonrectifying* contacts to semiconductors, whereas the metal-semiconductor contact with a depletion boundary layer exhibits rectification properties.

Before we demonstrate this by considering the behavior in the presence of current, we have to discuss the distribution of the electrostatic macropotential[1] V within the boundary layer. This layer is no longer neutral like the interior of the semiconductor, for with $n < n_{D^+}$ there are not enough negative electrons $\ominus$ available to compensate the charge of the positive donors D^+. The boundary layer contains, therefore, a positive space-charge density $\rho(x)$ which, according to the Poisson equation

$$V''(x) = - \frac{4\pi}{\varepsilon} \rho(x) \tag{IV.2.05}$$

bends the potential downward. A so-called "diffusion voltage" V_D is present at the boundary layer (see Fig. IV.2.3).

[1] See p. 337 concerning this term.

This potential difference within a conductor in the absence of current is very difficult to comprehend, as experience has shown. First we recall that absence of current does not necessarily exclude potential differences. For instance, the so-called Galvani voltage[1] is established between the *inner* potentials of two conductors of different material in the absence of current; in the same case the so-called Volta or contact potential[1] exists between the *surface* potentials, as is well known from the calculation of the effective grid bias in a vacuum tube. The reader who is interested in more detail concerning this subject and its connection with the diffusion voltage V_D is referred to Chap. X.

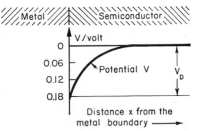

Fig. IV.2.3. Potential distribution in a depletion boundary layer.

It is, however, useful to realize that the diffusion voltage V_D is necessary to establish the zero-current condition. The large concentration gradient from n_S to n_B must lead to a large electron current from right to left. The zero-current condition is established solely by the electrical potential difference V_D which transports the negatively charged electrons from left to right in order to compensate the current resulting from the concentration gradient.

The stratification of the earth's atmosphere is a well-known analogy. Here, too, the absence of vertical motion of the air may be regarded as a compensation of two opposite air currents, namely, the rising air current from the lower high-pressure layers to the higher low-pressure layers and a downward air current due to the gravitational attraction of the earth. The resulting air pressure or the proportional concentration n of the air molecules obeys the so-called barometric equation:

$$n(x) = n(0) \, e^{-\frac{mgx}{kT}} \tag{IV.2.06}$$

where m = mass of a molecule
g = gravitational acceleration
k = Boltzmann constant
T = absolute temperature
x = altitude coordinate

If we substitute the electrostatic energy $(-e) \cdot V(x)$ of an electron $\ominus$ in the electrostatic potential $V(x)$ for the potential energy mgx of a molecule in the gravitational field of the earth, we obtain according to (IV.2.06)

[1] See pp. 342 to 345 concerning this term.

$$n(x) = n_S \, e^{+\frac{e V(x)}{kT}} \qquad\qquad \text{(IV.2.07)}$$

In particular, we find at the semiconductor boundary $x = 0$

$$V(0) = -V_D \qquad\qquad \text{(IV.2.08)}$$

and

$$n(0) = n_B \qquad\qquad \text{(IV.2.09)}$$

so that we arrive at

$$n_B = n_S \, e^{-\frac{e V_D}{kT}} \qquad\qquad \text{(IV.2.10)}$$

The relations (IV.2.06) and (IV.2.07) are special cases of the concentration distribution of a Boltzmann gas in a space with varying potential energy. Therefore we call spatial concentration distributions like (IV.2.06) and (IV.2.07) Boltzmann distributions and the mutual compensation of two opposite particle currents Boltzmann equilibrium. If, in Fig. IV.2.3, we plot the potential linearly and in Fig. IV.2.2 the concentration n logarithmically, Eq. (IV.2.07) leads to an identity of the $V(x)$ and $n(x)$ curves if the scales are chosen appropriately. The possibility of deducing the identity of the concentration and potential curves (plotted as indicated) from the existence of a Boltzmann equilibrium is often useful.

This concludes the discussion of the zero-current case. We shall see in §3 what currents arise if the potential difference V_D of the zero-current condition is changed by an externally applied voltage U.

§3. The Metal-Semiconductor Contact with Current

We begin with the assumption of an increase of the potential of the metal electrode by the voltage U_{forw}, while the potential on the semiconductor side is fixed at the far right (see Fig. IV.3.3). In this case the potential drop across the boundary layer is not V_D but only $V_D - U_{\text{forw}}$.

Actually one must distinguish between a voltage U_{forw}^* between the terminals of the rectifier and the portion U_{forw} which lies across the boundary layer itself and is smaller than U_{forw}^*. The neutral portion of the semiconductor adjacent to the boundary layer of Fig. IV.3.2 has also a finite resistance which we shall call the "base resistance R_B." The current through the base causes a voltage drop $R_B I$ which is in series with the boundary-layer voltage U_{forw}:

$$U_{\text{forw}}^* = U_{\text{forw}} + R_B I$$

From the current-voltage characteristics of the boundary layer

$$I = f(U_{\text{forw}})$$

one obtains the over-all characteristic $I = g(U^*_{\text{forw}})$ of the entire rectifier including the base resistance R_B (see Fig. IV.3.1). In the following
we shall deal only with the charac-
teristics $I = f(U_{\text{forw}})$ of the boundary layer.

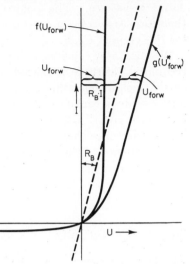

In order to establish the reduced
potential barrier $V_D - U_{\text{forw}}$, the
space charge which is responsible
must also be reduced. The density
ρ of this space charge is given very
nearly by the fixed concentration
n_{D^+} of the immobile donors D^+, for
the variable and therefore adjust-
able concentration n of the mobile
electrons $\ominus$ does not play any part
in comparison with n_{D^+} in the essential portion of the space-charge
boundary layer. A reduction of the
space charge, responsible for the
potential drop, is possible only
through a reduction in the width of
the total space charge. The con

FIG. IV.3.1. Modification of the
boundary-layer rectification characteristics $I = f(U_f)$ by the base resistance R_B.

centration n_S corresponding to neutrality must, therefore, be maintained
further to the left than in the zero-current condition (see Fig. IV.3.2).
One can visualize this in the form of a "conceptual aid"[1] by assuming

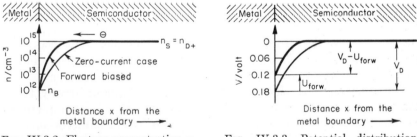

FIG. IV.3.2. Electron concentration n
with forward bias.

FIG. IV.3.3. Potential distribution
$V(x)$ with forward bias.

that the electrons which flow from the interior of the semiconductor
toward the positive electrode extend their concentration n_S somewhat
further into the boundary zone which, in the absence of current, is depleted of carriers. In any case, the carrier depletion is less intensive

[1] *Only* a "conceptual aid" and not a physically correct picture!

with the assumed bias than in the unbiased condition, and it is certainly plausible that this is accompanied by a reduction of the differential resistance. The polarity of the applied voltage corresponds, therefore, to *forward* current in the rectifier; hence the subscript "forw" for the voltage U^*_{forw}.

We shall now consider an applied voltage of opposite polarity where the metal electrode is biased negatively by U_{rev} relative to the zero-current condition, while the potential far to the right on the semiconductor side is again held constant. The potential barrier is thus increased from V_D to $V_D + U_{\text{rev}}$ (see Fig. IV.3.5), which requires an increase in space charge. This can take place only if the carrier depletion is widened at the boundary (see Fig. IV.3.4) leading to an increase

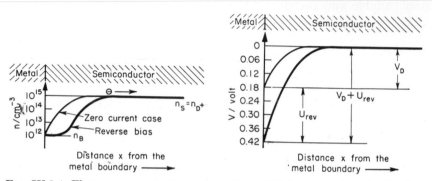

FIG. IV.3.4. Electron concentration n with reverse bias.

FIG. IV.3.5. Potential distribution $V(x)$ with reverse bias.

of the differential resistance. Thus we realize *reverse* current in the rectifier, indicated by the subscript "rev" for the voltage U_{rev}. The electrons $\ominus$ now flow from the negatively charged metal electrode into the semiconductor. This seems to cause the low concentrations of the boundary to extend somewhat further into the semiconductor.

The foregoing considerations will be utilized quantitatively for a computation of the characteristics in §4 and §5. To complete §3 we must indicate what happens in a p-type semiconductor in contrast to the previously treated n-type semiconductor. Here again we find that the metal contact effects a change of the hole concentration from the value p_S in the interior of the semiconductor which satisfies the neutrality condition. Again, only the depletion and not the accumulation boundary layers can be observed in view of the series connection of the "base resistance" of the entire semiconductor. The resistance of such layers is dependent on the load; thus, as in the n-type case, the depletion-layer width is reduced along with the differential rectifier resistance when the positive holes $\oplus$ are flowing from the interior of the semiconductor toward the metal electrode.   For this purpose a negative bias must be applied, which indicates that a p-type semiconductor requires a negative polarity of the metal electrode for forward current, whereas the previously described n-type semiconductor requires a positive polarity of the metal electrode.   This difference of the polarities between n-type and p-type conductors, which is easily remembered with the concept of the spreading of the carrier concentration, was predicted by Schottky[1] as early as 1935.   This prediction has often been checked experimentally since and has always been found correct.   In order to do this it was necessary to determine the conductivity type of the semiconductor in question by Hall effect or thermoelectric measurements.   By now the Schottky rule is so well accepted that it is used to determine the conductivity type of semiconductors, since it is generally much more convenient than Hall effect and thermoelectric measurements.   Above all it allows the determination of local transitions from p-type to n-type conductivity in a non-homogeneous semiconductor, because the metal electrodes can be spring-loaded *point* contacts which allow very high resolution.

§4. Calculation of Characteristics

We have seen in the zero-current case that the absence of current can be regarded as a consequence of the exact compensation of two currents in opposite directions.   Accordingly, even in the biased case the observed current must be the resultant of two opposite currents which compensate each other at least partially.   The analytical expressions for these two currents differ, depending on whether the thickness of the boundary depletion layer is large or small compared to the mean free path of the carriers.   First we shall consider the case of small boundary-layer thickness.

a. Boundary-layer Thickness Small Compared with the Mean Free Path of the Electrons (Diode Theory)

Here decelerations of the electrons by collisions with phonons[2] or with imperfections and impurities within the boundary layer can be neglected.   The number of electrons arriving per square centimeter and per second from the interior of the semiconductor at the semiconductor interface $x = l$ of the boundary layer (see Fig. IV.4.1) is

---

[1] W. Schottky: comment on the paper by Störmer, *Z. tech. Phys.*, **16**: 512 (1935).
[2] Concerning this term see pp. 13 to 14 and Fig. I.2.9 as well as p. 256.

equal to the unilateral thermal current density[1] $(1/\sqrt{6\pi})v_{\text{th}} \cdot n_S$ for the corresponding electron concentration n_S. The fraction

$$\exp - \left(\frac{e(V_D + U_{\text{rev}})}{kT}\right)$$

of these electrons possesses the necessary kinetic energy to pass over the peak $+e(V_D + U_{\text{rev}})$ of the potential barrier and can therefore reach the boundary of the semiconductor.[2] We thus find at a plane close to the semiconductor boundary $x = 0$ a particle current density from the right to the left

$$\overleftarrow{s} = \frac{1}{\sqrt{6\pi}} v_{\text{th}} \cdot n_S \cdot e^{-\frac{e(V_D + U_{\text{rev}})}{kT}} \qquad\text{(IV.4.01)}$$

In contrast to this "retarding field" of the electrons which run up against the rise in potential energy from the interior of the semiconductor, the current of electrons from the semiconductor boundary toward the interior is a "saturation current"; for it is aided rather than

---

[1] The unilateral thermal current density in a Boltzmann gas of the concentration n_S can be calculated to be

$$s = \int v_x \cdot dn = \int\limits_{v_x = -\infty}^{v_x = 0} v_x \cdot n_S \cdot \frac{1}{\sqrt{\pi}} \cdot \exp - \left(\frac{v_x}{\sqrt{\frac{2kT}{m_{\text{eff}}}}}\right)^2 \cdot d\left(\frac{v_x}{\sqrt{\frac{2kT}{m_{\text{eff}}}}}\right)$$

$$s = \frac{1}{\sqrt{\pi}} n_S \sqrt{\frac{2kT}{m_{\text{eff}}}} \int\limits_{u=0}^{\infty} u\, e^{-u^2}\, du = \frac{1}{\sqrt{\pi}} n_S \sqrt{\frac{2kT}{m_{\text{eff}}}} \cdot \frac{1}{2}$$

The "mean thermal velocity v_{th}" is given in this book in accordance with the law of equipartition

$$\frac{m_{\text{eff}}}{2} v_{\text{th}}^2 = \frac{3}{2} kT$$

as the quantity (pp. 256 and 264)

$$v_{\text{th}} = \sqrt{\frac{3kT}{m_{\text{eff}}}} \qquad\text{(VII.9.22)}$$

This yields the unilateral thermal current density

$$s = \frac{1}{\sqrt{6\pi}} n_S v_{\text{th}}$$

[2] In the computation of the fraction of electrons arriving at the peak, we must integrate not to $v = 0$ as in footnote 1, but rather only to

$$v_x = -\sqrt{\frac{2e(V_D + U_{\text{rev}})}{m_{\text{eff}}}}$$

obstructed by the potential distribution. This aid, however, cannot increase the current beyond the capacity of its source. The saturation current is

$$\overrightarrow{s} = \frac{1}{\sqrt{6\pi}} v_{th} \cdot n_B \qquad (IV.4.02)$$

because the electron concentration n_B at the semiconductor boundary is the source of the current (IV.4.02).

Equation (IV.4.01) corresponds to the reverse-current case, where according to §3 the electrons flow from the semiconductor boundary to

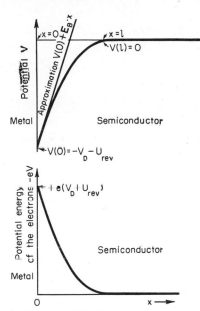

FIG. IV.4.1. The rise of the potential electron energy in a boundary layer. Top: linear approximation of the potential distribution at the metal side of the boundary layer.

the interior of the semiconductor. For the particle current density s, we find by forming the difference $s = \overrightarrow{s} - \overleftarrow{s}$

$$s = \frac{1}{\sqrt{6\pi}} v_{th}(n_B - n_S e^{-\frac{e}{kT}V_D} e^{-\frac{e}{kT}U_{rev}}) \qquad (IV.4.03)$$

Here we use Eq. (IV.2.10) and obtain

$$s = \frac{1}{\sqrt{6\pi}} v_{th} \cdot n_B(1 - e^{-\frac{e}{kT}U_{rev}}) \qquad (IV.4.04)$$

Multiplication with the elementary charge e yields a reverse current which flows in conventional terms from right to left:

$$i_{\text{rev}} = \frac{1}{\sqrt{6\pi}}\, e \cdot v_{\text{th}} \cdot n_B \left(1 - e^{-\frac{e}{kT}U_{\text{rev}}}\right) \tag{IV.4.05}$$

or

$$i_{\text{rev}} = i_S \left(1 - e^{-\frac{e}{kT}U_{\text{rev}}}\right)$$

In the forward direction i_{rev} and U_{rev} are replaced by $-i_{\text{forw}}$ and $-U_{\text{forw}}$, respectively:

$$i_{\text{forw}} = i_S \left(e^{+\frac{e}{kT}U_{\text{forw}}} - 1\right) \tag{IV.4.06}$$

For higher forward voltages $U_{\text{forw}} \gg kT/e$ the forward current increases exponentially (IV.4.06), whereas for higher reverse voltages $U_{\text{rev}} \gg kT/e$ the reverse current (IV.4.05) saturates. The saturation value is

$$i_S = \frac{1}{\sqrt{6\pi}}\, e \cdot v_{\text{th}} \cdot n_B \tag{IV.4.07}$$

According to Eq. (X.7.01), with the work function $\Psi_{\text{met sem}}$ we find the boundary density n_B

$$n_B = N_C\, e^{-\frac{\Psi_{\text{met sem}}}{kT}} \tag{X.7.01}$$

so that we obtain

$$i_S = \frac{1}{\sqrt{6\pi}}\, e \cdot v_{\text{th}} \cdot N_C\, e^{-\frac{\Psi_{\text{met sem}}}{kT}} \tag{IV.4.08}$$

If we introduce $e = 1.6 \cdot 10^{-19}$ coulomb, v_{th} from Eq. (VII.9.22), and N_C from Eq. (VIII.4.04) and utilize $kT = 25.9 \cdot 10^{-3}$ ev $(T/300°\text{K})$, we arrive at

$$i_S = 1.08 \cdot 10^7\, \frac{\text{amp}}{\text{cm}^2} \left(\frac{m_{\text{eff}}}{m}\right) \cdot \left(\frac{T}{300°\text{K}}\right)^2 \cdot e^{-38.6\left(\frac{\Psi_{\text{met sem}}}{e\,\text{volt}}\right)\cdot\left(\frac{300°\text{K}}{T}\right)} \tag{IV.4.09}$$

$$= 120\, \frac{\text{amp}}{\text{cm}^2} \cdot \left(\frac{m_{\text{eff}}}{m}\right) \cdot \left(\frac{T}{°\text{K}}\right)^2 \cdot e^{-\left(\frac{\Psi_{\text{met sem}}}{e\,\text{volt}}\right)\cdot\left(\frac{11,580°\text{K}}{T}\right)}$$

Equations (IV.4.05) and (IV.4.06) give the characteristics for thin boundary layers. We shall now consider the opposite case.

b. Boundary-layer Thickness Large Compared with the Mean Free Path of the Electrons (Diffusion Theory)

Here the electron suffers many collisions with phonons and imperfections or impurities. The electron current from right to left is caused by the concentration gradient and may be expressed as a diffusion current

$$\overleftarrow{s} = D_n \cdot n'(x) \tag{IV.4.10}$$

(D_n = diffusion constant of the electrons), whereas the current from left to right results from the potential gradient and may be expressed as a field current

$$\overrightarrow{s} = \mu_n n V'(x) \tag{IV.4.11}$$

The diffusion constant D_n and the mobility μ_n of the electrons are connected by the Nernst-Townsend-Einstein relation

$$D_n = \mu_n \cdot \frac{kT}{e} \tag{IV.4.12}$$

so that we find for the total current from left to right, which is source-free and hence independent of location,

$$s = \overrightarrow{s} - \overleftarrow{s} = \mu_n n V'(x) - \mu_n \frac{kT}{e} n'(x) \tag{IV.4.13}$$

According to §3 this particle current direction from the boundary to the interior corresponds to reverse current. We find the reverse-current density by multiplication with the elementary charge e

$$i_{\text{rev}} = e\mu_n n V'(x) - \mu_n kT n'(x) \tag{IV.4.14}$$

This is a linear differential equation of the first order for the concentration distribution $n(x)$. The solution is

$$n(x) = n_S \, e^{+\frac{e}{kT}V(x)} + \frac{i_{\text{rev}}}{\mu_n kT} \int_{\xi=x}^{\xi=l} e^{+\frac{e}{kT}(V(x)-V(\xi))} \, d\xi \tag{IV.4.15}$$

as can be verified by introducing it into (IV.4.14). The only integration constant occurring in the solution of the first-order differential equation has already been determined in (IV.4.15) so that the neutrality concentration n_S of the interior of the semiconductor is obtained at the semiconductor interface $x = l$ of the boundary layer.[1]

If, on the other hand, we apply (IV.4.15) to the metal interface $x = 0$ of the boundary layer, we find according to the qualitative considerations and the figures of §3

$$n(0) = n_B \tag{IV.4.16}$$

[1] The potential value $V(l)$ is made equal to zero at this point (see Fig. IV.4.1).

as well as

$$V(0) = -V_D - U_{\text{rev}} \qquad \text{(IV.4.17)}$$

so that

$$n_B = n_S \, e^{-\frac{e}{kT}V_D} \, e^{-\frac{e}{kT}U_{\text{rev}}} + \frac{i_{\text{rev}}}{\mu_n kT} \int_{\xi=0}^{\xi=l} e^{+\frac{e}{kT}(V(0)-V(\xi))} \, d\xi \qquad \text{(IV.4.18)}$$

Using the equation

$$n_S \, e^{-\frac{e}{kT}V_D} = n_B \qquad \text{(IV.2.10)}$$

we find for the reverse-current density

$$i_{\text{rev}} = e\mu_n n_B \cdot \frac{kT}{e} \frac{1 - e^{-\frac{e}{kT}U_{\text{rev}}}}{\displaystyle\int_{\xi=0}^{\xi=l} e^{+\frac{e}{kT}(V(0)-V(\xi))} \, d\xi} \qquad \text{(IV.4.19)}$$

If the potential function $V(x)$ is known, the integral in the denominator can be evaluated at least in principle, and (IV.4.19) already represents the characteristic $i_{\text{rev}} = f(U_{\text{rev}})$. The following reasoning often yields an adequate approximation.[1] The exponent $(e/kT)(V(0) - V(\xi))$ of the integral is always negative within the integration range $0 < \xi < l$ (see Fig. IV.4.1). The essential contributions, therefore, occur in the vicinity of $\xi = 0$ where the approximation

$$V(0) - V(\xi) = -\mathbf{E}_B \cdot \xi \qquad \text{(IV.4.20)}$$

is again applicable. ($\mathbf{E}_B$ = contribution of the boundary field strength, see Fig. IV.4.1.) The integral in the denominator thus becomes

$$\int_{\xi=0}^{\xi=l} e^{\frac{e}{kT}(V(0)-V(\xi))} \, d\xi \approx \int_{\xi=0}^{\xi=l} e^{-\frac{e\mathbf{E}_B}{kT}\xi} \, d\xi = \frac{kT}{e\mathbf{E}_B} [e^{-\frac{e\mathbf{E}_B}{kT}\xi}]_{\xi=l}^{\xi=0} \qquad \text{(IV.4.21)}$$

Since $e\mathbf{E}_B l/(kT) \gg 1$ the term corresponding to $\xi = l$ can be omitted. We find thus simply

$$\int_{\xi=0}^{\xi=l} \cdots d\xi \approx \frac{kT}{e\mathbf{E}_B} \qquad \text{(IV.4.22)}$$

and obtain from (IV.4.19) the equation of the characteristic

$$i_{\text{rev}} \approx e\mu_n n_B \mathbf{E}_B \left(1 - e^{-\frac{e}{kT}U_{\text{rev}}}\right) \qquad \text{(IV.4.23)}$$

[1] But not always! The case of unsaturated impurities in the boundary layer cannot be treated accurately in this manner.

For forward current the substitution $i_{rev} \to -i_{forw}$ and $U_{rev} \to -U_{forw}$ yields

$$i_{forw} \approx e\mu_n n_B \mathbf{E}_B (e^{+\frac{e}{kT}U_{forw}} - 1) \qquad \text{(IV.4.24)}$$

The comparison with the characteristic equations (IV.4.05) and (IV.4.06) of the diode theory shows the great similarity between the results of the two theories. The saturation current of the boundary concentration n_B

$$i_S = \frac{1}{\sqrt{6\pi}}\, ev_{th} n_B \qquad \text{(IV.4.07)}$$

is replaced by the field current corresponding to this concentration:

$$i_{field} = e\mu_n n_B \mathbf{E}_B \qquad \text{(IV.4.25)}$$

Unlike the previously mentioned saturation current, i_{field} is dependent also on the applied voltage through the boundary layer field strength $\mathbf{E}_B$. Compared to the exponential term in (IV.4.23) or (IV.4.24), this dependence is significant. The reader will find further particulars in the literature.[1]

§5. The Concentration Distribution in a Boundary Layer

Even with current flow the concentration distribution $n(x)$ follows the Boltzmann law $n(x) = n_S\, e^{+\frac{eV(x)}{kT}}$ in most of the boundary layer. Only in the immediate proximity of the metal is the concentration increased for reverse current and decreased for forward current (see Fig. IV.5.1) with respect to the Boltzmann distribution. For reverse current the diffusion current is so much reduced that i_{rev} is almost a pure field current in the boundary-layer regions adjoining the metal. For forward current the diffusion current is so much increased that i_{forw} is here almost a pure diffusion current.

Equation (IV.4.15) gave for the concentration distribution:

$$n(x) = n_S\, e^{+\frac{e}{kT}V(x)} + \frac{i_{rev}}{\mu_n kT} \int_{\xi=x}^{\xi=l} e^{+\frac{e}{kT}(V(x)-V(\xi))}\, d\xi \qquad \text{(IV.4.15)}$$

This can be simplified by noting the negative sign of the exponent in the integral, as in the calculation of the characteristics, hence deducing

[1] W. Schottky, Z. Physik, **118**: 539 (1942). E. Spenke, Z. Physik, **126**: 67 (1949); Z. Naturforsch., **4a**: 37 (1949).

that appreciable contributions occur only in the vicinity of $\xi = x$, where we can approximate as follows:

$$V(x) - V(\xi) \approx -\mathbf{E}(x)(\xi - x) \qquad \text{with } \mathbf{E}(x) > 0 \quad \text{(IV.5.01)}$$

We obtain the integral

$$\int_{\xi=x}^{\xi=l} e^{+\frac{e}{kT}(V(x)-V(\xi))} \, d\xi \approx \frac{kT}{e\mathbf{E}(x)} \left[1 - e^{-\frac{e\mathbf{E}(x)}{kT}(l-x)}\right] \quad \text{(IV.5.02)}$$

If we forego a description of the concentration conditions at $x \approx l$, we can neglect the exponential term in the parenthesis, and we obtain

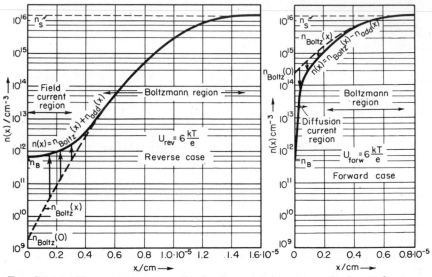

FIG. IV.5.1. The concentration distribution $n(x)$ is composed of a Boltzmann distribution $n_{\text{Boltz}}(x)$ and an added concentration $n_{\text{add}}(x)$. The figure is based on the values $n_S = 1.3.10^{16}$ cm^{-3} and $V_D = 10\frac{kT}{e} = 0.259$ volt. With respect to the additional assumptions and simplifications see E. Spenke, Z. Physik, **126**: 67 (1949).

for the concentration distribution in the reverse-current case

$$n(x) \approx n_S \, e^{+\frac{e}{kT}V(x)} + \frac{i_{\text{rev}}}{e\mu_n \mathbf{E}(x)} \qquad \text{for } x < l \quad \text{(IV.5.03)}$$

For forward current the substitution $i_{\text{rev}} \to -i_{\text{forw}}$ leads to

$$n(x) \approx n_S \, e^{+\frac{e}{kT}V(x)} - \frac{i_{\text{forw}}}{e\mu_n \mathbf{E}(x)} \qquad \text{for } x < l \quad \text{(IV.5.04)}$$

These equations contain very important physical information. They indicate that the electron distribution $n(x)$ is composed of two components (see Fig. IV.5.1) of which the first is the Boltzmann distribution

$$n_{\text{Boltz}}(x) = n_S \, e^{+\frac{e}{kT}V(x)} \qquad (\text{IV}.5.05)$$

and therefore does not correspond to any current, since the field and diffusion current compensate each other exactly.

However, the Boltzmann component $n_{\text{Boltz}}(x)$ has a boundary value which for reverse current is too small by a factor $e^{-\frac{e}{kT}U_{\text{rev}}}$

$$n_{\text{Boltz}}(0) = n_S \, e^{+\frac{e}{kT}V(0)} = n_S \, e^{-\frac{e}{kT}V_D} \, e^{-\frac{e}{kT}U_{\text{rev}}} = n_B \, e^{-\frac{e}{kT}U_{\text{rev}}} \qquad (\text{IV}.5.06)$$

and for forward current is too large by a factor $e^{+\frac{e}{kT}U_{\text{forw}}}$

$$n_{\text{Boltz}}(0) = n_B \, e^{+\frac{e}{kT}U_{\text{forw}}} \qquad (\text{IV}.5.07)$$

The correct boundary value n_B is now established if an additional concentration

$$n_{\text{add}}(x) = \frac{|i|}{e\mu_n \mathbf{E}(x)} \qquad (\text{IV}.5.08)$$

is added for reverse current according to (IV.5.03) and is subtracted for forward current according to (IV.5.04).

This influences not only the concentration $n(x)$ but also the concentration gradient $n'(x)$ (see Fig. IV.5.1). The concentration gradient and with it the diffusion current are tremendously reduced for reverse current when compared to the pure Boltzmann component $n_{\text{Boltz}}(x)$ with its exact compensation of field and diffusion current. For all practical purposes, the field current $i_{\text{field}} = e\mu_n n(x)\mathbf{E}(x)$ alone remains, which becomes simply

$$i_{\text{field}} \approx e\mu_n \cdot n_{\text{add}}\mathbf{E}(x) \qquad (\text{IV}.5.09)$$

since $n_{\text{Boltz}} \ll n_{\text{add}}$. This leads with (IV.5.08) to

$$i_{\text{field}} \approx i_{\text{rev}} \qquad (\text{IV}.5.10)$$

For forward current, however, the concentration gradient is increased as compared to the pure Boltzmann contribution (see Fig. IV.5.1). The diffusion current greatly predominates over the field current, and the entire forward current i_{forw} is for all practical purposes diffusion current.

Figure IV.5.1 shows, however, that the influence of n_{add} is noticed only at the metal interface of the boundary layer. Toward the interior of the semiconductor we find

$$n_{\text{Boltz}} \gg n_{\text{add}}$$

and the distribution is a Boltzmann distribution not only for zero current but also for reverse and forward current.   This is again very plausible.   Let us take, for instance, reverse current and go from left to right through the boundary layer in Fig. IV.5.1.   To the extreme left we find the field-current region, where the density increases at such a rate that, with the decreasing field strength, the required total current is carried as field current.   This increase leads to an increase of the concentration gradients.[1]   This in turn causes the diffusion current in the opposite direction to increase which, to begin with, is immaterial.   However, further to the right the diffusion current in the opposite direction approaches the same order of magnitude as the field current.   Both currents must then have become large compared to the total current i_{rev} in order to leave a residual current i_{rev} in spite of the mutual compensation.   We have now passed over from the field-current region on the left to the Boltzmann region on the right.

Thus in the region of the boundary layer adjoining the semiconductor, the Boltzmann distribution prevails substantially not only for zero current but also for current flow.   Therefore, the logarithmically plotted concentration distribution $n(x)$ and the potential distribution $V(x)$ are identical for current flow as well as for zero current as shown on page 78.

PART 2. THE p-n JUNCTION

§6. The Zero-current Condition of a p-n Junction

The first five paragraphs of this chapter were concerned with the properties of a semiconductor-metal contact.   A systematic procedure would require next the treatment of a contact between two different semiconductors.   However, the multitude of possible phenomena is

---

[1] When considering the concentration gradient, it must be pointed out that the concentration is plotted as $\log_{10} n(x)$ and not as $n(x)$.   Thus we obtain the concentration gradient dn/dx from the slope $d \ln n/dx$ by multiplying with the concentration $n(x)$ itself:

$$\frac{dn}{dx} = n(x) \cdot \frac{d \ln n}{dx}$$

The slope $d \ln n/dx$ increases somewhat from left to right.   However, the factor $n(x)$ increases much more rapidly, so that the concentration gradient dn/dx increases very rapidly from left to right.

here so large that we are forced to make a choice. In view of their practical importance, we shall limit ourselves to the so-called *p-n junctions*. A *p-n* junction is *not* a contact between two entirely different semiconductors such as selenium and cadmium selenide; the term "junction" is chosen to indicate that only one single host lattice is present and that there is a transition from a zone doped with acceptors producing holes into a zone doped with donors producing electrons.

Referring to the example discussed in §1, we imagine—see Figs. IV.1.1 and IV.6.1—that indium (In) is diffused into a germanium single crystal from the left, creating acceptor impurities A^- and holes $\oplus$. This leads to *p*-type germanium on the left. Antimony (Sb) is diffused into the crystal from the right, creating donor impurities D^+ and electrons $\ominus$. This leads to *n*-type germanium on the right. To begin with we consider the special case of a symmetrical *p-n* junction. Let us assume, for instance, an impurity concentration[1] of 10^{16} cm^{-3}:

$$n_{A^-} = n_{D^+} = 10^{16} \text{ cm}^{-3} \qquad \text{(IV.6.01)}$$

The mean distance between two impurities is thus

$$\sqrt[3]{\frac{4.52 \cdot 10^{22} \text{ cm}^{-3}}{10^{16} \text{ cm}^{-3}}} = 165$$

interatomic distances in germanium because the concentration of the germanium atoms is $4.52 \cdot 10^{22}$ cm^{-3}. For reasons of neutrality, the germanium on the left must contain a hole concentration

$$p_p = 10^{16} \text{ cm}^{-3} \qquad \text{(IV.6.02)}$$

and on the right an electron concentration

$$n_n = 10^{16} \text{ cm}^{-3} \qquad \text{(IV.6.03)}$$

In addition, the so-called thermal pair formation (see page 25ff) introduces throughout the germanium pairs of electrons and holes continuously so that the *p* germanium contains a certain electron concentration n_p and the *n* germanium contains a certain hole concentration p_n. For zero current these concentrations result from thermal equilibrium between pair formation and its counterprocess, recombination. The electron concentration n and the hole concentration p obey (but only in the case of thermal equilibrium) a law of mass action[2]

$$n \cdot p = n_i^2 \qquad \text{(IV.6.04)}$$

---

[1] Except at very low temperatures all the substitutional impurities in germanium at the concentrations considered here are dissociated.

[2] See pp. 26 and 305.

The so-called intrinsic density n_i for germanium at room temperature has approximately the value[1]

$$n_i \approx 10^{13} \text{ cm}^{-3} \qquad (\text{IV.6.05})$$

This results in an electron concentration on the left in the p germanium of

$$n_p = 10^{10} \text{ cm}^{-3} \qquad (\text{IV.6.06})$$

and an equal hole concentration on the right in the n germanium of

$$p_n = 10^{10} \text{ cm}^{-3} \qquad (\text{IV.6.07})$$

From the standpoint of space charge, these 10^6 times smaller concentrations can, of course, be neglected compared with n_n and p_p.

We make the unrealistic but convenient and fundamentally permissible assumption that the impurity concentrations n_{A^-} and n_{D^+} maintain a constant value in space of 10^{16} cm^{-3} on the left and on the right, dropping abruptly to zero at the center $x = 0$. This assumption introduces an abrupt transition from indium doping to antimony doping at the center. Such an abrupt transition is obviously not shared by the concentrations n and p of the *mobile* holes and electrons. The concentrations n and p must exhibit a spatial distribution differing from that of the impurity concentrations n_{A^-} and n_{D^+} because they do not drop from their neutrality values p_p and n_n, respectively, to zero after crossing the center $x = 0$ but rather to the equilibrium values $p_n = n_i^2/n_n$ and $n_p = n_i^2/p_p$, respectively, as required by the mass-action law (IV.6.04). In this §6 we shall discuss the distribution of p and n in the case of thermal equilibrium corresponding to zero current.

The transition from p_p to p_n and from n_n to n_p, respectively, must assume the form of an S-shaped curve (see Fig. IV.6.1). Space charges are formed on the left and on the right of the center $x = 0$. The positive space-charge density in the region $x > 0$ bends the electrostatic potential $V(x)$ downward (see Fig. IV.6.1) according to the Poisson equation

$$V''(x) = -\frac{4\pi}{\varepsilon}\,\rho(x) < 0 \qquad \text{for } x > 0 \qquad (\text{IV.6.08})$$

whereas the negative space-charge density connecting at the left bends the potential $V(x)$ back to horizontal:

$$V''(x) = -\frac{4\pi}{\varepsilon}\,\rho(x) > 0 \qquad \text{for } x < 0 \qquad (\text{IV.6.09})$$

---

[1] More accurately, $2.5 \cdot 10^{13}$ cm^{-3}. See E. M. Conwell, *Proc. IRE*, **40:** 1329 (1952), Table II.

The over-all result is—as for the boundary layer of a metal-semiconductor contact—a potential step[1] within which is established a Boltzmann distribution

$$p(x) = p_n \, e^{-\frac{e}{kT}V(x)} \tag{IV.6.10}$$

$$n(x) = n_n \, e^{+\frac{e}{kT}V(x)} \tag{IV.6.11}$$

The height of the step, i.e., the diffusion voltage V_D, can be calculated

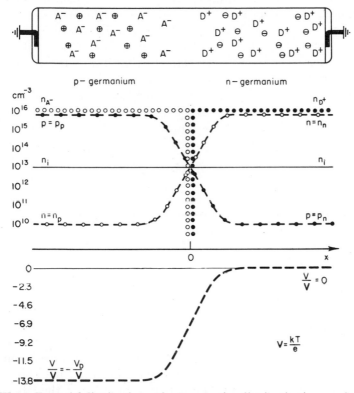

FIG. IV.6.1. Potential distribution and concentration distribution in a *p-n* junction. Zero-current case.

by solving these equations for $x \rightarrow -\infty$ with $V(-\infty) = -V_D$:

$$\frac{p_p}{p_n} = \frac{n_n}{n_p} = e^{+\frac{e}{kT}V_D} \tag{IV.6.12}$$

[1] The potential step is present in spite of the fact that the germanium crystal is grounded at both terminals! See also pp. 76 and 77 and pp. 359 to 361.

In the present case, V_D would be

$$V_D = \frac{kT}{e} \ln \frac{n_n}{n_p}$$

$$\approx 25.9 \text{ mv} \cdot \ln \frac{10^{16}}{10^{10}} = 25.9 \text{ mv} \cdot 13.8 \qquad \text{(IV.6.13)}$$

$$V_D \approx 0.358 \text{ volt}$$

Because of the Boltzmann equilibrium (IV.6.11), the logarithmically plotted electron concentration curve $n(x)$ is again identical with the potential curve $V(x)$ in Fig. IV.6.1. The logarithmic plot of the concentrations n and p has a further property which arises for p-n junctions but not for Schottky boundary layers with only one carrier type. The law of mass action (IV.6.04) requires that in Fig. IV.6.1 the n and p curves be symmetrical with respect to the horizontal line n_i. With the help of this criterion, we shall be able to determine the predominance of generation or recombination, respectively, in the nonequilibrium cases, i.e., when current is flowing.

§7. The p-n Junction with Current

What changes in the conditions just described when, for instance, a positive voltage $+U_{\text{forw}}$ is applied to the left p part of the rectifier while the potential of the right n part is fixed by grounding? The potential step is now reduced from V_D to $V_D - U_{\text{forw}}$ (see Fig. IV.7.1). The formation of this reduced step requires a diffuse double layer with less space charge than previously. The concentrations p and n must, therefore, maintain[1] their neutrality values $p_p = n_{A^-}$ and $n_n = n_{D^+}$ further into the transition region than in the previous condition of zero current. The concentrations p and n are no longer symmetrical to the intrinsic density n_i, and their product is now $p \cdot n > n_i^2$. This deviation from the law of mass action (IV.6.04) means that recombination exceeds pair formation in the entire transition region. This comes about in the following way: The potential increase at the left end of the rectifier drives the positive holes of the p region from left to right, namely, toward the transition region. The negative electrons of the right n region are attracted by the left positive electrode and thus flow, also, toward the transition region. Therefore the concentrations n and p increase within the transition region. This leads to an increase of the recombination rate $r \cdot n \cdot p$, whereas the generation g remains constant since it is independent of the concentration. A new steady-

---

[1] This argument should be made more precise as on p. 79.

state condition is established, when the excess of recombination over generation is just compensated by the influx into the transition region from both sides.   The foregoing shows furthermore that the total current i_{forw} is a pure hole current i_p on the left side and a pure electron current i_n on the right side (see Fig. IV.7.1, top).

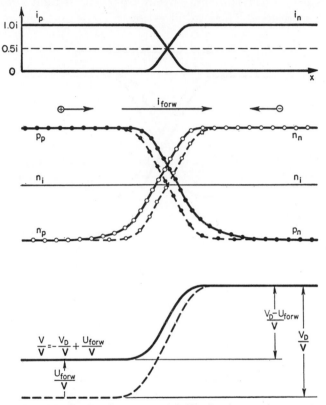

F IG. IV.7.1. Current distribution, potential distribution, and concentration distribution in a *p-n* junction.   The forward bias case.

It becomes now plausible that the experimentally observed high resistance of a *p-n* rectifier at small bias (the "zero-bias resistance" in Fig. IV.1.2) arises from carrier depletion in the transition region. There the carrier densities p and n drop to the intrinsic density n_i.   As we saw at the end of Chap. I (p. 27), this condition of intrinsic conduction corresponds to the highest attainable specific resistance in a semiconductor.   This cause of the high zero-bias resistance of the *p-n* rectifier has been reduced by the application of a positive voltage to the left *p* end of the rectifier.   The high carrier concentrations of the

p part and n part are, as we have seen, effectively carried along by the hole and electron currents directed toward the transition region, so that they are, so to speak, extended into the otherwise depleted transition region. The resulting reduction in resistance of the transition region, and hence of the p-n rectifier, shows that this polarity and the direction of the conventional current from left to right through the rectifier constitute the forward direction.

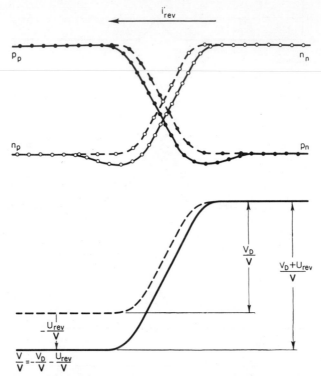

FIG. IV.7.2. Potential distribution and concentration distribution in a p-n junction. The reverse bias case.

The proof that the opposite direction of the conventional current is the reverse direction can now be made quite brief (see Fig. IV.7.2). A negative potential $-U_{rev}$ must be applied to the left end so that the conventional current flows from right to left. The potential step in the transition region increases thus to $V_D + U_{rev}$ and requires for its formation more space charge. This can be attained only by widening the depleted transition region. The widening of the high-resistance transition region increases the rectifier resistance. Thus the reverse direction is realized.

§8. The Special Case of a Low Recombination *p-n* Junction According to Shockley

Shockley has pointed out that the use of crystals with very low recombination rates leads to very special characteristics of *p-n* rectifiers. We shall again consider the case of the forward direction,

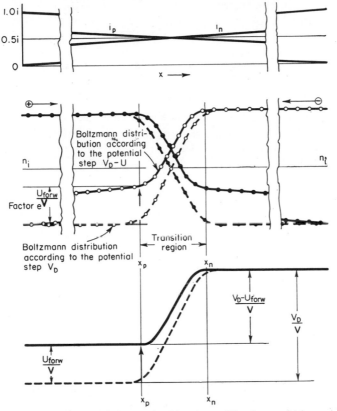

FIG. IV.8.1. *p-n* junction with low recombination. The forward-bias case. The potential in the forward-bias case is not strictly horizontal (constant) to the left of x_p and to the right of x_n, but rather a slight drop from left to right is present. In these "base regions" weak base fields are present which, however, are too small to be clearly incorporated in the above figure.

namely, the polarity shown in Fig. IV.7.1. We have pointed out previously that the current in the rectifier is carried by a hole current at the far left and by an electron current in the opposite direction at the far right and that the hole current passes over into the oppositely directed electron current in the transition region owing to the predominance of recombination.   If, according to Shockley, special measures, which we shall describe later, are taken to reduce the recombination appreciably, the holes will penetrate deeply into the n region and the electrons into the p region (see Fig. IV.8.1).   The $\oplus$ current begins to be taken over by the $\ominus$ current of opposite direction deep within the p region, long before the transition region is reached.   At the beginning x_p of the transition zone the exchange is already 49 per cent complete, in the middle of the transition region the ratio $i_p:i_n = 50:50$,[1] and at the end x_n of the transition region it is, for instance, 49:51, so that the remaining replacement of i_p by i_n takes place over a long distance in the n region.

Thus at the point x_p the numerous holes and the few electrons carry approximately the same current, namely, half of the total current i_{forw}. This stems from the fact that the holes are accelerated by only a very weak base field strength[2] whereas the few electrons contribute about the same current $\frac{1}{2}i_{\text{forw}}$ as a result of the relatively large concentration gradient.   The field contribution to the electron current can be completely neglected for all practical purposes.   While the weak field can contribute an equal hole current $\frac{1}{2}i_{\text{forw}}$ because of the large number of holes, the current contribution arising from the few electrons n is only of the order of $(n/p_p) \cdot \frac{1}{2}i_{\text{forw}} \approx \frac{1}{2} \cdot 10^{-4}i_{\text{forw}}$ in a typical example.

Thus we see that the electrons which are dragged into the p material carry their contribution to the total current in the form of a pure diffusion current.   This diffusion current is, however, not constant in space, but diminishes as the electrons penetrate further from right to left into the p material as a consequence of the predominance of the recombination $r \cdot n \cdot p$ over the generation g.   Hence, for two planes at x and $x + dx$ (see Fig. IV.8.2) we obtain

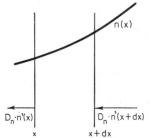

FIG. IV.8.2. Aid for the derivation of the diffusion equation.

$$D_n \cdot n'(x + dx) - D_n \cdot n'(x) = (r \cdot n(x) \cdot p_p - g)\, dx \quad \text{(IV.8.01)}$$

Applying the law of mass action (IV.6.04) to the p germanium, we obtain

$$g = r \cdot n_p \cdot p_p \quad\quad\quad\quad \text{(IV.8.02)}$$

and using this on the right side of (IV.8.01) we obtain

$$+D_n n''(x)\, dx = r p_p(n(x) - n_p)\, dx$$

[1] We still assume the symmetrical transition $n_n = n_p (= 10^{16}$ cm$^{-3})$.

[2] In this connection, see also the caption to Fig. IV.8.1.

or in another form

$$\frac{d^2}{dx^2}\left(n(x) - n_p\right) - \frac{1}{L_n^2}\left(n(x) - n_p\right) = 0 \qquad \text{(IV.8.03)}$$

where we have introduced the so-called diffusion length of the electrons in p germanium

$$L_n = \sqrt{\frac{D_n}{rp_p}} \qquad \text{(IV.8.04)}$$

In this connection we often use the concept of the "lifetime τ_n" of the electrons in p germanium, defined by[1]

$$\tau_n = \frac{1}{rp_p} \qquad \text{(IV.8.05)}$$

The justification of this definition would be too lengthy at this point. We refer the interested reader to Chap. IX, §1, where similar problems are discussed in detail. We shall note only that the combination of (IV.4.12), (IV.8.05), and the Nernst-Townsend-Einstein relation (IV.4.12) leads to

$$L_n = \sqrt{\frac{D_n}{rp_p}} = \sqrt{D_n \tau_n} = \sqrt{\mu_n \tau_n \frac{kT}{e}} \qquad \text{(IV.8.06)}$$

L_n and τ_n are added to the conductivity σ as material constants characterizing a given semiconductor sample. The solution of (IV.8.03) which fits the electron current as it diminishes toward $x = -\infty$ is

$$n(x) = n_p + C\,e^{\left|\frac{x - x_p}{L_n}\right.} \qquad \text{(IV.8.07)}$$

so that the logarithm of the concentration plotted in Fig. IV.8.1 shows a linear decrease toward $-\infty$ as long as $n(x)$ is large compared with the equilibrium value n_p. The slope of this straight line is determined by

---

[1] This relation applies to the specific reaction $\ominus + \oplus \to 0$. The carrier annihilation does not necessarily have to follow this recombination equation. Atomic imperfections and impurities as well as more extended lattice disorders, such as interfaces and surfaces, play an important role here. However, there is little doubt that in a first approximation the deviation $n - n_p$ from the equilibrium concentration n_p is the determining factor. Hence the expression

$$\frac{1}{\tau_n}\left(n - n_p\right)$$

for the number of carriers disappearing per unit time and volume has a rather general significance—independent of the particular recombination mechanism $\ominus + \oplus \to 0$. We shall, therefore, in the following always give the equations in a form which makes use of $\tau_n = 1/rp_p$ since this relation is tied to the specific reaction $\ominus + \oplus \to 0$.

the diffusion length L_n in such a fashion that the concentration $n(x)$ drops by a factor e over a distance L_n.

We shall now calculate the current which is carried by the diffusion tail; from (IV.8.07) we obtain

$$D_n n'(x) = \frac{D_n}{L_n} C\, e^{+\frac{x-x_p}{L_n}} = \frac{D_n}{L_n}\,(n(x) - n_p) \qquad \text{(IV.8.08)}$$

Thus i_n, the contribution to the total current i_{forw} which is carried by electrons, is at the point $x = x_p$:

$$i_n(x_p) = \frac{eD_n}{L_n}\,(n(x_p) - n_p) \qquad \text{(IV.8.09)}$$

For the computation of the characteristics, we must determine the concentration increase $n(x_p) - n_p$ at the beginning $x = x_p$ of the electron diffusion tail on the left (see Fig. IV.8.1) as a function of the voltage U_{forw} applied to the p-n junction. This can be done by stating the Shockley condition of "low" recombination more precisely. Low recombination means a small recombination coefficient and therefore, according to (IV.8.05), long lifetime τ_n and, according to (IV.8.04), long diffusion length L_n. The requirement of "low" recombination means actually that the diffusion length L_n is long compared with the width $x_n - x_p$ of the transition region. In this more precise form the Shockley condition has decisive consequences. The electron concentration drops within the small transition region $x_n - x_p$ by several or many powers of e, whereas in the diffusion tail the drop within the large diffusion length L_n is only by a factor e. The concentration gradient and with it the diffusion current must, therefore, increase enormously in the transition from diffusion tail to transition region. This is possible only if the excessive diffusion current in the transition region is compensated by a field current of almost equal magnitude, for the current contribution i_n of the electrons remains practically unchanged. This indicates that an approximate Boltzmann equilibrium exists in the transition region. This, in turn, leads to the potential curve $V(x)$, the logarithmically plotted electron concentration $n(x)$ being identical within the transition region. Since this applies also for zero current, it is evident from Fig. IV.8.1 that the rise by the forward bias U_{forw} of the potential curve $V(x)$ in the p region is associated with a rise in the concentration curve $n(x)$ at the point $x = x_p$ by the factor $e^{+\frac{e}{kT}U_{\text{forw}}}$:

$$n(x_p) = n_p\, e^{+\frac{e}{kT}U_{\text{forw}}} \qquad \text{(IV.8.10)}$$

This, however, is the relation between the voltage U_{forw} and the concentration $n(x_p)$ at the beginning $x = x_p$ of the electronic diffusion tail for which we were looking on page 100.

The characteristic equation $i_{\text{forw}} = f(U_{\text{forw}})$ of a *p-n* junction is now obtained without great effort. First we combine (IV.8.10) with (IV.8.09):

$$i_n(x_p) = \frac{eD_n}{L_n} \, n_p \, (e^{+\frac{e}{kT}U_{\text{forw}}} - 1) \qquad \text{(IV.8.11)}$$

In order to arrive at the total forward current i_{forw} the current contribution $i_p(x_p)$ carried by the holes $\oplus$ must be added to (IV.8.11):

$$i_{\text{forw}} = i_n(x_p) + i_p(x_p) \qquad \text{(IV.8.12)}$$

This current contribution i_p has essentially the same value at the point $x = x_p$ as at the point $x = x_n$, since the recombination in the transition region is to be neglected:

$$i_p(x_p) \approx i_p(x_n) \qquad \text{(IV.8.13)}$$

In analogy to (IV.8.11) we have

$$i_p(x_n) \approx \frac{eD_p}{L_p} \, p_n \, (e^{+\frac{e}{kT}U_{\text{forw}}} - 1) \qquad \text{(IV.8.14)}$$

The combination of (IV.8.12) with (IV.8.13) and (IV.8.14) leads to the characteristic equation for the forward current

$$i_{\text{forw}} = e\left(\frac{D_n n_p}{L_n} + \frac{D_p p_n}{L_p}\right)(e^{+\frac{e}{kT}U_{\text{forw}}} - 1)$$

and for the reverse current

$$i_{\text{rev}} = e\left(\frac{D_n n_p}{L_n} + \frac{D_p p_n}{L_p}\right)(1 - e^{-\frac{e}{kT}U_{\text{rev}}})$$

$$\qquad \text{(IV.8.15)}$$

We obtain, therefore, the same exponential characteristics for the Shockley *p-n* junction with low recombination as from the diode theory for the metal-semiconductor contact. The saturation current, however, is now

$$i_S = e\left(\frac{D_n n_p}{L_n} + \frac{D_p p_n}{L_p}\right) \qquad \text{(IV.8.16)}$$

With (IV.8.06), the Nernst-Townsend-Einstein relation (IV.4.12), and the mass-action law (IV.6.04) we find

$$i_S = \sqrt{e\,kT} \cdot n_i^2 \cdot \left(\sqrt{\frac{\mu_n}{\tau_n}}\frac{1}{p_p} + \sqrt{\frac{\mu_p}{\tau_p}}\frac{1}{n_n}\right) \qquad \text{(IV.8.17)}$$

which yields, with Eq. (IV.8.05), applicable to the specific reaction

$\ominus + \oplus \to 0$

$$i_S = \sqrt{e \cdot r \cdot kT}\, n_i^2 \left(\sqrt{\frac{\mu_n}{p_p}} + \sqrt{\frac{\mu_p}{n_n}} \right) \qquad \text{(IV.8.18)}$$

These saturation-current values are much lower than those derived from the diode theory for metal-semiconductor contacts. With the help of (IV.4.07), (IV.8.17), and (VII.9.22) we obtain with $n_B = n_i$ in the diode theory,[1] setting the two terms in (IV.8.17)[2] equal to each other,

$$\frac{i_S \text{ (metal semiconductor)}}{i_S \text{ (p-n junction)}} = \frac{1}{2} \frac{1}{\sqrt{2\pi}} \sqrt{\frac{e\tau_n}{m\mu_n}} \cdot \frac{p_p}{n_i}$$

$$= \sqrt{7.0 \cdot 10^{13} \frac{(\tau_n/\text{sec})}{(\mu_n/\text{cm}^2 \text{ volt}^{-1} \text{ sec}^{-1})} \cdot \frac{p_p/\text{cm}^{-3}}{n_i/\text{cm}^{-3}}} \qquad \text{(IV.8.19)}$$

For germanium with $\tau_n = 100\ \mu\text{sec}$, $\mu_n = 3{,}500\ \text{cm}^2/\text{volt-sec}$, $p_p = 10^{16}\ \text{cm}^{-3}$, and $n_i = 10^{13}\ \text{cm}^{-3}$, we thus obtain

$$\frac{i_S \text{ (metal semiconductor)}}{i_S \text{ (p-n junction)}} = 1.4 \cdot 10^{+6}$$

We hope that the foregoing discussion has shown that the physical reason for the unipolarity of a p-n rectifier with long diffusion length no longer lies in carrier-concentration extension effects within the transition region. The actual transition region, within which the carrier concentration is approximately equal to the intrinsic density n_i, is no longer of decisive importance for the magnitude of the actual current, for this current is readily provided by small deviations from the Boltzmann equilibrium.[3] The decisive effect is the current yield of the diffusion tails. The current yield of a diffusion tail is, however, vastly different for the two current directions (see Fig. IV.8.3). In

---

[1] For $n_B < n_i$ an inversion occurs within the boundary region (see p. 26). The neglect of carriers of opposite polarity in the diode theory is no longer permissible in the boundary region.

[2] This is permissible for order-of-magnitude considerations.

[2] For the reverse direction this is, however, approximately correct only to $U_{\text{rev}} < V \ln ([L/x_0] \sqrt{2/\pi})$, where $V = kT/e = 25.9$ mv $(T/300°K)$, $L = L_n$ or L_p is one of the two diffusion lengths, and $x_0 = \sqrt{\varepsilon V/4\pi e n_{D^+}}$ or $\sqrt{\varepsilon V/4\pi e n_{A^-}}$ is the so-called Debye length of the semiconductor. This was calculated by Herlet for the case of constant impurity concentrations n_{A^-} and n_{D^+} changing abruptly at the junction. The term Debye length stems from the similarity of x_0 with the characteristic length in the Debye-Hückel theory of strong electrolytes. As an aid for visualizing this length, we recall that a constant space charge produces a parabolic potential distribution according to the Poisson equation (IV.2.05). At the beginning of this parabolic potential distribution, the potential difference of $\frac{1}{2}V$ is established within a Debye length.

one direction the necessary concentration increases are possible without limit so that currents of any magnitude can be carried.   The concentration decrease required for the other current direction, however, rapidly approaches a limit because the concentration at the beginning of the diffusion tail cannot be made less than zero.   This should help in visualizing the saturation of the current for reverse polarity.

These *p-n* rectifiers with long diffusion lengths exhibit excellent reverse characteristics since the diffusion tails with their extremely low concentrations govern the process.   This was demonstrated in the comparison with a metal-semiconductor contact.   From the practical standpoint, high diffusion lengths are attained by using crystals of greatest possible perfection since recombination takes place primarily at surfaces and crystal imperfections.   It is not only necessary to have single crystals, but the

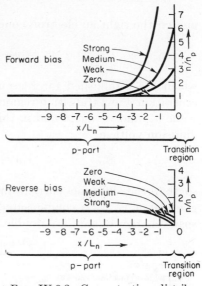

Fig. IV.8.3. Concentration distribution of the electrons in the diffusion tail within the *p* part. Linear plot.

single crystals must have a high degree of perfection without dislocations and domain structures.

This leads to an entirely new chapter of the physics of electronic semiconductors which cannot be entered upon here.[1]

§9. Supplementary Remarks on *p-n* Junctions

a. Abrupt and Gradual Change of Impurity Concentrations in the Junction Region

Up to now we have made the rather unrealistic assumption that the impurity concentrations n_{A^-} and n_{D^+} maintain their constant values up to the center $x = 0$ of the *p-n* junction, where they drop abruptly to zero.   If we examine the reasoning of the previous paragraphs, including §8, we find that this unrealistic assumption does not affect the results appreciably.   Assuming, for instance, $n_{A^-}(x)$ and $n_{D^+}(x)$ curves

[1] See in this connection W. Shockley and W. T. Read, Jr., *Phys. Rev.*, **87**: 835 (1952).

as shown in Fig. IV.9.1, we find in analogy to the previously considered case (Fig. IV.6.1) on the left a hole concentration

$$p_p = n_A\text{-}(-\infty) + n_p = n_A\text{-}(-\infty) + \frac{n_i^2}{p_p} \approx n_A\text{-}(-\infty) \quad \text{(IV.9.01)}$$

and on the right an electron concentration

$$n_n = n_{D^+}(+\infty) + p_n = n_{D^+}(+\infty) + \frac{n_i^2}{n_n} \approx n_{D^+}(+\infty) \quad \text{(IV.9.02)}$$

which are established for reasons of neutrality. The electron concentration n in a transition region drops again from the value n_n to the value n_p, and we again find in this transition region for zero current a diffusion voltage

$$V_D = \frac{kT}{e} \ln \frac{n_n}{n_p} \quad \text{(IV.9.03)}$$

so that the diffusion current in the direction of the concentration gradient $n_n \to n_p$ is compensated by an opposite field current. The space charges of a diffuse double layer are necessary for the formation

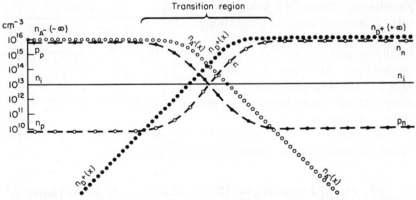

FIG. IV.9.1. p-n junction with gradually changing (graded) impurity densities.

of the potential step V_D. Hence, it is not possible for n and p to have, in the entire transition region, values prescribed by the neutrality condition

$$n + n_{A^-} = p + n_{D^+} \quad \text{(IV.9.04)}$$

and the law of mass action

$$n \cdot p = n_i^2 \quad \text{(IV.9.05)}$$

These would be

$$n_{\text{neutral}}(x) = +\tfrac{1}{2}[n_{D^+}(x) - n_A\text{-}(x)] \\ + \sqrt{\tfrac{1}{4}[n_{D^+}(x) - n_A\text{-}(x)]^2 + n_i^2} \quad \text{(IV.9.06)}$$

$$p_{\text{neutral}}(x) = -\tfrac{1}{2}[n_{D^+}(x) - n_{A^-}(x)]$$
$$+ \sqrt{\tfrac{1}{4}[n_{D^+}(x) - n_{A^-}(x)]^2 + n_i^2} \quad \text{(IV.9.07)}$$

For *abrupt* transitions of the impurity concentrations n_{A^-} and n_{D^+} (extreme case: Fig. IV.6.1), the deviations $p(x) - p_{\text{neutral}}(x)$ and $n(x) - n_{\text{neutral}}(x)$ will have the order of magnitude of $n_{A^-}(x)$ or $n_{D^+}(x)$, respectively. For very gradual transitions, these deviations $p(x) - p_{\text{neutral}}(x)$ and $n(x) - n_{\text{neutral}}(x)$ will be small compared to $n_{A^-}(x)$ or $n_{D^+}(x)$, respectively. In both cases, however, the same diffusion voltage V_D prescribed by (IV.9.03) must be formed in a double layer— in one case in a relatively thin layer with space-charge densities $\rho(x) \approx -en_{A^-}(x)$ or $\rho(x) \approx +en_{D^+}(x)$, in the other case in a layer with the space-charge densities $\rho(x) \ll -en_{A^-}(x)$ or $\rho(x) \ll +en_{D^+}(x)$.

These details do not, at least at this stage, prevent a distinction between the transition region and the two diffusion tails in the case of current flow. For current flow, too, the Boltzmann equilibrium is approximately maintained. In the regions adjacent to the transition region, the dominant carrier type (the "majority carriers") carries its current contribution as pure field current in a small "base field" and the minority carrier type (the "minority carriers") carries its current contribution in the form of a pure diffusion current. Therefore, Eq. (IV.8.09) applies again for the current contribution of the electrons beyond the transition region. The concentration value at the beginning of the diffusion tail is again determined by the Boltzmann distribution in the adjacent transition region [Eq. (IV.8.10)]. Thus we find again (IV.8.11) for the current contribution i_n of the electrons and finally (IV.8.15) for the total current.

The realization that the validity of the characteristic equation (IV.8.15) depends solely on the adjacency of a Boltzmann region and two diffusion tails, and not on the variation of the concentration within the Boltzmann region, will be fruitful when we consider unsymmetrical p-n junctions later in this paragraph. However, we should point out here that the maximum field strength is of course appreciably higher in a thin transition region than in a wide one, since the height of the potential step is always given, in the critical reverse case, by $V_D + U_{\text{rev}}$ independent of the width. Experience indicates that at field strengths of 10^5 to 10^6 volt cm^{-1} breakdown occurs, which may lead to destruction of the crystal. However, reversible secondary phenomena precede this stage; we shall mention here only the so-called Zener effect,[1] where valence electrons are transferred into the conduction band by high field strengths. K. B. McAfee, E. J. Ryder,

[1] See, for instance, pp. 223ff.

W. Shockley, and M. Sparks[1] have explained the reversible steep rise
of the reverse current above a critical reverse voltage by the Zener
effect.[2]   Disregarding the actual mechanism, it is known that the failure of rectifiers above a certain reverse voltage is associated with
excessive field strengths, and this shows that the impurity transition
must be as gradual as possible in order to attain the highest possible
reverse voltages.[3]   The only limitation in this direction is the original
assumption that the transition region must be small compared with
the diffusion length which, in turn, calls for the greatest possible
diffusion lengths.   This requires the use of single crystals with very
low imperfection content, as pointed out previously.

b. Asymmetrical p-n junctions

We have already pointed out that the characteristic Eqs. (IV.8.15)
and (IV.8.17) are based on the adjacency of a Boltzmann region and
two diffusion tails and that the details of the concentration distributions, particularly within the Boltzmann region, are unimportant.
This allows us to apply the characteristic Eqs. (IV.8.15) and (IV.8.17)
to the unsymmetrical p-n junction.

We dope, for instance, the p region with 10^{18} acceptors/cm³ and the
n region with only 10^{15} donors/cm³.   Then we have

$$p_p = 10^{18} \text{ cm}^{-3} \gg n_n = 10^{15} \text{ cm}^{-3}$$

The first term of the sum in the expressions (IV.8.16) and (IV.8.17) for
the saturation current represents the electrons and disappears for all
practical purposes in comparison with the hole contribution.   Since
the saturation current is not only decisive in the reverse direction but
determines the *entire* characteristic (IV.8.15), the forward current
consists essentially of holes which flow from the p germanium to the
n germanium.   The forward-biased p-n junction of a highly doped p

[1] K. B. McAfee, E. J. Ryder, W. Shockley, and M. Sparks. *Phys. Rev.*, **83**: 650
(1951).   The exponent in Eq. (1) of this paper is, however, too large by a factor 2.
This appears to be only a printing error, for in the numerical equation (3) of the
same paper the exponent has again the right value.

[2] See also G. K. McKay and K. B. McAfee, *Phys. Rev.*, **91**: 1079 (1953).

[3] R. N. Hall and W. C. Dunlap, *Phys. Rev.*, **80**: 467 (1950).   We would like to
suggest the use of the expression *p-n junction* also for very steep impurity concentration variations, i.e., for very abrupt transitions between p and n germanium.
As a criterion for the distinction between *transition* or *junction* and *contact* or
boundary, we shall use the uniformity or change of the crystal lattice.   W. Shockley
had probably the same distinction in mind when in his original paper [*Bell System
Tech. J.*, **28**: 444 (1949)], he considered abruptly changing impurity distributions
under the heading "junction."

and lightly doped n material acts, therefore, as a good "emitter" of holes into the n material. This will be of importance in transistor physics.

In this connection we mention another fact which is not restricted to the asymmetry of the p-n contact but is also important for the mechanism of a p-n-p transistor. The reverse current of a p-n junction is small because of the small current yield of the diffusion tails with reverse bias. If, therefore, in a p-n junction with reverse bias, carrier pairs are introduced by other means than the normal *thermal* excitation such as light incidence (internal photoelectric effect) or by high field strengths (Zener effect), the reverse current will be affected by these additional minority carriers. The same will apply if the carrier depletion is alleviated by the injection of carriers from a foreign carrier source. This means that a p-n junction with a reverse bias acts as a good "collector." We shall treat these matters in more detail in the next chapter.

§10. Junction Capacitance

It is clear from the preceding paragraphs that for any given voltage there is a certain distribution of charge carriers at and near the p-n junction. If the voltage is changed, this charge distribution has to be readjusted, too. This means that, during a change in voltage, the current is not equal to the current which corresponds to the instantaneous voltage but that there is an additional current which is proportional to the *rate* of change of voltage. Such a current is a capacitive current, and we therefore have to attribute a certain capacitance to a p-n junction.

The mobile charges in a semiconductor are minority carriers and majority carriers. Both contribute to the junction capacitance, but in a markedly different way. We treat the minority carriers first, and we restrict ourselves to junctions with low internal recombination (Shockley case).

When a p-n junction is biased in the forward direction, a diffusion tail of minority carriers extends to a depth of about a diffusion length into the bulk semiconductor, as shown for the p-type side in Fig. IV.8.3.

On the p side the electron density of the diffusion tail—that is, the total electron density minus the equilibrium density—is, according to Eqs. (IV.8.07) and (IV.8.10),

$$n(x) - n_p = n_p \, (e^{\frac{e}{kT} U_{\text{forw}}} - 1) \, e^{\frac{x - x_p}{L_n}} \qquad \text{(IV.10.01)}$$

The total number of electrons stored per unit area in this diffusion tail follows by integration

$$\frac{Q_n}{e} = \int_{-\infty}^{x_p} [n(x) - n_p]\, dx = n_p L_n\, (e^{\frac{e}{kT} U_{\text{forw}}} - 1) \quad \text{(IV.10.02)}$$

If now the voltage is changed by dU_{forw}, the stored electron charge changes by dQ_n, resulting in what may be termed the *differential storage capacitance for electrons*

$$C_n = \frac{dQ_n}{dU_{\text{forw}}} = \frac{e^2 n_p L_n}{kT}\, e^{\frac{e}{kT} U_{\text{forw}}} \quad \text{(IV.10.03)}$$

In addition, we have a similar differential storage capacitance for holes

$$C_p = \frac{dQ_p}{dU_{\text{forw}}} = \frac{e^2 p_n L_p}{kT}\, e^{\frac{e}{kT} U_{\text{forw}}} \quad \text{(IV.10.04)}$$

so that the total storage capacitance is

$$C_{\text{stor}} = C_n + C_p = \frac{e^2}{kT}\, (n_p L_n + p_n L_p)\, e^{\frac{e}{kT} U_{\text{forw}}} \quad \text{(IV.10.05)}$$

We have called this capacitance a differential capacitance because it is not the total charge divided by the voltage but rather the change in the charge for a small change in the voltage. Whenever, as in our case, the charge is not directly proportional to the voltage, this is a more useful definition because it is the differential capacitance which is seen by a small a-c signal superimposed on a d-c signal.

The storage capacitance is also often called diffusion capacitance because it arises from the carriers diffusing across the junction.

From (IV.10.05) it follows that the storage capacitance increases rapidly with the forward bias. The forward current increases in a similar fashion, and for $eU_{\text{forw}} \gg kT$ the storage capacitance is directly proportional to the current.

For a reverse bias, the storage capacitance drops off very rapidly to zero. However, the total capacitance of the junction does not vanish; there is an additional capacitance of the space-charge transition region itself, generally called the transition capacitance. This is the capacitance due to the *majority* carriers which was mentioned earlier. As we will show, it also varies with voltage, but much less so; in the forward direction, the transition capacitance is normally much smaller than the storage capacitance so that it can be neglected (see the problems in §11). We therefore can restrict our discussion of the transition capacitance to the reverse direction, where the opposite is true.

As shown already in Fig. IV.3.4 for the metal-semiconductor contact, the space-charge region widens for increasing reverse bias. The same is true, of course, for a *p-n* junction. This widening arises from the displacement of the majority carriers which neutralize the ionized impurities. As a result, a capacitive current flows. But contrary to the case of the minority carrier storage capacitance, the capacitive current of the transition capacitance is not a *carrier* current across the junction but rather a *displacement* current as in an ordinary condenser.

This similarity between the transition capacitance and an ordinary condenser capacitance holds quantitatively. To show this, we introduce the concept of an "equivalent condenser" that corresponds to a reverse-biased *p-n* junction. This is an ordinary plate condenser which is filled with a dielectric of the same dielectric constant as the semiconductor and which has a plate distance equal to the width of the space-charge region of the junction. If the boundaries of the space-charge layer are parallel planes, the equivalent condenser is a parallel-plate condenser; if they are curved in any arbitrary way, the plates of the equivalent condenser may be assumed to be of the same shape. The equivalent condensers that correspond to different reverse-bias values of the same junction are, of course, different.

If we now apply a small bias dU_{rev} across the equivalent condenser, its plates will charge up by a small amount dQ. Let us then take away this charge from the plates of the condenser and transfer every charge element, point by point, to the equivalent position at the space-charge layer boundary of the junction. This can be done by displacing this boundary by an infinitesimal amount. These charge elements are then arranged in the semiconductor in an identical geometry and in a medium of identical dielectric constant as before in the condenser. They therefore produce—superposed on the already present field distribution inside the space-charge layer—an additional field that is identical with the field inside the condenser, because the original charge distribution itself is not affected by the new charges. The additional voltage that develops across the *p-n* junction is then equal to the dU_{rev} that had been applied across the condenser. This means that the differential transition capacitance dQ/dU_{rev} is equal to the capacitance of the equivalent plate condenser.

For parallel-junction boundaries with a plate separation $x_n - x_p$, the capacitance per unit area is then

$$C_{tr} = \frac{\varepsilon}{4\pi(x_n - x_p)} \qquad \text{(IV.10.06)}$$

The problem therefore reduces to a determination of the space-charge region width as a function of the voltage.

This problem can be solved as follows: The space-charge region of a *p-n* junction is an electric double layer containing an equal number of positive and negative charges.   Therefore, if ρ is the local space-charge density

$$\int_{x_p}^{x_n} \rho \, dx = 0 \qquad (IV.10.07)$$

The electrical dipole moment per unit area of the layer is

$$\boldsymbol{M} = \int_{x_p}^{x_n} \rho x \, dx$$

and the potential difference ΔV across such a double layer is known to be equal to

$$\Delta V = \frac{4\pi}{\varepsilon} \boldsymbol{M}$$

In a *p-n* junction biased in the reverse direction, the total potential difference is $U_{\text{rev}} + V_D$, where V_D is the diffusion potential.   Therefore,

$$U_{\text{rev}} + V_D = \frac{4\pi}{\varepsilon} \int_{x_p}^{x_n} \rho x \, dx \qquad (IV.10.08)$$

If $\rho(x)$ were known, one could determine x_n and x_p and thereby $x_n - x_p$ from the two equations (IV.10.07) and (IV.10.08).

From the interior of a reverse-biased junction, all mobile carriers are swept out.   The charge density, then, is equal to the charge density of the ionized impurities and, if all impurities are ionized,

$$\rho(x) = e[n_D(x) - n_A(x)] \qquad (IV.10.09)$$

Near the ends of the boundaries of the space-charge layer, however, the mobile carriers are only partially swept out and the charge density approaches zero gradually, as shown in Fig. IV.3.4.   This tailing off takes place in that region where the electrostatic potential differs from the potential of the adjoining neutral semiconductor by only a few kT/e.   For every deviation kT/e from the outside potential, the majority carrier density drops by e^{-1} so that the remaining mobile carrier density is negligible as soon as the potential has changed by more than a few kT/e.   Now, kT/e is a very small voltage, at room temperature about 0.026 volt.   This tail region, therefore, contributes only a small amount of the total potential difference whenever $U_{\text{rev}} + U_D$ is large compared to kT/e, and this is practically always the case, since generally V_D alone is large compared to kT/e.

It has therefore been suggested by Schottky,[1] and justified by a detailed mathematical analysis, that one can replace the actual gradual drop-off in the space charge with negligible error by an abrupt drop-off.[2] This means that x_p and x_n are determined from the two equations

$$\int_{x_p}^{x_n} [n_D(x) - n_A(x)]\, dx = 0 \qquad (IV.10.10)$$

$$\int_{x_p}^{x_n} [n_D(x) - n_A(x)] \cdot x\, dx = \frac{\varepsilon}{4\pi e} (U_{rev} + V_D) \qquad (IV.10.11)$$

Actually, it is this introduction of an abrupt transition that gives a well-defined meaning to the quantities x_p and x_n; with a gradual transition, it is not immediately clear which coordinate is to be chosen as the "end" of the space-charge layer. Schottky showed that the values derived from the last two equations actually are the proper values.

Equations (IV.10.10) and (IV.10.11) can be solved in closed form only for a number of simple distributions. In the case of an abrupt transition, say

$$n_D(x) - n_A(x) = \begin{cases} - n_A \\ + n_D \end{cases} \quad \text{for} \quad \begin{cases} x < 0 \\ x > 0 \end{cases} \qquad (IV.10.12)$$

we find

$$-x_p = \sqrt{\frac{\varepsilon}{2\pi e} \frac{n_D}{n_A\,(n_D + n_A)}\,(U_{rev} + V_D)} \qquad (IV.10.13)$$

$$x_n = \sqrt{\frac{\varepsilon}{2\pi e} \frac{n_A}{n_D\,(n_D + n_A)}\,(U_{rev} + V_D)} \qquad (IV.10.14)$$

$$x_n - x_p = \sqrt{\frac{\varepsilon}{2\pi e} \frac{n_D + n_A}{n_D\,n_A}\,(U_{rev} + V_D)} \qquad (IV.10.15)$$

An important special case of this is the extremely unsymmetrically doped junction because it occurs in many practical alloy junctions and describes the behavior of the semiconductor side of a metal-semiconductor contact as well. For $n_A \gg n_D$, we obtain

$$-x_p = \sqrt{\frac{\varepsilon}{2\pi e} \frac{n_D}{n_A^2}\,(U_{rev} + V_D)} \qquad (IV.10.16)$$

$$x_n = \sqrt{\frac{\varepsilon}{2\pi e} \frac{1}{n_D}\,(U_{rev} + V_D)} \qquad \text{independent of } n_A \qquad (IV.10.17)$$

$$x_n - x_p \approx x_n \qquad (IV.10.18)$$

[1] W. Schottky, Z. Physik, **118**: 539 (1942).
[2] Note that Fig. IV.3.4 has a logarithmic scale. If replotted linearly, it shows that the real charge distribution drops off rather abruptly.

Since the junction width always increases with increasing voltage, it follows already from (IV.10.06) that the transition capacitance decreases with increasing U_{rev}. But while the storage capacitance decreases exponentially, the decrease of C_{tr} is fairly slow. In our example we found a decrease with the inverse square root of the total potential difference. Other impurity distributions lead to other variations. For further details we refer the reader to the problems in §11.

§11. Problems

1. In analogy to a differential capacitance dQ/dU, a differential conductance can be defined as di/dU. Give a formula for the differential conductance of a p-n junction both as a function of the voltage and as a function of the current.

2. An abrupt p-n junction in germanium may have the following physical parameters:

$$n_A = 10^{16} \text{ cm}^{-3} \qquad n_D = 10^{15} \text{ cm}^{-3} \qquad \tau_n = 10 \ \mu\text{sec} \qquad \tau_p = 50 \ \mu\text{sec}$$

Assuming the values for n_i, ε, μ_n, and μ_p given in the text, calculate the following electrical properties of this junction:

a. The diffusion voltage V_D.

b. The thickness of the space-charge region and the transition capacitance per unit area for zero bias.

c. The diffusion capacitance per unit area for zero bias.

d. The reverse saturation current density and the forward current density for a bias of 0.2 volt.

3. For the p-n junction in the preceding problem, determine graphically or numerically the voltage for which the diffusion capacitance becomes equal to the transition capacitance.

4.* The following experimental data are known about a particular germanium p-n junction:

a. The transition capacitance per unit area follows the relationship:

$$\frac{1}{C^2} = 1.77 \cdot 10^{-8} \left(\frac{U_{\text{rev}}}{1 \text{ volt}} + 0.314 \right) \frac{\text{cm}^4}{(\mu\mu\text{f})^2}$$

b. The reverse saturation current at room temperature is 192 μa/cm^2.

c. The diffusion capacitance per unit area at zero bias is 0.363 μf/cm^2.

Determine from these values the physical parameters of the junction, such as the impurity densities and the lifetimes, assuming the junction to be abrupt and assuming the values for n_i, ε, μ_n, and μ_p given in the text.

What is the uncertainty in the physical parameters if the contact potential varies by ± 0.001 volt, provided that the other experimental data are accurate?

5. Verify Eqs. (IV.10.13) to (IV.10.15).

6. What is the capacitance-voltage relationship for a graded junction for which the impurity density is given by

$$n_D(x) - n_A(x) = ax \qquad\qquad\qquad (\text{IV.11.01})$$

where a is a constant of the dimension cm^{-4}? Assume, for example, a value of $a = 10^{19}$ cm^{-4}. At what voltage, then, is the capacitance equal to 10^4 $\mu\mu$f/cm^2?

7. What is the capacitance-voltage relationship for a so-called p-i-n junction, that is, a junction where the p region and the n region are separated by an intrinsic region of a certain thickness, say w_i?

$$n_D(x) - n_A(x) = \begin{cases} -n_A & x < 0 \\ 0 & \text{for } 0 < x < w_i \\ +n_D & w_i < x \end{cases} \qquad \text{(IV.11.02)}$$

How does the result differ from the behavior of an abrupt junction without the intrinsic layer but with otherwise identical structure? Calculate the zero bias capacitance for a germanium junction with $n_D = 10^{15}$ cm^{-3}, $n_A = 10^{16}$ cm^{-3}, $w_i = 10^{-4}$ cm.

CHAPTER V

The Physical Mechanism of Crystal Amplifiers (Transistors)

§1. Introduction

The transistor is a device for the amplification of electrica¹ signals; so it may not be too far-fetched to refer in the discussion of its mechanism to the oldest and simplest device of this type, namely, the electromagnetic telegraph relay (see Fig. V.1.1). Here, a weak current arriving over a long transmission line actuates a switch which starts or blocks the strong current from a local source. The essential part of this process can be described as a signal which varies the conductivity in a current path of a local current source, effected in this particular case by a variation of the cross section at a certain point.

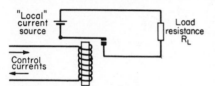

FIG. V.1.1. Amplification by a telegraph relay.

As an alternative of such a modification of the geometric dimensions of the current path, one could also consider a change of the specific conductivity, for instance, by varying the number of carriers. This actually happens in a number of transistor types, namely, by more or less intensive injection of additional charge carriers. Within the range of this common mechanism, the various types differ only in the nature of the affected current path. If the injection occurs into an ohmic conductor, we have the filamentary transistor (§2). If the affected current path is a p-n junction, we have the n-p-n transistor (§3). Finally, in the point-contact transistor, the boundary layer of a metallic point contact is affected by injected carriers (§4). The last transistor type to be discussed, namely, the unipolar transistor, operates like the relay by means of continuously variable geometrical dimensions of the current path (§5). This can again be interpreted as a variation of the carrier concentration as in the other transistor types. In contrast to the other types, it is here restricted to more or less extended boundary regions of the current cross section.   Furthermore, this variation applies to the majority carriers and not the minority carriers.

§2. The Filamentary Transistor

As was pointed out in the introduction, in this transistor type additional charge carriers are injected into an ohmic conductor.   So far, we have used the term injection as though it required no further explanation.   The error of this notion is evident from the fact that effective carrier injection is possible only into a semiconductor, but not into a metal.   Therefore we must first discuss carrier injection and the associated time effects.

a. Time Effects with Carrier Injection

We choose the example of a grounded germanium crystal which is doped with $n_{D^+} = 10^{16}$ arsenic atoms/cm³ and is, therefore, an n-type semiconductor.[1]   The neutrality condition requires in this case an electron concentration n of

$$n = n_{D^+} = 10^{+16} \text{ cm}^{-3} \qquad (V.2.01)$$

Now we want to increase the concentration n by electron bombardment, for instance, by $\delta n = 10^{15}$ cm⁻³ to $n + \delta n = 1.1 \cdot 10^{16}$ cm⁻³. This can be accomplished for only an extremely short period of time because the additionally introduced electrons repel each other and flow to ground.   Expressing this more precisely, the introduction of $\delta n = 10^{+15}$ electrons/cm³ disturbs the neutrality of the conductor, and the resulting space charge ρ creates an electric field which sets the entire electron concentration $n + \delta n$ in motion.   The resulting currents reduce the additional concentration again to zero.   Not only the few additional δn electrons participate in this process but predominantly the $n (\gg \delta n)$ electrons which were already present before the disturbance.   This disturbance is, therefore, rapidly removed and can exist only for a very short time.

In a quantitative treatment of the time decay of a space charge $\rho(t)$ we start from the continuity equation:

$$\frac{\partial \rho}{\partial t} = - \operatorname{div} \mathbf{i} \qquad (V.2.02)$$

[1] Substitutional imperfections or impurities in germanium can be assumed to be fully ionized—except at extremely low temperatures and very high doping concentrations.   Hence we can put $n_D = n_{D^+}$.

With the current

$$i = \sigma \, \mathbf{E} = - \, \sigma \, \text{grad} \, V \qquad (\text{V.2.03})$$

we obtain from (V.2.02)[1]

$$\frac{\partial \rho}{\partial t} = + \, \sigma \cdot \Delta V \qquad (\text{V.2.04})$$

Combination with Poisson's equation

$$\Delta V = - \frac{4\pi}{\varepsilon} \rho \qquad (\text{V.2.05})$$

results in

$$\frac{\partial \rho}{\partial t} = - \frac{4\pi\sigma}{\varepsilon} \rho \qquad (\text{V.2.06})$$

with the solution

$$\rho(t) = \rho(0) \, e^{-\frac{t}{T_{\text{relax}}}} \qquad (\text{V.2.07})$$

from which we find the relaxation time

$$T_{\text{relax}} = \frac{\varepsilon}{4\pi\sigma} \qquad (\text{V.2.08})$$

The germanium with 10^{16} cm^{-3} electrons just mentioned would have a conductivity

$$\sigma = e\mu_n n$$
$$= 1.6 \cdot 10^{-19} \text{ coulomb} \cdot 3.6 \cdot 10^{+3} \text{ cm}^2/\text{volt-sec} \cdot 10^{+16} \text{ cm}^{-3}$$
$$= 5.76 \text{ ohm}^{-1} \text{ cm}^{-1}$$
$$= 5.76 \cdot 9 \cdot 10^{+11} \text{ sec}^{-1} = 5.19 \cdot 10^{+12} \text{ sec}^{-1} \qquad (\text{V.2.09})$$

With $\varepsilon_{Ge} = 16.2$ we find from (V.2.08) in this case

$$T_{\text{relax}} = 2.49 \cdot 10^{-13} \text{ sec} \qquad (\text{V.2.10})$$

From (V.2.08) and (V.2.09) we obtain the relation for the relaxation time

$$T_{\text{relax}} = \frac{\varepsilon}{4\pi e \mu_n n} \qquad (\text{V.2.11})$$

which shows that the speed of the decay process is determined not by the disturbance itself but by the undisturbed concentration n. T_{relax} becomes very small because of the magnitude of n. Hence, if one introduces electrons into an n-type conductor, the change of concentration is maintained for only 10^{-12} to 10^{-13} sec.

[1] With $\Delta = \text{div} \, \text{grad} = \partial^2/\partial x^2 + \partial^2/\partial y^2 + \partial^2/\partial z^2$.

The situation is, however, vastly different if $\delta p = 10^{15}$ holes/cm^3 can be introduced additionally into the n germanium under consideration. These additional holes also repel each other, but only their own small concentration $\delta p = 10^{15}$ cm^{-3} is available for the decay of the concentration increase δp. Therefore the slow decay process does not take place at all. Instead, the electrons increase their concentration $n = 10^{16}$ cm^{-3} by $\delta n = 10^{15}$ cm^{-3} to $1.1 \cdot 10^{16}$ cm^{-3}; because their own high concentration 10^{16} cm^{-3} is available for this build-up process it proceeds very rapidly. Neutrality is again established as soon as the electrons have increased their concentration $1.0 \cdot 10^{16}$ cm^{-3} to $1.1 \cdot 10^{16}$ cm^{-3}, and there are no fields left which could remove any electrons or holes.

However, this condition is not maintained indefinitely either. In Chap. I, §3, we have shown that in all semiconductors a thermally determined carrier generation g and a carrier annihilation $r \cdot n \cdot p$ by recombination counteract each other continually. Time changes in carrier concentrations $n(t)$ and $p(t)$ must follow the law[1]

$$\frac{dn(t)}{dt} = \frac{dp(t)}{dt} = g - r \cdot n(t) \cdot p(t) = r[n_i^2 - n(t) \cdot p(t)] \quad \text{(V.2.12)}$$

The intrinsic density n_i in this law has approximately[2] the value 10^{13} cm^{-3} in germanium at room temperature. In equilibrium a hole concentration $p = 10^{10}$ cm^{-3} must coexist[3] with the electron concentration $n = 10^{16}$ cm^{-3}, because the time-independent equilibrium concentrations n and p are, according to (V.2.12),

$$0 = g - r \cdot n \cdot p = r(n_i^2 - n \cdot p) \quad \text{(V.2.13)}$$

The time-dependent disturbances $\delta n(t) = \delta p(t) \approx 10^{11}$ cm^{-3} introduced into (V.2.12) lead, in conjunction with (V.2.13), to

$$\frac{d}{dt}\,\delta n = \frac{d}{dt}\,\delta p = r[n_i^2 - (n + \delta n)(p + \delta p)]$$
$$= -r(n\,\delta p + p\,\delta n + \delta n\,\delta p)$$

In view of the relative orders of magnitude of $n = 10^{16}$ cm^{-3},

---

[1] Provided concentration changes are not effected by other causes such as the divergence of a carrier flow.

[2] E. M. Conwell gives $n_i = 2.5 \cdot 10^{13}$ cm^{-3}. *Proc. IRE*, **40**: 1329 (1952), Table II.

[3] The concentration $p = 10^{10}$ cm^{-3} does not play any role in the neutrality condition compared with $n = 10^{16}$ cm^{-3} and $n_{D^+} = 10^{16}$ cm^{-3}. Even in the problem of the dispersion of the injected holes $\delta p = 10^{15}$ cm^{-3}, it is for all practical purposes not necessary to consider the already present equilibrium density $p = 10^{10}$ cm^{-3}.

$p = 10^{10}$ cm^{-3}, and $\delta n = \delta p \approx 10^{11}$ cm^{-3}, we obtain

$$\frac{d}{dt}\,\delta n = \frac{d}{dt}\,\delta p = -rn\,\delta p = -\frac{\delta n}{\tau_p} \qquad (V.2.14)$$

$$\delta n = \delta p \sim e^{-\frac{t}{\tau_p}} \qquad (V.2.15)$$

We can now see that even a *neutral* deviation $\delta n = \delta p$ from thermal equilibrium ($n = 10^{16}$ cm^{-3}, $p = 10^{10}$ cm^{-3}) cannot last forever but decays exponentially with a "lifetime $\tau_p = 1/(rn)$ of the holes in the n conductor." This lifetime τ_p and also the lifetime $\tau_n = 1/(rp)$ of electrons in a p conductor are strongly dependent on the perfection of the crystal lattice through the recombination coefficient[1] r. Exceptionally perfect crystals exhibit lifetimes as high as 10^{-3} sec, and even relatively poor single crystals rarely have lifetimes less than 10^{-7} sec. The lifetimes τ_p and τ_n are therefore much higher than the relaxation times T_{relax}.

Summarizing and generalizing we can now state: The electrons in n semiconductors and the holes in p semiconductors, i.e., the "majority carriers," remove disturbances of quasi-neutrality in a semiconductor within extremely short times $T_{\text{relax}} \approx 10^{-13}$ sec. It is immaterial here how the particular disturbance has come about. If the disturbance is, for instance, caused by the injection of "minority carriers," the majority-carrier concentration is increased within the short time T_{relax} in order to establish neutrality. Both concentrations decay thereafter exponentially with the lifetime τ_{minor} as the time constant, which is very large compared with the relaxation time T_{relax}.

b. The Filamentary Transistor

The foregoing discussion shows that it is useless to inject majority carriers in order to influence the conductivity of a current path. The additional carrier concentrations decay within much too short times T_{relax} or within much too short distances $v_{\text{drift}} \cdot T_{\text{relax}}$ if the injected carriers are transported with a drift velocity v_{drift}.

When minority carriers are injected, however, the equalizing flow of majority carriers reestablishes neutrality within a few relaxation times T_{relax} so that the space-charge field with its dissipating tendency is removed. The conductance in the current path in question is thus increased by the additional minority carriers as well as by the neutralizing concentration rise of the majority carriers.

The question arises now as to how the injection of minority carriers is accomplished. The introduction by bombardment from the outside

[1] See also footnote 1, p. 99.

requires a vacuum, high voltages, and electron-optical structures and is, therefore, very cumbersome. Furthermore, this method would be restricted to electrons and could be applied only to a p-type semiconductor. The following two methods are much more elegant. First, light excitation may be used to increase the pair generation above its thermally determined value. The creation of *pairs* of positive and negative carriers leads not even to a momentary deviation from neutrality. This effect is utilized in the so-called phototransistor. Second, charge displacement effects known from rectifier theory may be utilized. Thus holes may be carried from a p semiconductor into an n semiconductor. This is the emitter action of a p-n junction biased in the forward direction, as mentioned on page 106. Finally, it has been

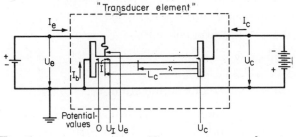

Fɪɢ. V.2.1. The filamentary transistor. The current arrows do not represent the direction of the actual currents but rather the direction in which the current in question is considered positive. Accordingly, the voltage arrows do not represent the actual potential drop but rather the direction in which the potential drop (voltage) in question is considered positive. The schematic batteries, however, are represented with the correct polarities as they are applied in the operation of the transistor.

found empirically that the forward current of a metal-semiconductor contact on germanium may consist largely—possibly entirely—of minority carriers. The interpretation of this effect is believed to lie in a disguised p-n action.

Be that as it may, forward-biased p-n junctions and metal-semiconductor point contacts represent simple "emitters" for the injection of minority carriers.

In conjunction with the introductory remarks of §1 we obtain the following arrangement of a crystal amplifier (see Fig. V.2.1). A rod or filament of single-crystal n germanium is provided with *large-area* electrodes at each end to make good ohmic connections. The left "base electrode" is grounded, and a negative bias $[|U_c| \gg + kT/e]$ is applied to the right "collector electrode." An emitter is applied to the rod near the base with a positive bias with respect to the base in order to produce emitter action. A fraction γ of the current I_e which flows from the emitter into the germanium rod consists of holes (γ = injection efficiency = the fraction of the emitter current carried by minority carriers). These holes are collected by the negative collector after entering the n germanium so that they modulate the conductivity of the current path between emitter and collector, depending on their number. Therefore, variation of the emitter voltage U_e must be capable of controlling the power supplied by the battery in the collector circuit.

c. Survey of Procedure and Objective of the Following Calculations

The preceding rough description of the effects under discussion will now be refined quantitatively. The mathematical formulation of the mechanisms, however, is not a goal in itself. Our goal is, rather, to develop clearly the physical concepts of

Injection efficiency γ
Transport factor β
Inherent (or *true*) current amplification α_i

and to single out the fundamental physical effects so as to indicate their significance for the operation of the over-all structure, namely, for the amplification properties of the transistor.

The transistor is a special case of a switching or rather a transducer element in which a primary or input circuit controls a secondary or output circuit. The behavior of such a transducer element is, accordingly, determined by two current-voltage relations (namely, one for the primary and one for the secondary circuit):

$$U_e = f(I_e, I_c) \tag{V.2.16}$$
$$U_c = g(I_c, I_e) \tag{V.2.17}$$

For small deviations u_e, u_c, i_e, i_c, from an operating point, these equations can be linearized:

$$u_e = r_{11}i_e + r_{12}i_c \tag{V.2.18}$$
$$u_c = r_{21}i_e + r_{22}i_c \tag{V.2.19}$$

where r_{11} and r_{22} are the differential primary and secondary resistances. The coupling resistance r_{21} furnishes the desired influence of the primary circuit on the secondary circuit. The feedback resistance r_{12} determines the feedback effect of the secondary circuit on the primary circuit.

The amplification and transfer properties, respectively, of a circuit element with a primary and a secondary circuit are described appropriately by the short-circuit current amplification, the open-circuit voltage amplification, and the power amplification in the matched condition. These amplification values are generally derived from the resistances $r_{11} \cdots r_{22}$. This will be done in §6, since the relations in question and their derivation have nothing to do with the physical mechanism of the filamentary transistor.

The following calculations for the filamentary transistor relate the values of the resistances $r_{11} \cdots r_{22}$ to the structural data and the characteristic constants of this type of transistor. The equations of §6 are used in the same way for the amplification factors. A discussion of the equations which we derive will help us to understand the importance of the individual effects for the performance of the filamentary transistor.

d. The Current-Voltage Equations of the Filamentary Transistor

First we must establish certain sign conventions. We adopt the choice of signs customary in transistor literature, so that the flow of positive charge carriers into the semiconductor constitutes positive currents I_e and I_c. Within the single crystal rod, we measure a coordinate x positive from the collector end $x = 0$ toward the left (see Fig. V.2.1). The electrical field strength E within the crystal is taken as positive in the direction of increasing x values as usual.

We shall now consider a certain location x of the single crystal rod between the point I (immediately in front of the emitter) and the collector c (see Fig. V.2.1). Here we find a field strength directed from the left to the right, and hence negative according to our convention. Its value is $E_0 + E_1(x) < 0$; E_0 is the component present before injection. The corresponding electron concentration is $n_0 + n_1$ and the hole concentration $n_i^2/n_0 + p_1(x) \approx p_1(x)$, because the injected hole concentration $p_1(x)$ even at low injection levels is large compared with the already present hole density n_i^2/n_0 ($= 10^{10}$ cm^{-3} in our example). Restricting the analysis to low injection levels where we can neglect terms of the second order, we find for the current density I_c/Q of the collector current (Q being the cross-sectional area of the germanium rod):

$$\frac{1}{Q} I_c = e\mu_n n_0 E_0 + e\mu_n n_1(x)E_0 + e\mu_p p_1(x)E_0 + e\mu_n n_0 E_1(x) \quad (V.2.20)[1]$$

[1] The signs in this equation are correct, since I_c and $E_0 + E_1$ are positive in the same direction, namely, from right to left. In transistor operation I_c as well as $E_0 + E_1$ are negative, at least for the n semiconductor here assumed.

It is carried partly by electrons and partly by holes in this region of the current path.   Introducing the mobility ratio

$$b = \frac{\mu_n}{\mu_p} \qquad (\text{V.2.21})$$

we find

$$e\mu_n n_0 Q(E_0 + E_1(x)) = I_c - e\mu_p[bn_1(x) + p_1(x)]QE_0 \quad (\text{V.2.22})$$

The injected hole concentration p_1 decays with time according to the exponential law (V.2.15) by recombination.   If we consider an arbitrarily chosen number of holes at a distance $L_c - x$ from the point I, the concentration $p(x)$ has decreased by a factor

$$\mathrm{e}^{-t/\tau_p} = \mathrm{e}^{-(L_c-x)/\tau_p v_{\text{drift}}}$$

compared with the original concentration $p(L_c)$, and a time

$$t = \frac{L_c - x}{v_{\text{drift}}}$$

has passed since the introduction of these holes into the n germanium. The same applies to the additional electron concentration $n_1(x)$ which has the same value as $p_1(x)$ for reasons of neutrality.   We find therefore

$$n_1(x) = p_1(x) = p_1(L_c)\, \mathrm{e}^{-\frac{L_c-x}{\tau_p v_{\text{drift}}}} \qquad (\text{V.2.23})$$

We substitute this in (V.2.22) and introduce the hole contribution of the collector current I_c at point I

$$e\mu_p p_1(L_c)E_0 \cdot Q = I_{c_p}(L_c) \qquad (\text{V.2.24})$$

and finally integrate (V.2.22) from $x = 0$ to $x = L_c$:

$$e\mu_n n_0 Q \int_{x=0}^{x=L_c} (E_0 + E_1(x))\, dx$$

$$= I_c \cdot L_c - I_{c_p}(L_c) \cdot (b+1) \int_{x=0}^{x=L_c} \mathrm{e}^{-\frac{L_c-x}{\tau_p v_{\text{drift}}}}\, dx \quad (\text{V.2.25})$$

Since $E_0 + E_1(x) = -\mathrm{grad}\ V$, the field-strength integral on the left side leads to the value $-(U_I - U_c) = U_c - U_I$, i.e., the total voltage between the collector c and point I.   Introducing the unmodulated "collector resistance,"

$$r_c = \frac{L_c}{e\mu_n n_0 Q} \qquad (\text{V.2.26})$$

dividing by L_c, and carrying out the integration on the right side of

(V.2.25) results in

$$\frac{1}{r_c}(U_c - U_I) = I_c - (1 + b)I_{c_p}(L_c) \cdot \frac{\tau_p v_{\text{drift}}}{L_c}[1 - e^{-\frac{L_c}{\tau_p v_{\text{drift}}}}] \quad (V.2.27)$$

We introduce an abbreviation

$$\beta = \frac{\tau_p v_{\text{drift}}}{L_c}(1 - e^{-\frac{L_c}{\tau_p v_{\text{drift}}}}) \quad (V.2.28)$$

In terms of the transit time between point I and collector **c**

$$t_{\text{tr}} = \frac{L_c}{v_{\text{drift}}} \quad (V.2.29)$$

we obtain

$$\beta = \frac{\tau_p}{t_{\text{tr}}}(1 - e^{-\frac{t_{\text{tr}}}{\tau_p}}) \quad (V.2.30)$$

This "transport factor β" represents the fraction of the holes injected by the emitter at $x = L_c$ which actually arrives at the collector, i.e., which is not lost by recombination. From (V.2.27) we find then

$$\frac{1}{r_c}(U_c - U_I) = I_c - (1 + b)\beta I_{c_p}(L_c) \quad (V.2.31)$$

Finally we can replace $I_{c_p}(L_c)$ by the negative hole contribution $-I_{e_p}$ of the emitter current or use the injection efficiency mentioned on page 120 so that

$$I_{c_p}(L_c) = -\gamma I_e \quad (V.2.32)$$

This equation is obtained by resolving Kirchhoff's law

$$I_b + I_e + I_c = 0 \quad (V.2.33)$$

into an equation for the electron currents

$$I_b + (1 - \gamma)I_e + I_{c_n}(L_c) = 0 \quad (V.2.34)$$

and for the hole currents[1]

$$0 + \gamma I_e + I_{c_p}(L_c) = 0 \quad (V.2.35)$$

Equations (V.2.31) and (V.2.32) combine to yield

$$U_c - U_I = (1 + b)\beta\gamma r_c I_e + r_c I_c \quad (V.2.36)$$

If we apply Ohm's law to the path between the base and point I and, further, use (V.2.33) after introducing the quantity

$$0 - U_I = +r_b I_b \quad (V.2.37)$$

---

[1] The hole contribution to the base current I_b is zero, because the field E_0 draws the injected holes away toward the collector on the right.

we obtain finally

$$\alpha_e = (1 + b)\beta\gamma \tag{V.2.38}$$

or
$$U_c - r_b(I_e + I_c) = \alpha_e r_c I_e + r_c I_c$$
$$U_c = (r_b + \alpha_e r_c)I_e + (r_b + r_c)I_c \tag{V.2.39}$$

This is the current-voltage relation in the *secondary* circuit of the filamentary transistor. The equation for the primary circuit can be obtained in a much simpler way.

Between the metal of the emitter point and the body of the germanium at point I, we find the voltage $U_e - U_I$ (see Fig. V.2.1). The relation between this voltage and the current I_e, i.e., the emitter characteristic, is not linear:

$$U_e - U_I = f(I_e) \tag{V.2.40}$$

Equations (V.2.37) and (V.2.33) yield for the current-voltage relation in the primary circuit of the filamentary transistor

$$U_e = r_b I_e + f(I_e) + r_b I_c \tag{V.2.41}$$

These equations are usually linearized by considering only small deviations u_e, u_c, i_e, i_c from the d-c operating point U_e, U_c, I_e, I_c. Introducing the differential emitter resistance

$$r_e = f'(I_e) \tag{V.2.42}$$

we find

$$u_e = (r_b + r_e)i_e + r_b i_c \tag{V.2.43}$$
$$u_c = (r_b + \alpha_e r_c)i_e + (r_b + r_c)i_c \tag{V.2.44}$$

e. The Amplification Properties of the Filamentary Transistor

Comparing (V.2.43), (V.2.44) with (V.2.18), (V.2.19), we obtain

$$r_{11} = r_b + r_e \qquad r_{12} = r_b$$
$$r_{21} = r_b + \alpha_e r_c \qquad r_{22} = r_b + r_c \tag{V.2.45}$$

With the help of (V.2.45) we can now evaluate the general amplification formulas (V.6.06), (V.6.07), and (V.6.08) for the special case of the filamentary transistor: Short-circuit current amplification ($R_L = 0$):

$$\left[\frac{i_c}{i_e}\right]_{\text{short circuit}} = -\frac{r_b + \alpha_e r_c}{r_b + r_c} \tag{V.2.46}$$

Open-circuit voltage amplification ($R_L = \infty$):

$$\left[\frac{u_L}{u_e}\right]_{\text{open circuit}} = -\frac{r_b + \alpha_e r_c}{r_b + r_e} \tag{V.2.47}$$

Power amplification under matched conditions ($R_L = r_{22} = r_b + r_c$):

$$\left[\frac{u_L i_c}{u_e i_e}\right]_{\text{matched}} = +\frac{1}{4}\frac{(r_b + \alpha_e r_c)^2}{(r_b + r_e)(r_b + r_c)}\frac{1}{1 - \frac{1}{2}\frac{(r_b + \alpha_e r_c)r_b}{(r_b + r_e)(r_b + r_c)}} \quad (V.2.48)$$

If we succeed in eliminating the base resistance r_b, which causes instabilities,[1] by proper structural design, i.e., by locating the emitter as far as possible to the left near the base, we obtain:

Short-circuit current amplification ($R_L = 0$):

$$\left[\frac{i_c}{i_e}\right]_{\text{short circuit}} = -\alpha_e \quad (V.2.49)$$

Open-circuit voltage amplification ($R_L = \infty$):

$$\left[\frac{u_L}{u_e}\right]_{\text{open circuit}} = -\alpha_e\frac{r_c}{r_e} \quad (V.2.50)$$

Power amplification under matched conditions ($R_L = r_{22} = r_c$):

$$\left[\frac{u_L i_c}{u_e i_e}\right]_{\text{matched}} = +\frac{1}{4}\alpha_e^2\frac{r_c}{r_e} \quad (V.2.51)$$

If we finally add Eq. (V.2.38)

$$\alpha_e = (1 + b)\beta\gamma \quad (V.2.38)$$

with (V.2.21)

$$b = \frac{\mu_n}{\mu_p} \quad (V.2.21)$$

and with (V.2.30)

$$\beta = \frac{\tau_p}{t_{\text{tr}}}\left(1 - e^{-\frac{t_{\text{tr}}}{\tau_p}}\right) \quad (V.2.30)$$

we arrive at a very clear picture of the physical relations:

1. The largest possible injection efficiency γ, namely, unity, is advantageous for all three types of amplification. This is plausible since the emitter current i_e, which is controlled by the emitter voltage u_e, consists then entirely of modulating holes. On the other hand, all amplification properties are lost as $\gamma \to 0$. The conductance of the current path cannot be modulated by the injection of electrons into n germanium.

2. The largest possible transport factor β, namely, unity, is advantageous for all three types of amplification. This is plausible since all

[1] See in this connection p. 148. According to Eq. (V.2.43) we have $r_{12} = r_b$ for the filamentary transistor.

injected holes are then effective along the entire path from the emitter to the collector and are not lost by recombination before reaching the latter.

3. The largest possible mobility ratio b is advantageous for all three types of amplification. This is plausible since many electrons of high velocity, contributing correspondingly little to the space charge, are required to neutralize holes of low velocity, contributing greatly to the space charge. The current amplification which is attained with an ideal emitter ($\gamma = 1$) and ideal transport factor ($\beta = 1$) is often called the *true* current amplification α_i. It is in the case of the filamentary transistor

$$\alpha_i = 1 + b$$

and therefore depends here on the space-charge action of the holes.

In general, α_i gives the effectiveness of a hole arriving at the collector in modulating the collector current. α_i is, therefore, defined as the ratio of the *total* collector current variation i_c to the initiating variation i_{c_p} of the hole current arriving at the collector

$$\alpha_i = \left[\frac{i_c}{i_{c_p}} \right]_{u_c=0} \tag{V.2.52}$$

The secondary condition $u_c = 0$ assures that the collector current variation is caused only by i_{c_p}.

4. Let us consider the special case $\gamma = 1$, $\beta = 1$, $b = 0$. The emitter current thus consists entirely of modulating minority carriers which are not reduced by recombination but are all captured by the collector. They are assumed to be much faster than the majority carriers, so that they modulate the conductance of the path from emitter to collector only with their own conductivity and not with the conductivity of additional majority carriers needed for reestablishing neutrality.

In this case, the current amplification is unity, e.g., no current amplification takes place. However, voltage and power amplification are still obtained, if it is possible to make the collector resistance r_c large compared to the emitter resistance r_e—for instance, by means of a long and thin current path from emitter to collector.[1]

This special case represents, in a way, the pure and unadulterated transistor effect: Injected minority carriers modulate the conductance of the current path of a "local" battery merely by their presence.

---

[1] The difficulty in realizing such a condition lies in the fact that it is hard to keep the recombination small in spite of the length and the small cross section. A consequent reduction of β and hence α_e much below 1 would spoil everything.

This results in voltage and power amplification without current amplification. Current amplification is possible only if, in addition, the space-charge action of the minority carriers, requiring a concentration increase of the majority carriers, comes into play.

§3. The *n-p-n* Transistor

We have emphasized in the introduction, as a common principle of the mechanism of some transistor types, that the conductance of a current path containing a strong "local" current source is influenced by the small controlling power of a current coming from "far away." In the filamentary transistor the influenced current path is a piece of ohmic conductor, whereas in the *n-p-n* transistor[1] it is a reverse-biased *p-n* junction (see Fig. V.3.1). The cause of the blocking effect of such a *p-n* junction is the depletion of minority carriers in the diffusion tails, which ordinarily act as current sources.[2] Counteracting this carrier depletion by the injection of a varying number of minority carriers results in a control action on the reverse current of the junction. The injector or emitter in an *n-p-n* transistor is not a forward-biased point contact but another *p-n* junction which is biased in the forward direction, in contrast to the collector.[3] Thus we arrive at the *n-p-n* transistor shown in Fig. V.3.1 as the final stage. The operation of this transistor type is, therefore, based roughly on the following mechanisms: The left *n-p* junction, which is biased in the forward direction,

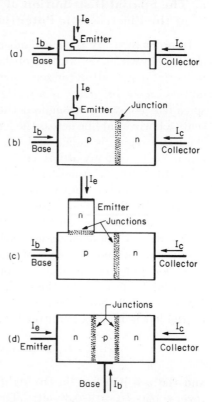

FIG. V.3.1. The transformation of the filamentary transistor into the *n-p-n* transistor.

[1] W. Shockley, *Bell System Tech. J.*, **28**: 435 (1949). W. Shockley, M. Sparks, and G. K. Teal, *Phys. Rev.*, **83**: 151 (1951).

[2] See pp. 102 to 103.

[3] See p. 106.

emits electrons into the central p layer; these electrons are collected by the p-n junction on the right which is biased in the reverse direction, and the reverse resistance of this p-n junction acting as collector is a sensitive function of the number of captured electrons. The *electron* currents flowing in the n-p-n transistor are therefore essential for its functioning. However, it will be necessary to consider also the hole components of the emitter and collector currents in the following quantitative treatment.

a. The Spatial Distribution of the Carriers and the Variation of the Electrostatic Potential

In order to study the mechanism of an n-p-n transistor in detail, we shall begin with a description of the concentration distribution and the potential distribution for zero current (see Fig. V.3.2). The intrinsic density[1] $n_i \approx 10^{13}$ cm^{-3} is a guide for the concentration distribution, since it is constant throughout the entire crystal and therefore represents a horizontal line across the figure. We assume that, for instance, the left n region is doped with $n_{Dl} = 10^{16}$ and the right n region with $n_{Dr} = 10^{14}$ antimony atoms/cm^3, whereas the central p region contains $n_A = 10^{15}$ indium atoms/cm^3 (see Fig. V.3.2).[2] This leads to the p and n distributions shown in the middle of Fig. V.3.2, which are symmetrical to the intrinsic density $n_i \approx 10^{13}$ cm^{-3} because we have assumed zero current and hence thermal equilibrium. The potential distribution V, plotted underneath, is identical with the electron distribution n as a consequence of the Boltzmann principle (IV.6.11), the *logarithmic* plot of the electron concentration n, the *linear* plot of the potential V, and finally, the choice of suitable scales.

Figure V.3.3 shows the changes which take place if the n-p junction on the left is made an emitter by applying forward bias

$$U_e = -\,0.078 \text{ volt} \approx -\frac{3kT}{e}$$

and the p-n junction on the right is made a collector by applying a reverse bias $U_c = +0.3$ volt. The concentration distributions within the transition regions of both p-n junctions maintain almost entirely the original Boltzmann character[3] in spite of the current flow.

The hole concentration p is therefore increased by the factor $e^{e|U_e|/kT} = e^{-eU_e/kT}$ at the point x_e and is decreased by the factor

---

[1] E. M. Conwell quotes for germanium at room temperature the more accurate value $n_i = 2.5 \cdot 10^{13}$ cm^{-3}. See *Proc. IRE*, **40:** 1329 (1952), Table II.

[2] The subscripts l and r in n_{Dl} and n_{Dr} indicate left and right.

[3] See p. 100 and Fig. IV.8.1.

$e^{-e|U_c|/kT} = e^{-eU_c/kT}$ at the point x_c. The increase at the point x_e leads to a diffusion tail which decreases toward the left and in which p is reduced by the factor e for each diffusion length L_{pl}.[1] This diffusion tail determines the hole component of the emitter current. In the evaluation of the decrease at the point x_c, we must bear in mind the

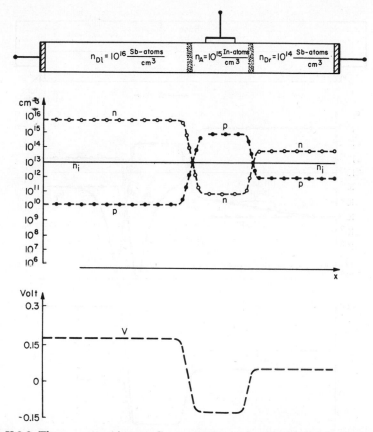

FIG. V.3.2. The *n-p-n* transistor. Concentration and potential distribution. The zero-current case.

logarithmic plot of p. The concentration decreases from the value p_{nr} to the value $p_{nr}\, e^{-eU_c/kT}$, which can here be regarded as practically equal to zero. This decrease from right to left takes place within a few diffusion lengths[2] L_{pr} and determines the hole component of the collector current.

[1] See p. 99. The subscripts l and r in L_{pl} and L_{pr} indicate again left and right.
[2] See Fig. IV.8.3, lower part.

The increase of the electron concentration n at the point x_{bl} leads to a diffusion tail which decays toward the right and extends in principle over several diffusion lengths L_n. The adjoining concentration decrease to the right, from the equilibrium density $n_p = n_i^2/n_{A^-}$ in the interior of the p region to practically zero at the point x_{br} extends, in

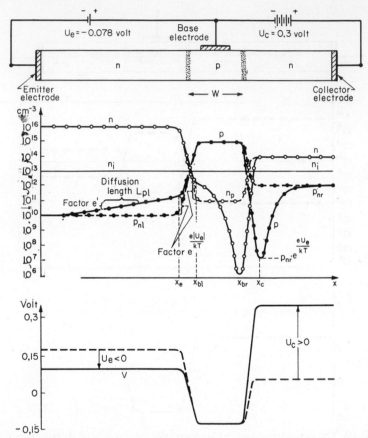

FIG. V.3.3. The n-p-n transistor.   Concentration and potential distribution.   The operating case.

principle, also over several diffusion lengths L_n.   In Fig. V.3.3 we have made the assumption that the width W of the p layer is smaller than, or at most equal to, the diffusion length L_n, in contrast to Fig. V.3.4, so that the left and the right diffusion tails overlap and electrons are transported in a single diffusion process from the emitter at the left to the collector at the right.   Thus the small electron supply from the p layer which is limited to the saturation-current value is enhanced and modulated by the injection from the emitter. We see here already that this is possible only if the condition $W \leq L_n$ is fulfilled. If the p layer becomes too wide ($W \gg L_n$, Fig. V.3.4), the diffusion tail on the left drops to zero so that the electron concentration n remains horizontal for a certain distance at the thermal equilibrium value $n_p = n_i^2/n_{A^-}$; the diffusion decay sets in beyond this point, in front of the collector junction. In the region of the p layer where n is now horizontal, we find essentially a pure hole current; for the electrons

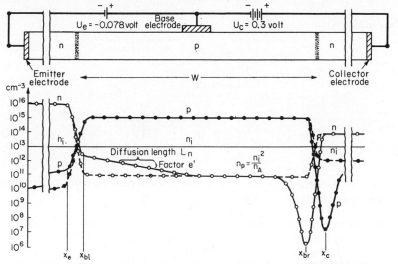

FIG. V.3.4. The *n-p-n* transistor with too wide a base width ($W \gg L_n$).

with their low concentration could furnish a substantial contribution to the current only in the presence of a nonexistent concentration gradient. The great majority of the electrons injected by the emitter are lost through recombination long before they reach the collector.

b. The Current-Voltage Equations of the *n-p-n* Transistor

The conditions in a diffusion tail were calculated in connection with the *p-n* rectifier. The fact that the divergence of the diffusion current is equal to the difference between recombination and pair formation leads to the differential equation

$$\frac{d^2}{dx^2}\left(n(x) - n_p\right) - \frac{1}{L_n^2}\left(n(x) - n_p\right) = 0 \qquad \text{(IV.8.03)}$$

We were then satisfied with the particular solution $A\,e^{+x/L_n}$ which corresponds to an electron current vanishing at minus infinity. Now we require for the description of the electron concentration in the

p layer of our n-p-n transistor the complete solution

$$n(x) - n_p = A\, e^{+\frac{x}{L_n}} + B\, e^{-\frac{x}{L_n}} \qquad (V.3.01)$$

The integration constants A and B are determined by the boundary conditions

$$n(x_{bl}) = n_p\, e^{-\frac{eU_e}{kT}} \qquad (V.3.02)$$

$$n(x_{br}) = n_p\, e^{-\frac{eU_c}{kT}} \qquad (V.3.03)$$

We obtain with $x_{br} - x_{bl} \approx W$

$$n(x) = n_p \left[1 + (e^{-\frac{eU_e}{kT}} - 1)\, \frac{\sinh \dfrac{x_{br} - x}{L_n}}{\sinh \dfrac{W}{L_n}} \right.$$

$$\left. + (e^{-\frac{eU_c}{kT}} - 1)\, \frac{\sinh \dfrac{x - x_{bl}}{L_n}}{\sinh \dfrac{W}{L_n}} \right] \qquad (V.3.04)$$

The electron component I_{e_n} of the emitter current I_e can be calculated as a diffusion current at the point x_{bl}:

$$I_{e_n} = (-e) \cdot D_n \cdot (-n'(x_{bl})) \cdot A \qquad (V.3.05)$$

$$= + e\, \frac{D_n}{L_n}\, n_p \left[- (e^{-\frac{eU_e}{kT}} - 1)\, \coth \frac{W}{L_n} \right.$$

$$\left. + (e^{-\frac{eU_c}{kT}} - 1)\, \frac{1}{\sinh \dfrac{W}{L_n}} \right] \cdot A \quad (V.3.06)$$

A is here the cross-sectional "area" of the n-p-n transistor.

If we use the Nernst-Townsend-Einstein relation $D_n = \mu_n kT/e$ in (V.3.06) and define the following conductances

$$e\mu_n n_p\, \frac{A}{L_n}\, \coth \frac{W}{L_n} = G_{ll_n} \qquad (V.3.07)$$

$$-e\mu_n n_p\, \frac{A}{L_n}\, \frac{1}{\sinh \dfrac{W}{L_n}} = G_{lr_n} \qquad (V.3.08)$$

we find for the electron component I_{e_n} of the emitter current I_e

$$I_{e_n} = -G_{ll_n}\, \frac{kT}{e}\, (e^{-\frac{eU_e}{kT}} - 1) - G_{lr_n}\, \frac{kT}{e}\, (e^{-\frac{eU_c}{kT}} - 1) \quad (V.3.09)$$

A hole component must be added; for a hole diffusion tail extends into the left n region

$$p(x) = p_{nl} + p_{nl} \, (e^{-\frac{eU_e}{kT}} - 1) \, e^{\frac{x - x_e}{L_{pl}}} \qquad (V.3.10)$$

At the beginning $x = x_e$ of the diffusion tail there is a diffusion current

$$I_{e_p} = (+e) \cdot D_p \cdot (-p'(x_e)) \cdot A$$

$$= -e\mu_p p_{nl} \cdot \frac{A}{L_{pl}} \cdot \frac{kT}{e} \cdot (e^{-\frac{eU_e}{kT}} - 1) \qquad (V.3.11)$$

or in simplified form

$$I_{e_p} = -G_{u_p} \cdot \frac{kT}{e} \, (e^{-\frac{eU_e}{kT}} - 1) \qquad (V.3.12)$$

Here we have introduced the "conductance"

$$G_{u_p} = e\mu_p p_{nl} \frac{A}{L_{pl}} \qquad (V.3.13)$$

Finally we obtain for the emitter current $I_e = I_{e_n} + I_{e_p}$ with the help of Eqs. (V.3.09) and (V.3.12)

$$I_e = +Gu \frac{kT}{e} \, (1 - e^{-\frac{eU_e}{kT}}) + G_{lr} \frac{kT}{e} \, (1 - e^{-\frac{eU_c}{kT}}) \qquad (V.3.14)$$

and correspondingly for the collector current

$$I_c = +G_{rl} \frac{kT}{e} \, (1 - e^{-\frac{eU_e}{kT}}) + G_{rr} \frac{kT}{e} \, (1 - e^{-\frac{eU_c}{kT}}) \qquad (V.3.15)$$

with the conductances

$$G_u = G_{u_n} + G_{u_p} = e\mu_n n_p \frac{A}{L_n} \coth \frac{W}{L_n} + e\mu_p p_{nl} \frac{A}{L_{pl}} \qquad (V.3.16)$$

$$G_{lr} = G_{lr_n} \qquad = -e\mu_n n_p \frac{A}{L_n} \frac{1}{\sinh \dfrac{W}{L_n}} \qquad (V.3.17)$$

$$G_{rl} = G_{rl_n} \qquad = -e\mu_n n_p \frac{A}{L_n} \frac{1}{\sinh \dfrac{W}{L_n}} \qquad (V.3.18)$$

$$G_{rr} = G_{rr_n} + G_{rr_p} = e\mu_n n_p \frac{A}{L_n} \coth \frac{W}{L_n} + e\mu_p p_{nr} \frac{A}{L_{pr}} \qquad (V.3.19)$$

If we replace I_e in (V.3.14) and (V.3.15) by $I_e + i_e$, I_c by $I_c + i_c$, U_e by $U_e + u_e$, and U_c by $U_c + u_c$, and if we expand on the right side the small quantities u_e and u_c and make use of (V.3.14) and (V.3.15), we find for the small variations i_e, u_e, . . . about the operating point

$I_e, U_e, \ldots$ the equations

$$i_e = G_{ll} \, e^{-\frac{eU_e}{kT}} \, u_e + G_{lr} \, e^{-\frac{eU_c}{kT}} \, u_c = g_{11}u_e + g_{12}u_c \qquad (V.3.20)$$

$$i_c = G_{rl} \, e^{-\frac{eU_e}{kT}} \, u_e + G_{rr} \, e^{-\frac{eU_c}{kT}} \, u_c = g_{21}u_e + g_{22}u_c \qquad (V.3.21)$$

Thus we have found the current-voltage characteristics of the n-p-n transistor in the conductance form, whereas for the filamentary transistor we arrived at the resistance form [(V.2.43) and (V.2.44)].

c. The Transport Factor β and the Efficiencies γ_e and γ_c for the n-p-n Transistor

The foregoing equations allow us to obtain a more accurate quantitative picture of our previous qualitative concepts of the mechanism of the n-p-n transistor.   The emitter has the task of emitting toward the collector a number of electrons proportional to the emitter-voltage variation u_e.   This task is better fulfilled, the more *electrons* are contained in the emitter current resulting from u_e alone

$$[i_e]_{u_c=0} = g_{11}u_e = (G_{ll_n} + G_{ll_p}) \, e^{-\frac{eU_e}{kT}} \, u_e$$

A measure of merit of the emitter is the injection efficiency

$$\gamma_e = \frac{[i_{en}]_{u_c=0}}{[i_e]_{u_c=0}} = \frac{G_{ll_n}}{G_{ll_n} + G_{ll_p}} = \frac{G_{ll_n}}{G_{ll}} \qquad (V.3.22)$$

We shall later find it useful to introduce a corresponding collection efficiency for the collector

$$\gamma_c = \frac{G_{rr_n}}{G_{rr}} \qquad (V.3.23)$$

The effectiveness of the emitter is not assured solely by an adequate content of electrons.   The emitted electrons must also be collected by the collector and must not be lost by recombination.   A measure of the proper functioning of the collector is, therefore, the ratio of the electron current[1] $[-i_{c_n}]_{u_c=0}$ arriving at the collector and the electron current $[i_{e_n}]_{u_c=0}$ emitted by the emitter.   The transport factor β is thus given by

$$\beta = \frac{[-i_{c_n}]_{u_c=0}}{[i_{e_n}]_{u_c=0}} = \frac{-G_{rl_n}}{G_{ll_n}} = \frac{1}{\cosh \dfrac{W}{L_n}} \qquad (V.3.24)$$

[1] The minus sign is required because for i_c the positive direction is defined oppositely to that for i_e.

We see now that

$$\beta = \frac{1}{\cosh \dfrac{W}{L_n}} \leq 1 \qquad (V.3.25)$$

and that the optimum value 1 is dependent on $W \ll L_n$ as we found on page 131 in a qualitative manner. The differential conductances $g_{11} \cdots g_{22}$ can be described with the help of γ_e, γ_c, and β, as we can see from Eqs. (V.3.16) to (V.3.25):

$$\left.\begin{aligned}
g_{11} &= + \frac{1}{\beta \gamma_e} G \cdot e^{-\frac{e}{kT} U_e} & g_{12} &= - \quad G \cdot e^{-\frac{e}{kT} U_c} \\
g_{21} &= - \quad G \cdot e^{-\frac{e}{kT} U_e} & g_{22} &= + \frac{1}{\beta \gamma_c} G \cdot e^{-\frac{e}{kT} U_c}
\end{aligned}\right\} \qquad (V.3.26)$$

For brevity we use the substitution

$$G = e \mu_n n_p \frac{A}{L_n} \frac{1}{\sinh \dfrac{W}{L_n}} \qquad (V.3.27)$$

d. Current and Voltage Amplification of the n-p-n Transistor

We gain further insight into the mechanism of the n-p-n transistor if we derive the current amplification for the short-circuited collector ($u_c = 0$) from the current-voltage equations (V.3.20) to (V.3.21) and the conductances (V.3.26):

$$\left[\frac{i_c}{i_e} \right]_{u_c = 0} = \frac{g_{21}}{g_{11}} = - \beta \cdot \gamma_e \qquad (V.3.28)$$

The current amplification can at best reach the value 1 when the transport factor β and the injection efficiency γ_e of the emitter have their optimum values 1. This requirement for maximum current amplification is thus the same as for the filamentary transistor. However, in contrast to Eqs. (V.2.49) and (V.2.38) we do not have the favorable factor $1 + b = + \mu_n/\mu_p$ in addition to $\beta \gamma_e$. The *true* current amplification α_i is, therefore, equal to 1, as can also be seen from a suitable modification of the defining equation (V.2.52)

$$\alpha_i = \left[\frac{i_c}{i_{c_n}} \right]_{u_c = 0} \qquad (V.3.281)$$

provided that the secondary current-voltage equation (V.3.21) and the fact that $G_{rl} = G_{rl_n}$ (V.3.18) are utilized in the evaluation of (V.3.281).

$\alpha_i = 1 + b$ for the filamentary transistor because of the space-charge compensation of the injected minority carriers by additional majority carriers. Such an increase of the majority carrier concentration exists also in the n-p-n transistor. However, it does not affect the current as long as the latter is determined by the yield of the diffusion tails. Only when the ohmic resistance of the path becomes important, namely, at high currents, may a similar effect be expected in the n-p-n transistor.[1]

The voltage amplification with open-circuited collector ($i_c = 0$) is, according to (V.3.21) and (V.3.26),

$$\left[\frac{u_c}{u_e}\right]_{i_c=0} = -\frac{g_{21}}{g_{22}} = +\beta\gamma_c\, e^{+\frac{e}{kT}(U_c-U_e)} \qquad (V.3.29)$$

We have now $U_c > 0$ and $U_e < 0$, and the difference is

$$U_c - U_e \gg \frac{kT}{e} = 26 \text{ mv} > 0$$

so that the exponential factor is large compared with 1. Even if β and γ_c do not have their optimum value, large voltage amplifications are obtained. In the n-p-n transistors described by Shockley, Sparks, and Teal[2] the conductivity of the collector n layer is, incidentally, about an order of magnitude smaller than that of the p layer with the base electrode. Accordingly, the collector current consists predominantly of holes. Despite a γ_c appreciably smaller than 1, these transistors exhibit high voltage amplification in accordance with (V.3.29). However, apart from the practical importance of the case $\gamma \ll 1$, the discussion of this condition is informative.

e. The Special Case[3] $\gamma_c \ll 1$, $\gamma_e = 1$, $\beta = 1$

With $\gamma_e = 1$ and $\beta = 1$, the two current-voltage equations (V.3.20) and (V.3.21), utilizing (V.3.26), can be written in the form

$$i_e = \quad G\cdot e^{-\frac{e}{kT}U_e}\, u_e - \quad G\cdot e^{-\frac{e}{kT}U_c}\, u_c \qquad (V.3.30)$$

$$i_c = -G\cdot e^{-\frac{e}{kT}U_e}\, u_e + \frac{1}{\gamma_c}G\cdot e^{-\frac{e}{kT}U_c}\, u_c \qquad (V.3.31)$$

The feedback term $G\cdot e^{-\frac{e}{kT}U_c}\, u_c$ can now be omitted in (V.3.30).

---

[1] Early shows that, in weakly doped collectors, the minority carrier current is a field current and not a diffusion current. Thus *inherent* current amplification becomes possible. See J. M. Early, *Bell System Tech. J.*, **32**: 1271 (1953), particularly pp. 1306ff.

[2] W. Shockley, M. Sparks, and G. K. Teal, *Phys. Rev.*, **83**: 151 (1951).

[3] To bring out the principles involved, we assume that $\gamma_e = 1$ and $\beta = 1$ in addition to $\gamma_c \ll 1$.

Unlike the term below it, it contains the very small factor $e^{-\frac{e}{kT}U_c}$ uncompensated by $1/\gamma_c$, which, according to our assumptions, is large. The current-voltage equations then assume the form

$$i_e = \quad G \cdot e^{-\frac{e}{kT}U_e}\, u_e$$

$$i_c = -G \cdot e^{-\frac{e}{kT}U_e}\, u_e + \frac{1}{\gamma_c} G \cdot e^{-\frac{e}{kT}U_c}\, u_c = -i_e + \frac{1}{\gamma_c} G \cdot e^{-\frac{e}{kT}U_c}\, u_c$$

By solving for the voltages we obtain the resistance form:

$$u_e = \quad \frac{1}{G}\, e^{+\frac{e}{kT}U_e}\, i_e \tag{V.3.32}$$

$$u_c = \gamma_c \frac{1}{G}\, e^{+\frac{e}{kT}U_c}\, i_e + \gamma_c \frac{1}{G}\, e^{+\frac{e}{kT}U_c}\, i_c \tag{V.3.33}$$

These equations have now become identical with the current-voltage equations (V.2.43) and (V.2.44) of the filamentary transistor if they are written for the special case $r_b = 0$, $\beta = 1$, $\gamma = 1$, $b = 0$ discussed on page 124

$$u_e = r_e i_e \tag{V.3.34}$$
$$u_c = r_c i_e + r_c i_c \tag{V.3.35}$$

In fact, we can now see an almost complete analogy between the filamentary transistor and the n-p-n transistor:

1. In both cases an ideal emitter ($\gamma = 1$ or $\gamma_e = 1$) injects minority carriers which are collected without loss by the collector ($\beta = 1$).

2. A space-charge action and with it a *true* current amplification α_i is absent in both cases, in the filamentary transistor because of the somewhat artificial assumption $b = \mu_n/\mu_p \approx 0$ and in the n-p-n transistor because of the fundamental reasons discussed on page 135.

3. The injected minority carriers influence the conductance of a current path whose conductivity, without injection, is predominantly determined by carriers of the opposite polarity. This is, in contrast to point 2, a rather natural assumption for the filamentary transistor, whereas it seems somewhat artificial for the n-p-n transistor.[1]

This makes a detailed discussion of the opposite limiting case $\gamma_c = 1$ desirable, because characteristic features in the mechanism of

---

[1] Inasmuch as (V.3.29) shows that for high amplification γ_c ought to be as large as possible, namely, $\gamma_c \to 1$. Then the entire collector current consists of electrons which, in contrast to the holes, are subject to modulation. The fact that real transistors can, nevertheless, have $\gamma_c \ll 1$ (see pp. 135 to 136) is probably a consequence of the particular method of preparation.

the *n-p-n* transistor will appear which have no analogies in the filamentary transistor.

f. The Special Case $\gamma_c = 1$, $\gamma_e = 1$, $\beta = 1$

The current-voltage equations (V.3.30) and (V.3.31) assume in this case the form

$$i_e = \quad G \cdot e^{-\frac{e}{kT}U_e}\, u_e - G \cdot e^{-\frac{e}{kT}U_c}\, u_c \qquad\qquad \text{(V.3.36)}$$

$$i_c = -G \cdot e^{-\frac{e}{kT}U_e}\, u_e + G \cdot e^{-\frac{e}{kT}U_c}\, u_c \qquad\qquad \text{(V.3.37)}$$

and we see that the base current is zero, independently of u_e and u_c:

$$i_b = -(i_e + i_c) \equiv 0 \qquad\qquad \text{(V.3.38)}$$

This particular case exhibits a certain analogy between the *n-p-n* transistor and the vacuum tube. Thus the base corresponds to the control grid by way of the absence of current, the emitter corresponds to

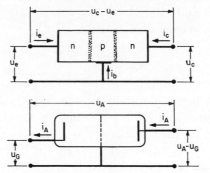

FIG. V.3.5. Comparison of the *n-p-n* transistor in the special case $\alpha_c = 1$, $\alpha_e = 1$, $\beta = 1$ with the vacuum tube.

the cathode by way of emission, and the collector corresponds to the anode by way of collection (see Fig. V.3.5).

If we write (V.3.37) in the form

$$i_c = G[e^{-\frac{e}{kT}U_e} - e^{-\frac{e}{kT}U_c}]\left\{(-u_e) + \frac{e^{-\frac{e}{kT}U_c}}{e^{-\frac{e}{kT}U_e} - e^{-\frac{e}{kT}U_c}}\,(u_c - u_e)\right\}$$

we see with the aid of Fig. V.3.5 and by comparison with the vacuum-tube equation[1]

$$i_A = S\{u_G + Du_A\}$$

[1] i_A = plate current, u_A = plate voltage, u_G = grid voltage, S = transconductance, D = reciprocal voltage amplification.

that the reciprocal voltage amplification is

$$D = \frac{1}{e^{\frac{e}{kT}(U_c - U_e)} - 1} \approx e^{-\frac{e}{kT}(U_c - U_e)} \ll 1$$

This extremely small reciprocal voltage amplification is the reason for the strong similarity between the pentode and the n-p-n transistor characteristics. The similarity is, incidentally, not tied to the foregoing special case (see Fig. V.3.6) and results from the saturated character of the collector current.[1]

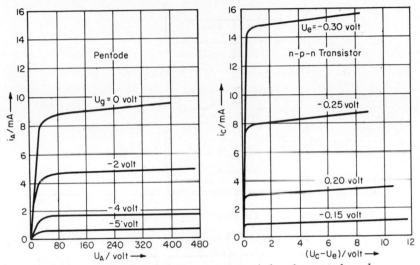

FIG. V.3.6. Comparison of the family of characteristics of a pentode and an n-p-n transistor.

§4. The Point-contact Transistor

a. Qualitative Treatment

Historically, the first transistor is the so-called type A transistor shown in Fig. V.4.1, whose discovery in 1948 by John Bardeen and W. H. Brattain[2] created, rightly, a sensation. The transistor with double surface of J. N. Shive[3] (see Fig. V.4.2) and the "coaxial tran-

[1] Concerning the comparison of the n-p-n transistor and the vacuum tube, see also L. J. Giacoletto, *Proc. IRE*, **40**: 1490 (1952). Figure V.3.6 is based on data from this paper.

[2] J. Bardeen and W. Brattain, *Phys. Rev.*, **74**: 230 and 231 (1948); **75**: 1208 (1949).

[3] J. N. Shive, *Phys. Rev.*, **75**: 689 (1949).

sistor" of W. E. Kock and R. L. Wallace[1] (see Fig. V.4.3) are, as was found shortly afterward, only geometric modifications of the type A transistor and fall within the general concept of the "point-contact transistor." The physically significant mechanism is the same for all these transistors. It consists in the fact that the boundary layer of a point contact, biased in the reverse direction, represents the current

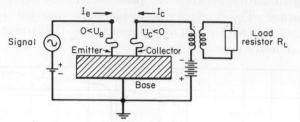

FIG. V.4.1. The type A transistor.

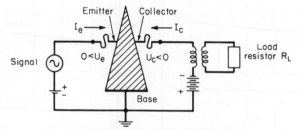

FIG. V.4.2. Transistor with double surface.

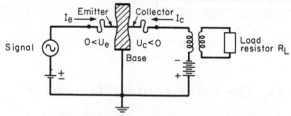

FIG. V.4.3. The coaxial transistor.

path which is influenced by carrier injection and that the emitter is also a point contact, biased, however, in the forward direction. A transistor of n germanium shall be considered for the qualitative description of the mechanism. A current I_e (e.g., 0.75 ma) enters the n germanium from a positively biased (e.g., $+ 0.15$ volt) emitter. A small fraction $1 - \gamma$ of this current consists of electrons which come from the large area nonrectifying base and flow into the emitter after passing through the body of the germanium. The major part γI_e

[1] W. E. Kock and R. L. Wallace, *Elec. Eng.*, **68**: 222 (1949).

of the emitter current, however, consists of holes which are naturally attracted by the negatively biased collector in the immediate vicinity, $U_c < 0$ (e.g., -20 volts). Hence the major portion β of the hole current γI_e is captured by the collector and thus modifies the conductance of the collector boundary layer which is depleted of carriers as a result of the reverse bias. In this manner the current path of the battery in the collector circuit, which includes the collector boundary layer, can be modulated with very little power in the emitter circuit.

An attempt to develop these concepts quantitatively fails because the physical mechanism of the point contacts—as previously pointed out on page 73—is described only very approximately by the Schottky boundary-layer theory. The favorable operation of point-contact detectors depends largely on certain empirically determined surface treatments and forming processes. This clearly points to chemical changes in the pure metal-semiconductor contact which have only recently been discovered, at least in a qualitative way.[1]

The only way to arrive at a "theory" of the point-contact transistor is to apply the concepts used for the filamentary transistor to the geometry of the type A transistor, although this is only partly possible. However, the following difficulty is even more serious. While in the filamentary transistor the control of the conductivity of the current path between emitter and collector can be described and followed theoretically,[2] we have for the point-contact transistor only the formal definition of the current-amplification factor α_i for this important part of the theory. In view of this unsatisfactory situation, we shall deal with this subject only briefly in the next section.

b. The Quantitative "Theory" of the Type A Transistor

We begin with a discussion of the emitter, and we consider first the properties of the emitter alone, ignoring the influence of the collector. For this purpose we must keep the collector in the zero-current condition and measure the emitter current-voltage characteristics:

$$I_e = f_{e0}(U_e) \qquad (V.4.01)$$

With positive collector current I_c, the potential of the germanium surrounding the emitter would be $R_b \cdot I_c$ higher than before. According

[1] R. Thedieck, *Physik. Verhandl.*, **3**: 31 and 212 (1952). L. B. Valdes, *Proc· IRE*, **40**: 445 (1952).

[2] The pertinent theoretical concepts have also been experimentally verified. See W. Shockley, G. L. Pearson, and J. R. Haynes, *Bell System Tech. J.*, **288**: 344 (1949).

to Fig. V.4.4, R_b is the resistance between the equipotential surface through the emitter and the grounded base, assuming the current to spread out radially from the collector.

A positive collector current I_c creates in the germanium with the conductivity σ a hemispherical potential distribution

$$V(r) = \frac{I_c}{2\pi\sigma r} \qquad (V.4.02)$$

With the collector as center point, the resulting field strength

$$E(r) = -V'(r) = +\frac{I_c}{2\pi\sigma r^2} \qquad (V.4.03)$$

then produces with the conductivity σ exactly the required current I_c through each hemisphere $2\pi r^2$.

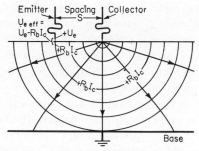

FIG. V.4.4. The origin of the effective emitter voltage

$$U_{e\ eff} = U_e - R_b I_c$$

If the emitter is at a distance S from the collector, the equipotential surface intersecting the emitter has the potential

$$V(S) = \frac{I_c}{2\pi\sigma S} \qquad (V.4.04)$$

The base is identified with the infinitely distant hemisphere and therefore has the potential

$$V(\infty) = 0 \qquad (V.4.05)$$

The voltage between the equipotential surface through the emitter and the base is, therefore,

$$V(S) - V(\infty) = \frac{I_c}{2\pi\sigma S} \qquad (V.4.06)$$

and the resistance between the two surfaces in question is

$$R_b = \frac{V(S) - V(\infty)}{I_c} = \frac{1}{2\pi\sigma S} \qquad \text{(V.4.07)}$$

For $\sigma = \frac{1}{10}$ ohm^{-1} cm^{-1} and $S = 50 \cdot 10^{-4}$ cm, by way of example, the resistance is

$$R_b = \frac{10 \text{ ohm cm}}{6.28 \cdot 5 \cdot 10^{-3} \text{ cm}} = 318 \text{ ohms} \qquad \text{(V.4.08)}$$

Inasmuch as with a collector current I_c the potential of the germanium near the emitter exceeds that for zero collector current by $R_b \cdot I_c$, it seems reasonable to regard $U_e - R_b \cdot I_c$ as the effective emitter voltage and to write in place of (V.4.01)

$$I_e = f_{e0}(U_e - R_bI_c) \qquad \text{(V.4.09)}$$

We have here assumed, it is true, that potentials created by the emitter current and the collector current can be superposed without interaction. This assumption is certainly not strictly correct because the conductivity of the germanium is modified by the injected holes. Taking this effect into account would lead to appreciable complications and will not be attempted here.[1]

After having treated the conditions on the emitter side, though in a somewhat incomplete manner, and having obtained Eq. (V.4.09) for the emitter current I_e, we shall now consider the collector current I_c. Without the influence of the emitter, I_c is given by the unmodified collector characteristic

$$I_c = f_{c0}(U_c) \qquad \text{for } I_e = 0 \qquad \text{(V.4.10)}$$

In addition to this component, arising directly from the collector voltage U_c, a further component is introduced by the injection from the emitter. A fraction γ of the emitter current I_e consists of holes, a fraction β of which, in turn, is captured by the collector. The hole current $\beta\gamma I_e$ arriving at the collector releases a collector-current component $\alpha_i\beta\gamma I_e = \alpha I_e$ which is larger by the true current-amplification factor α_i and which is added to (V.4.10) though with negative sign, since according to our definition a positive emitter current traverses the collector circuit in a negative direction:

$$I_c = f_{c0}(U_c) - \alpha I_e \qquad \text{(V.4.11)}$$

Equations (V.4.09) and (V.4.11) are the two equations which relate

---

[1] L. B. Valdes, *Proc. IRE*, **40**: 1429 (1952), has also neglected this effect. Valdes considers the finite thickness of the Ge wafer in his calculation, which leads to a deformation of the hemispherical propagation of the collector current, in contrast to the above treatment.

the currents I_e and I_c and the voltages U_e and U_c. If we consider small deviations i_e, i_c, u_e, u_c from an operating point I_e, I_c, U_e, U_c, we obtain from (V.4.09) and (V.4.11) by linearization

$$i_e = \frac{1}{r_e} (u_e - R_b i_c)$$

$$i_c = \frac{1}{r_c} u_c - \alpha i_e$$

and
$$u_e = r_e i_e + R_b i_c \tag{V.4.12}$$
$$u_c = \alpha r_c i_e + r_c i_c \tag{V.4.13}$$

Here r_e and r_c are the differential resistances which can be calculated from the unperturbed characteristics (V.4.01) and (V.4.10) for the operating points I_e and I_c, respectively. R_b is given approximately by

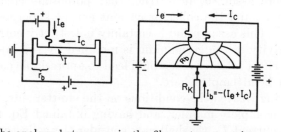

Fig. V.4.5. The analogy between r_b in the filamentary transistor and the *external* coupling resistor R_K in the point-contact transistor. The *internal* base resistance R_b does not have an analogue in the filamentary transistor.

Eq. (V.4.07). The current-amplification factor α of the point-contact transistor is formally expressed by the product

$$\alpha = \alpha_i \beta \gamma \tag{V.4.14}$$

but it is not possible to relate any of the three factors α_i, β, and γ to the geometrical dimensions and the material constants of the device.[1] Thus the theory of the point-contact transistor has a rather formal character compared with the theories of the n-p-n transistor and particularly the filamentary transistor.

We shall add a few remarks concerning the obvious comparison with the current-voltage characteristics of the filamentary transistor:

$$u_e = (r_b + r_e)i_e + r_b \cdot i_c \tag{V.2.43}$$
$$u_c = (r_b + \alpha_e r_c)i_e + (r_b + r_c)i_c \tag{V.2.44}$$

As can be seen, the resistance R_b of the point-contact transistor does not act in a manner analogous to the base resistance r_b in the filamen-

[1] See further, J. Bardeen, *Bell System Tech. J.*, **29**: 469 (1950).

tary transistor (resistance between point I and the base electrode in Fig. V.4.5). The latter acts rather as a feedback resistance R_K which can be added between base electrode and ground in the point-contact transistor. In view of

$$U_e^* = U_e - R_K I_b = U_e + R_K(I_e + I_c) \qquad \text{(V.4.15)}$$
$$U_c^* = U_c - R_K I_b = U_c + R_K(I_e + I_c) \qquad \text{(V.4.16)}$$

and the corresponding equations for the deviations u_e^* . . . from the operating point, we obtain from (V.4.12) and (V.4.13)

$$u_e^* = (R_K + r_e)i_e + (R_K + R_b)i_c \qquad \text{(V.4.17)}$$
$$u_c^* = (R_K + \alpha r_c)i_e + (R_K + r_c)i_c \qquad \text{(V.4.18)}$$

Comparison with (V.2.43) and (V.2.44) shows the analogy between r_b in the filamentary transistor and R_K in the point-contact transistor, whereas there is no analogue in the filamentary transistor to the resistance R_b of the point-contact transistor.

In conclusion we shall refer very briefly to an extensive field which is extremely important for practical applications. On page 124 we

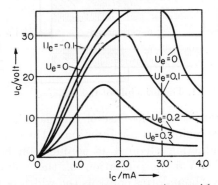

Fig. V.4.6. Family of characteristics of a transistor with regions of negative resistance.

already touched upon the internal feedback in a transistor which can lead to instability.[1] In such cases the input impedance, measured from the primary or secondary side, of a transistor is negative, indicated by falling characteristics (see Fig. V.4.6). This phenomenon is utilized in switching circuits and has led to numerous applications of the transistor in pulse, switching, and electronic computing techniques.[2]

[1] See in this connection also p. 148.
[2] See in this connection, for instance, B. A. E. Anderson, *Proc. IRE*, **40**: 1541 (1952).

§5. The Unipolar Transistor

In contrast to the previously discussed three transistor types, the injection of *minority* carriers plays no part in the unipolar transistor; instead use is made of displacement effects of *majority* carriers in the transition regions of *p-n* junctions. We may recall that there is a potential step V_D in a *p-n* junction even for zero current (see Fig. IV.6.1). The establishment of this step requires space charges which stem from the fact that, on both sides of the transition region, the respective majority carrier concentration is smaller than the corresponding impurity density. If, by application of a reverse voltage U, the potential step is increased to $V_D + U$, the space-charge regions which are depleted of carriers must increase in width (see Fig. IV.7.1). All this has been discussed in detail in Chap. IV, §6 and §7, in connection with the rectifying action of a *p-n* junction.

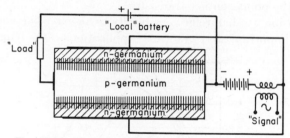

Fig. V.5.1. The principle of the unipolar transistor.

The unipolar transistor makes use of the majority carrier depletion in the space-charge region of a *p-n* junction in the following way. For instance, a *p*-conducting channel is confined on both sides by *p-n* junctions (see Fig. V.5.1). Variation of the voltage between the *p* channel and the *n* boundaries controls the width of the space-charge regions so that a varying width of the boundary strip on each side of the *p* channel is depleted of carriers. This boundary strip is subtracted from the conducting cross section for a current in the *longitudinal direction* of the channel. In the limit the entire channel width can be made carrier-free by applying sufficiently high reverse voltages between the *p* channel and the *n* boundaries. The channel is then apparently "pinched off," and the longitudinal current is blocked.

Thus the over-all effect is that the width of the channel, and with it the conductance for the longitudinal current, is controlled by the reverse voltage. The control requires only very little power, because the control voltages are in the reverse direction and the reverse currents of p-n junctions are extremely small. At the time of writing, no experimental realization of this unipolar transistor has been published, although it has already been announced by Shockley.[1]

§6. Appendix: The Amplification of Current, Voltage, and Power for a Transducer Element with Output Load

We employ the linearized current-voltage relations (V.2.18) and (V.2.19) for the treatment of these equations:

$$u_e = r_{11}i_e + r_{12}i_c \qquad (V.2.18)$$
$$u_c = r_{21}i_e + r_{22}i_c \qquad (V.2.19)$$

According to Fig. V.6.1 we have

$$u_c = -u_L = -R_L i_c \qquad (V.6.01)$$

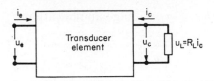

Fig. V.6.1. Transducer element with a load resistor at the output side.

where R_L is the load resistor in the secondary circuit:

$$0 = r_{21}i_e + (r_{22} + R_L)i_c \qquad (V.6.02)$$

From the preceding we obtain for the current amplification

$$\frac{i_c}{i_e} = -\frac{r_{21}}{r_{22}} \frac{r_{22}}{r_{22} + R_L} \qquad (V.6.03)$$

For the voltage amplification[2] we obtain with (V.6.03), (V.6.01), and (V.2.18)

---

[1] W. Shockley, *Proc. IRE*, **40**: 1365 (1952), particularly end of p. 1376. See also G. L. Pearson, *Phys. Rev.*, **90**: 336 (1953); and G. C. Dacey and I. M. Ross, *Proc. IRE*, **41**: 970 (1953).

[2] We define the ratio of the secondary terminal voltage u_c to the primary terminal voltage u_e as the voltage amplification. The maximum voltage which the primary voltage source is capable of producing without transducer element is often taken as the reference quantity instead of u_e. This would be the emf e_g of the primary *generator*. In this case we would have to introduce an internal resistance r_g of the generator in Fig. V.6.1, and we would have to distinguish between the emf e_g and the terminal voltage u_e. For our discussion, which is directed at the physical essentials, we can refrain from considering these more detailed differences.

$$\frac{u_L}{u_e} = - \frac{r_{21}}{r_{11}} \frac{R_L}{r_{22} + R_L} \frac{1}{1 - \frac{r_{21}}{r_{11}} \frac{r_{12}}{r_{22} + R_L}} \qquad (V.6.04)$$

Equations (V.6.04) and (V.6.03) together lead to the power amplification[1]

$$\frac{u_L i_c}{u_e i_e} = \frac{r_{21}^2}{r_{11} \cdot r_{22}} \frac{r_{22} R_L}{(r_{22} + R_L)^2} \frac{1}{1 - \frac{r_{21}}{r_{11}} \frac{r_{12}}{r_{22} + R_L}} \qquad (V.6.05)$$

In both of these equations, the second factor $r_{22}/(r_{22} + R_L)$, $R_L/(r_{22} + R_L)$, and $r_{22}R_L/(r_{22} + R_L)^2$ represents the effect of the voltage division between the circuit element and the load resistance on the secondary side.[2] The physically important information is obtained from the short-circuit ($R_L = 0$) current amplification

$$\left[\frac{i_c}{i_e} \right]_{\text{short circuit}} = - \frac{r_{21}}{r_{22}} \qquad (V.6.06)$$

the open-circuit ($R_L = \infty$) voltage amplification

$$\left[\frac{u_L}{u_e} \right]_{\text{open circuit}} = - \frac{r_{21}}{r_{11}} \qquad (V.6.07)$$

and the power amplification under matched ($R_L = r_{22}$) conditions[3]

$$\left[\frac{u_L i_c}{u_e i_e} \right]_{\text{matched}} = \frac{1}{4} \frac{r_{21}^2}{r_{11} r_{22}} \frac{1}{1 - \frac{1}{2} \frac{r_{21} r_{12}}{r_{11} r_{22}}} \qquad (V.6.08)$$

The factor on the right of (V.6.08) is significant. It shows the feedback effect of the resistance r_{12} and the resulting tendency toward

---

[1] We take the power $u_e \cdot i_e$ which is delivered to the four-pole element by the primary voltage source as the reference quantity for the definition of the power amplification. Instead, the maximum power $\frac{1}{4} \cdot (e_g^2/r_g)$ which can be taken out of the primary generator e_g, r_g without the transducer element is often used as reference quantity for the power amplification.

[2] In this connection we may recall the, possibly trivial, fact that for an a-c short circuit ($R_L = 0$) the voltage amplification and for an a-c open circuit ($R_L = \infty$) the current amplification is zero. Whether a circuit element exhibits mostly current amplification or voltage amplification depends *also* very strongly on the magnitude of the load resistance and should, therefore, not be used for the characterization of the physical mechanism of the particular circuit element.

[3] If we designate $R_L = r_{22}$ as "matching," we neglect the feedback resistance r_{12} and its effect on the input resistance $r_{22} - r_{12}r_{21}/(r_{11} + r_g)$ on the secondary side. This, too, is not essential for our discussion which is aimed at the basic principles.

instability which can occur if the magnitude of r_{12} is such that the denominator of this factor can become zero so that the power amplification becomes ∞, leading to destruction of the transducer element. Much as an increase of the power amplification is desirable, the utilization of the feedback r_{12} is risky because of the danger of instability, so that one tries in general to make r_{12} as small as possible.[1]

§7. Problems

1. What is the average transit time required for the injected minority carriers to diffuse through a base region of the thickness w, assuming $w \ll L$? Give the numerical values for germanium transistors of both polarities with $w = 10^{-4}$ cm.

2. Compare the diffusion transit time through the base region of a transistor (see Prob. 1) with the drift transit time under the influence of an electric field E. The drift transit time can be defined as the transit time due to the field only. What potential difference across the base region would be necessary in a transistor so that the drift transit time becomes equal to the diffusion transit time? For lower electric fields, the transport process is mostly diffusion-determined, for higher fields mostly field-determined.

3. Calculate the drift transit time in an n-type germanium point-contact transistor with an emitter-collector distance of 5×10^{-3} cm, for a collector electron current of 0.1 mA, assuming a germanium resistivity of 1 ohm-cm.

4.* In a semiconductor with nonuniform impurity density, the free carrier density will be nonuniform, too. On the other hand, the carrier density in thermal equilibrium can vary only when the electrostatic potential varies. This is true not only for p-n junctions but for inhomogeneous n-type or p-type doping as well. In all cases, the equilibrium carrier densities and the potential are connected by a pair of equations analogous to (IV.6.10) and (IV.6.11):

$$p(x) = p(0) \exp\left\{ - \frac{e}{kT} [V(x) - V(0)] \right\} \tag{V.7.01}$$

$$n(x) = n(0) \exp\left\{ + \frac{e}{kT} [V(x) - V(0)] \right\} \tag{V.7.02}$$

a. What is the potential distribution inside the base layer of a transistor if the donor density decreases exponentially from the emitter to the collector, according to, say,

$$n_D(x) = n_D(0) \cdot e^{-\frac{x}{\lambda}} \tag{V.7.03}$$

b. What is the drift transit time for holes (see Prob. 2) in a p-n-p germanium transistor with $n_D(0) = 1.5 \cdot 10^{17}$ cm^{-3}, $\lambda = 6.25 \cdot 10^{-5}$ cm, and $w = 5 \cdot 10^{-4}$ cm?

5. Calculate the current amplification factor α_i for an n-p-n germanium transistor with the following physical parameters: $n_D = 10^{17}$ cm^{-3}, $n_A = 2 \cdot 10^{15}$ cm^{-3}, $\tau_p = 10^{-6}$ sec, $\tau_n = 5 \cdot 10^{-5}$ sec, $w = 5 \cdot 10^{-4}$ cm. How much of the deviation of α_i from unity is due to recombination losses, and how much is due to incomplete injection?

---

[1] In contrast to the feedback resistance r_{12}, the coupling resistance r_{21} must never be zero. For $r_{21} = 0$ there would be no effect of the primary circuit on the secondary circuit, much less an *amplification* of the primary signal.

6. When the injected minority-carrier density in the base region increases with increasing emitter current, the majority-carrier density increases by the same amount in order to neutralize the charge of the injected carriers, as described in §2a. The result is the same as though the increase in the majority carrier density had been caused by an increase in the impurity density. In the case of an n-p-n transistor, this means that the hole current flowing out of the base into the emitter is not proportional to the injected electron current, as would be the case for a constant hole density in the base. Instead, this "lost" hole current rises faster with increasing emitter voltage than the electron current, so that the emitter efficiency γ_e decreases.[1] Calculate the dependence of γ_e alone and of the total current amplification factor α_i on the current. Plot the variation of the current-amplification factor for the transistor of Prob. 5.

7. With increasing collector voltage the width of the collector junction increases, thereby reducing the width of the base region.[2] If the emitter voltage is held constant, the diffusion gradient in the base region becomes steeper and the current increases. This means that the collector has a low, but finite, conductance, as already shown in Fig. V.3.6. If, however, the emitter current rather than the emitter voltage is held constant, the emitter voltage will drop with increasing collector voltage by such an amount that the diffusion gradient in the base region remains constant. This means that there exists a negative feedback from the collector to the emitter. Calculate the collector conductance for constant emitter voltage $(\partial i_c / \partial U_c)_{u_e}$ and the feedback factor for constant emitter current $(\partial U_e / \partial u_c)_{i_e}$ for an n-p-n transistor with an abrupt collector junction. For simplicity, make the following additional assumptions: $n_{D,\text{collector}} \gg n_{A,\text{base}}$, $\alpha_i = 1$. Give numerical values for germanium, assuming $W = 10^{-4}$ cm, $n_{A,\text{base}} = 5 \cdot 10^{15}$ cm^{-3}, $i_e = 1$ mA, $U_c = 3$ volts.

[1] W. M. Webster, *Proc. IRE*, **42**: 914 (1954).
[2] J. M. Early, *Proc. IRE*, **40**: 1401 (1952).

Fundamentals of
Semiconductor Physics

Detailed deductions of concepts and theorems from the fundamentals of semiconductor physics have been avoided in the preceding five chapters, since such deductions would not have been in the interest of the application-minded reader. However, the physicist who wishes to delve deeper in the semiconductor field will want to distinguish between the elements in modern solid-state physics which are based on fundamental physical laws and those which rest on hypotheses and simplifying assumptions. Chapters VI to X, on fundamentals, may here be helpful.

A solid body, with its enormous number of atomic nuclei and electrons, represents a many-body problem whose exact treatment is out of the question. Since a crystal is, in a sense, a single giant molecule, it seems reasonable to transfer to crystals the approximation methods found useful for molecules. This has, in fact, taken place. For instance, the approximation method of Heitler and London has been applied by Heisenberg[1] to the theory of ferromagnetism and by Hylleraas[2] and Landshoff[3] to the theory of the cohesive forces in ionic crystals. Thus a wave-mechanical basis is provided for the *atomistic* picture, which is employed mainly by crystal and physical chemists and is best suited for insulators and ionic crystals. In the last two decades this picture has unjustly been regarded as antiquated and as unduly influenced by the corpuscular viewpoint. This may arise in part from the fact that the other approximation method, the band model, is particularly suited to metals and that, for historical reasons, the long-known and well-defined phenomenon of metallic conduction

[1] W. Heisenberg, Z. *Physik*, **49**: 619 (1928).
[2] E. A. Hylleraas, Z. *Physik*, **63**: 771 (1930).
[3] H. Landshoff, Z. *Physik*, **102**: 201 (1936); *Phys. Rev.*, **52**: 246 (1937).

was investigated first.   By comparison, semiconductor physics, initially so confused, has expanded its scope only in the last three decades. In fact, in the minds of most physicists it lost a slightly scurrilous character only a few years ago.

In the field of molecular structure, the band model has its starting point in the methods of Hund and Mulliken.   To demonstrate clearly the equal standing[1] of the band model and the atomistic picture, it seemed appropriate to compare, in Chap. VI, the methods of London and Heitler on the one hand and of Hund and Mulliken on the other as applied to the simplest molecule, namely, the hydrogen molecule.   In Chap. VII we shall discuss the band model in detail.   We cannot enter upon the atomistic picture to the same extent.   Quantitative results have been derived from the atomistic picture only for the theory of ferromagnetism and the theory of cohesive forces in ionic crystals. These topics lie, however, outside the scope of this book.

Instead, Chap. VIII covers the quantitative results of the Fermi statistics of electrons in crystals within the scope of the band model. We return here to the concepts of lattice-defect reactions and the laws of mass action introduced in Chap. II.   In Chap. II wep ointed out that this approach was proper only for sufficient dilution of the participants in the reaction.   A quantitative formulation of this assumption becomes possible only with the aid of Fermi statistics in Chap. VIII.   These statistics also provide a basis for the value of the mass-action constant which, in Chap. II, could be given only without proof.

The law of mass action, which is so important for semiconductor physics, is discussed once more in Chap. IX, this time from the kinetic standpoint.   Here we find relations between the mass-action constant, the so-called recombination coefficient (or the effective cross section), and the lifetime.   These matters are of importance in the theory of phosphors and may be of significance in the high-frequency behavior of rectifiers and detectors.

Finally, in Chap. X, the phenomena are discussed which occur when two different solids are brought into contact.   Here we obtain a representation of the concepts of the Galvani voltage, Volta potential difference (= contact potential), work function, photoelectric activation energy, and diffusion voltage.

In this connection we shall also enter into a discussion of surface states and their possible effect on the contact between two solids.

[1] See F. Stöckmann, Z. physik. Chem., **198**: 215 (1951).

CHAPTER VI

Approximation Methods in the Quantum Mechanics of the Hydrogen Molecule

§1. Introduction

Our concern with the theory of the hydrogen molecule is not an end in itself.   Instead, we wish to recognize in the approximation methods used in this two-electron problem those characteristic traits which we shall meet again in the multielectron problem of a solid.[1]   In such an approximation method,[2] the Schrödinger function $\psi(\mathbf{r}_1, \mathbf{r}_2)$ of the complete molecule, which contains the position vectors $\mathbf{r}_1$ and $\mathbf{r}_2$ of both electrons 1 and 2, is initially approximated by a product of two functions $u(\mathbf{r}_1)$ and $v(\mathbf{r}_2)$, which each contain the position vector of only one electron:

$$\psi(\mathbf{r}_1, \mathbf{r}_2) = u(\mathbf{r}_1) \cdot v(\mathbf{r}_2) \qquad \text{(VI.1.01)}$$

A nonidentical[3] eigenfunction with the same total energy would be

[1] Hence we need not consider the refined approximation methods of S. C. Wang, *Phys. Rev.*, **31**: 579 (1928); of E. Hylleraas, *Z. Physik*, **71**: 739 (1931); or of H. M. James and A. S. Coolidge, *J. Chem. Phys.*, **1**: 825 (1933).

[2] We are not dealing here with Schrödinger's original perturbation method in which the problem to be treated differs by only a slight perturbation from an accurately solvable problem and where the solution of the perturbed problem is expanded in the eigenfunctions of the unperturbed problem.   In principle, this is an infinite process which, at least theoretically, is capable of arbitrary refinement and, in case of convergence, will yield arbitrarily precise results.   The methods to be described are, rather, specific realizations of a finite procedure.   The historical starting point for them is the treatment of the hydrogen molecule by W. Heitler and F. London, *Z. Physik*, **44**: 455 (1927), which is to be discussed next.   The general scheme was indicated by J. C. Slater, *Phys. Rev.*, **38**: 1109 (1931).   See also F. Hund in H. Geiger and K. Scheel, "Handbuch der Physik," vol. XXIV, part 1, pp. 572ff., Springer-Verlag OHG, Berlin, 1933.

[3] The eigenfunctions of a square membrane clamped on the edge

$$\cos x \cdot \sin 2y$$
$$\sin 2x \cdot \cos y$$

indicate how, by the exchange of two coordinates or degrees of freedom, a non-identical eigenfunction with the same characteristic frequency can be obtained (see Fig. VI.1.1).

that in which electrons 1 and 2 have exchanged their role

$$\psi(\mathbf{r}_1, \mathbf{r}_2) = v(\mathbf{r}_1) \cdot u(\mathbf{r}_2) \qquad \text{(VI.1.02)}$$

since, for a measurable quantity such as the energy, it is a matter of indifference which electron is denoted by 1 and which is denoted by 2. The two functions (VI.1.01) and (VI.1.02) are hence degenerate and, consequently, the correct eigenfunction will, in general, be neither of the two, but rather a linear combination of them:

cos x·sin 2y

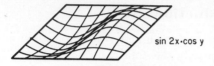
sin 2x·cos y

$$\psi(\mathbf{r}_1, \mathbf{r}_2) = c \cdot u(\mathbf{r}_1)v(\mathbf{r}_2)$$
$$+ d \cdot v(\mathbf{r}_1)u(\mathbf{r}_2) \quad \text{(VI.1.03)}$$

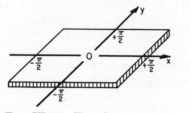

FIG. VI.1.1. Two degenerate characteristic vibrations of the square membrane with clamped boundaries.

The values of the coefficients c and d and of the total energy E are obtained in effect by solving a variation problem replacing the Schrödinger differential equation within the limits imposed by restricting the choice of functions to the manifold (VI.1.03). We need not enter upon this here in greater detail.[1] It is merely important for us that this procedure yields as correct eigenfunctions

$$\psi(\mathbf{r}_1, \mathbf{r}_2) = u(\mathbf{r}_1)v(\mathbf{r}_2) - v(\mathbf{r}_1)u(\mathbf{r}_2) \qquad \text{(VI.1.04)}$$
$$\psi(\mathbf{r}_1, \mathbf{r}_2) = u(\mathbf{r}_1)v(\mathbf{r}_2) + v(\mathbf{r}_1)u(\mathbf{r}_2) \qquad \text{(VI.1.05)}$$

An exchange of the two electrons 1 and 2 does not change the "symmetric" eigenfunction (VI.1.05) at all and changes only the sign of the "antisymmetric" eigenfunction (VI.1.04).[2] This was to be expected since the measurable quantities deducible from the Schrödinger function such as energy, probability density, etc., cannot depend on the numbering of the electrons. A change of sign of ψ with an exchange of

[1] The interested reader is referred to Geiger and Scheel, *op. cit.*, vol. XXIV, part 1, pp. 572ff.

[2] The fact that the eigenfunction which is *symmetric* in the *position* coordinates of the electrons is retained and not eliminated from the consideration is only apparently a violation of the Pauli principle. The restriction to eigenfunctions antisymmetric in the electron coordinates required by this principle demands the simultaneous consideration of the electron spin, which may occur at least formally by the introduction of the spin variables σ and the spin functions $\alpha(\sigma)$ and $\beta(\sigma)$. See H. A. Bethe in Geiger and Scheel, *op. cit.*, vol. XXIV, part 2, pp. 587–598.

electrons 1 and 2 is permissible since the Schrödinger function always occurs quadratically in these quantities.

The approximation methods of Hund and Mulliken on the one hand and of Heitler and London on the other, to be discussed below, differ first of all in the formulation of the one-electron functions $u(\mathbf{r})$ and $v(\mathbf{r})$.

§2. The Approximation Method of Hund[1] and Mulliken[2]

We proceed here from the case of closely adjoining hydrogen nuclei. Since the fields of the two nuclei overlap to a large extent, it becomes meaningless to distinguish between the electron being in the field of one nucleus a or its being in the field of the other nucleus b. From this

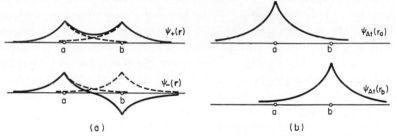

(a)   (b)

FIG. VI.2.1. The starting points of the procedures of Hund and Mulliken and of Heitler and London. (a) Hund and Mulliken: The eigenfunctions $\Psi_+(r)$ and $\Psi_-(r)$ of the molecular ion H_2^+ are chosen as one-electron functions. (b) Heitler and London: The atomic eigenfunctions $\Psi_{at}(r_a)$ and $\Psi_{at}(r_b)$ are chosen as one-electron functions.

standpoint the eigenfunctions of one electron in the field of two nuclei a and b, i.e., the eigenfunctions of the hydrogen molecular ion (see Fig. VI.2.1), appear appropriate for $u(\mathbf{r})$ and $v(\mathbf{r})$. The exact treatment of this one-electron–two-center problem is possible with the use of elliptical coordinates. However, the utilization of the resulting exact eigenfunctions of the hydrogen molecular ion in the procedure of Hund and Mulliken is awkward. Hence we shall be content with approximate expressions for the eigenfunction of an electron in the field of the two nuclei a and b obtained when the separation ab is relatively large:[3]

$$\psi_+ (\mathbf{r}) = \psi_{at}(r_a) + \psi_{at}(r_b) \qquad (VI.2.01)$$
$$\psi_- (\mathbf{r}) = \psi_{at}(r_a) - \psi_{at}(r_b) \qquad (VI.2.02)$$

[1] F. Hund, *Z. Physik*, **51**: 759 (1928); **63**: 719 (1930).
[2] R. S. Mulliken, *Phys. Rev.*, **32**: 186, 761 (1928); **33**: 730 (1928).
[3] This is unquestionably a logical difficulty in our procedure, since it was stated at the start that the Hund-Mulliken approximation corresponded to the case of

Here, according to Fig. VI.2.2, $\mathbf{r}$ is the position vector of the electron referred to an arbitrary origin. r_a and r_b are the distances of the electron from the nucleus a and b, respectively. Hence the atomic eigenfunction[1]

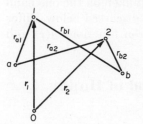

$$\psi_{\mathrm{at}}(r_a) = \frac{1}{\sqrt{\pi a_0^3}}\, e^{-\frac{r_a}{a_0}} \qquad (VI.2.03)$$

is centered about the nucleus a. A corresponding statement applies of course for $\psi_{\mathrm{at}}(r_b)$. a_0 is the radius of the first Bohr orbit

FIG. VI.2.2. Two electrons 1 and 2 in the field of two hydrogen nuclei a and b.

$$a_0 = \frac{h^2}{4\pi^2 m e^2} = 0.5281 \cdot 10^{-8}\ \text{cm} \qquad (VI.2.04)$$

The eigenfunction (VI.2.01) which is symmetrical in the nuclei a and b pertains to the normal state of the hydrogen molecular ion; a higher[2] energy of the electron in the field of the two nuclei a and b corresponds to the eigenfunction (VI.2.02) which is antisymmetric in the nuclei. In carrying out the program of §1 with the functions (VI.2.01) and (VI.2.02) for the description of the normal state of the H_2 molecule, we shall give both electrons the smallest possible energy and hence put both

$$u(\mathbf{r}) = \psi_+(\mathbf{r})$$
and
$$v(\mathbf{r}) = \psi_+(\mathbf{r})$$

Since $u \equiv v$ we obtain for the normal state of the hydrogen molecule only the eigenfunction (VI.1.05) which is symmetrical in electrons 1

---

closely adjoining nuclei. In this limiting case, however, no simple relation is obtained between the eigenfunction of the molecular ion and the atomic eigenfunctions $\psi_{\mathrm{at}}(r_a)$ and $\psi_{\mathrm{at}}(r_b)$. In view of the intended comparison with the results of Heitler and London, such a relation is more important to us here than the attainment of the highest possible accuracy in the numerical results. Hence we make use of the approximate expressions (VI.2.01) and (VI.2.02) for the eigenfunction of the molecular ion which apply for large separation of the nuclei.

[1] Hydrogen problem, normal state!

[2] This can be recognized intuitively, even without calculation. The plane of symmetry between the two nuclei is a region of (relatively) high potential. For the antisymmetric eigenfunction, the probability density of the electron in the plane of symmetry is zero (because of $r_{a1} = r_{b1}$), and it is small in the neighborhood of the plane of symmetry. The large negative contributions to the potential energy made by this region for the symmetrical eigenfunction drop out for the antisymmetric eigenfunction, so that the total energy is reduced less. Hence the normal state with the lowest energy corresponds to the symmetrical eigenfunction, whereas an excited state with higher (or less negative) energy corresponds to the antisymmetric eigenfunction. The symmetric eigenfunction (VI.2.01) thus represents a "binding state," the antisymmetric eigenfunction (VI.2.02) a "loosening state."

and 2, whereas the antisymmetric eigenfunction (VI.1.04) is identically equal to zero.   With (VI.2.01) we obtain[1]

$$\psi_+(\mathbf{r}_1) \cdot \psi_+(\mathbf{r}_2) = [\psi_{at}(r_{a1}) + \psi_{at}(r_{b1})] \cdot [\psi_{at}(r_{a2}) + \psi_{at}(r_{b2})]$$

With the readily understood abbreviations $a1$, $b1$, $a2$, $b2$ for the atomic eigenfunctions $\psi_{at}(r_{a1})$, $\psi_{at}(r_{b1})$, $\psi_{at}(r_{a2})$, $\psi_{at}(r_{b2})$ we obtain for the eigenfunction of the normal state

$$[a1 + b1] \cdot [a2 + b2]$$
$$= (a1 \cdot a2 + b1 \cdot b2) + (a1 \cdot b2 + b1 \cdot a2) \quad (VI.2.05)$$

If, next, we wish to consider an excited state of the hydrogen molecule, we must give only one of the electrons the lowest possible energy. Accordingly, we substitute in the scheme of §1

$$u(\mathbf{r}) = \psi_+(\mathbf{r})$$
$$v(\mathbf{r}) = \psi_-(\mathbf{r})$$

Then (VI.1.04) and (VI.1.05) lead to the following two molecular eigenfunctions for two excited states:[2]

$$\psi_+(\mathbf{r}_1) \cdot \psi_-(\mathbf{r}_2) - \psi_-(\mathbf{r}_1) \cdot \psi_+(\mathbf{r}_2)$$
$$= [a1 + b1] \cdot [a2 - b2] - [a1 - b1] \cdot [a2 + b2]$$
$$\sim (a1 \cdot b2 - b1 \cdot a2) \quad (VI.2.06)$$

$$\psi_+(\mathbf{r}_1) \cdot \psi_-(\mathbf{r}_2) + \psi_-(\mathbf{r}_1) \cdot \psi_+(\mathbf{r}_2)$$
$$= [a1 + b1] \cdot [a2 - b2] + [a1 - b1] \cdot [a2 + b2]$$
$$\sim (a1 \cdot a2 - b1 \cdot b2) \quad (VI.2.07)$$

Finally, accommodating both electrons 1 and 2 in the antisymmetric state (VI.2.02) and carrying out, correspondingly, the program of §1 with

$$u(\mathbf{r}) = \psi_-(\mathbf{r})$$
$$v(\mathbf{r}) = \psi_-(\mathbf{r})$$

leads, as for the normal state, to a single molecular function which is symmetrical in the electrons:

$$\psi_-(r_1) \cdot \psi_-(r_2) = [a1 - b1] \cdot [a2 - b2]$$
$$= (1a \cdot a2 + b1 \cdot b2) - (a1 \cdot b2 + b1 \cdot a2) \quad (VI.2.08)$$

Altogether, the procedure of Hund and Mulliken thus leads to the following four eigenfunctions:

Normal state:

$$(a1 \cdot a2 + b1 \cdot b2) + (a1 \cdot b2 + b1 \cdot a2) \quad (VI.2.05)$$

---

[1] We omit the factor 2 in front of the complete eigenfunction which follows from (VI.1.04) for $u \equiv v \equiv \psi_+$ since it would be changed again at any rate in carrying out the normalization procedure.

[2] Factors -2 and $+2$, respectively, have been omitted from the final expressions.

Excited states:

$$(a1 \cdot b2 - b1 \cdot a2) \qquad \text{(VI.2.06)}$$
$$(a1 \cdot a2 - b1 \cdot b2) \qquad\qquad\qquad \text{(VI.2.07)}$$
$$(a1 \cdot a2 + b1 \cdot b2) - (a1 \cdot b2 + b1 \cdot a2) \qquad \text{(VI.2.08)}$$

§3. The Original Procedure of Heitler and London

In contrast with the program of Hund and Mulliken, we proceed here from the case of widely separated hydrogen nuclei. We see immediately that the state of neutral H atoms is energetically much more favorable than the state $H^+ + H^-$. Starting from two neutral H atoms we reach the state $H^+ + H^-$ by the ionization of one of the hydrogen atoms (energy required: 13.54 ev)[1] and capture of the electron thus freed by the other neutral H atom (energy liberated: 0.76 ev).[2] This would require the very material expenditure of energy of $(13.54 - 0.76)$ ev = 12.78 ev. From this point of view it appears appropriate to approximate at least the normal state of the H_2 molecule by regarding one electron as bound to one nucleus and the other bound to the other nucleus. Accordingly, we substitute in the relations of §1

$$u(\mathbf{r}) = \psi_{at}(r_a) = \frac{1}{\sqrt{\pi a_0^3}} \, e^{-\frac{r_a}{a_0}}$$

$$v(\mathbf{r}) = \psi_{at}(r_b) = \frac{1}{\sqrt{\pi a_0^3}} \, e^{-\frac{r_b}{a_0}}$$

Then (VI.1.04) and (VI.1.05) yield as eigenfunctions

$$\psi_{at}(r_{a1}) \cdot \psi_{at}(r_{b2}) - \psi_{at}(r_{b1}) \cdot \psi_{at}(r_{a2}) = a1 \cdot b2 - b1 \cdot a2$$
$$\psi_{at}(r_{a1}) \cdot \psi_{at}(r_{b2}) + \psi_{at}(r_{b1}) \cdot \psi_{at}(r_{a2}) = a1 \cdot b2 + b1 \cdot a2$$

The sign of the so-called exchange integral determines for which of the two functions the energy is lower and which, hence, represents the normal state. For most molecules, including the hydrogen molecule, the exchange integral is negative, so that the normal state corresponds to the eigenfunction which is symmetrical in the position coordinates of the electrons:[3]

Normal state: $a1 \cdot b2 + b1 \cdot a2$ (VI.3.01)

Excited state: $a1 \cdot b2 - b1 \cdot a2$ (VI.3.02)

---

[1] See J. D'Ans and E. Lax, "Taschenbuch für Chemiker und Physiker," p. 113, Springer-Verlag OHG, Berlin, 1943.

[2] *Ibid.*, p. 116.

[3] See, e.g., H. A. Bethe in Geiger and Scheel, *op. cit.*, vol. XXIV, part 2, p. 592.

§4. Extension of the Procedure of Heitler and London by the Inclusion of Polar States. Comparison of the Approximations of Hund and Mulliken and Those of Heitler and London

In a comparison of the results (VI.3.01) and (VI.3.02) of the original procedure of Heitler and London with those of the procedure of Hund and Mulliken, the omission of polar states with H^+ and H^- in the former, resulting in the absence of the products $a1 \cdot a2$ and $b1 \cdot b2$, proves disturbing. Furthermore, an application of the original procedure of Heitler and London to a crystal could never lead to conductivity. The transition of an electron from an atom a to an atom b must invariably be accompanied by a compensating transition of another electron from atom b to atom a if we limit ourselves to states in which every atom has at all times one electron, and only one electron. Thus we must supplement the results (VI.3.01), (VI.3.02) of the original procedure of Heitler and London by two additional excited states $a1 \cdot a2 - b1 \cdot b2$ and $a1 \cdot a2 + b1 \cdot b2$. The comparison now takes the form:

Heitler and London

Normal state:	$a1 \cdot b2 + b1 \cdot a2$	(VI.4.01)
	$a1 \cdot b2 - b1 \cdot a2$	(VI.4.02)
Excited states: $\begin{cases} a1 \cdot a2 - b1 \cdot b2 \\ a1 \cdot a2 + b1 \cdot b2 \end{cases}$		(VI.4.03)
		(VI.4.04)

Hund and Mulliken

Normal state:	$(a1 \cdot a2 + b1 \cdot b2) + (a1 \cdot b2 + b1 \cdot a2)$	(VI.4.05)
	$a1 \cdot b2 - b1 \cdot a2$	(VI.4.06)
Excited states: $\begin{cases} a1 \cdot a2 - b1 \cdot b2 \\ (a1 \cdot a2 + b1 \cdot b2) - (a1 \cdot b2 + b1 \cdot a2) \end{cases}$		(VI.4.07)
		(VI.4.08)

We now see that the two approaches differ in the estimation of the normal state and of what is here the highest excited state; according to Hund and Mulliken these are quite definite linear combinations of the two corresponding states as adjudged by London and Heitler. According to Hund and Mulliken the heteropolar states $a1 \cdot a2$ and $b1 \cdot b2$ participate with equal weight in the normal state as the homopolar states $a1 \cdot b2$ and $b1 \cdot a2$. Simply expressed, the electrons are, according to Hund and Mulliken, as frequently together at one and the same nucleus as distributed between the two nuclei. By contrast, according to London and Heitler, the electrons are always distributed between the two nuclei in the normal state and never at one and the same nucleus.

At the same time it is intuitively obvious that the actual circumstances are reflected in the procedure of Heitler and London only for very widely separated nuclei and in the procedure of Hund and Mulliken only for the converse case of very closely adjoining nuclei. These are, indeed, the starting points of the two procedures.

We can conclude, hence, that neither procedure describes the actual circumstances correctly for intermediate nuclear separations. The foregoing comparison of the results of the approximation of Hund and Mulliken and the extended approximation of Heitler and London indicates, however, how the approximation might be improved without the introduction of functions more complex than the atomic eigenfunction (VI.2.03). The scheme of §1 or, more precisely, the range of functions admitted to comparison will have to be extended and Slater's perturbation theory will have to be carried out with the formulation

$$\psi(\mathbf{r}_1, \mathbf{r}_2) = A[a1 \cdot b2 + b1 \cdot a2] + B[a1 \cdot b2 - b1 \cdot a2]$$
$$+ C[a1 \cdot a2 - b1 \cdot b2] + D[a1 \cdot a2 + b1 \cdot b2] \quad \text{(VI.4.09)}$$

Considerations of symmetry lead to the conclusion that there will be three types of eigenfunctions:

Nuclei antisymmetric; electrons antisymmetric:

$$a1 \cdot b2 - b1 \cdot a2 \quad \text{(VI.4.10)}$$

Nuclei antisymmetric; electrons symmetric:

$$a1 \cdot a2 - b1 \cdot b2 \quad \text{(VI.4.11)}$$

Nuclei symmetric; electrons symmetric:

$$A(a1 \cdot b2 + b1 \cdot a2) + D(a1 \cdot a2 + b1 \cdot b2) \quad \text{(VI.4.12)}$$

Carrying through the perturbation calculation again leads for the two intermediate states to the types (VI.4.10) and (VI.4.11) as in the procedure of Heitler and London [(VI.4.02) and (VI.4.03), respectively] and that of Hund and Mulliken [(VI.4.06) and (VI.4.07), respectively]. However, eigenfunctions of the type (VI.4.12) are obtained for the normal state and the highest excited state. The heteropolar components vanish for the normal state and the homopolar components for the highest excited state only for the limiting case of very widely separated nuclei (Heitler and London). Correspondingly, homopolar and heteropolar components participate equally in the normal state and the highest excited state only in the limiting case of very closely adjoining nuclei (Hund and Mulliken). In any case, the heteropolar component of the normal state is surprisingly large even for the finite nuclear separation of the actual H_2 molecule. The probability of finding both electrons at one nucleus is 37 per cent, whereas according to Hund and Mulliken it would be 50 per cent and according to Heitler and London, 0 per cent.[1]

What conclusions may be drawn for a giant molecule such as a crystal from the relationships just described in the hydrogen molecule? The approximation of Heitler and London with the inclusion of polar states corresponds to the atomistic picture in solid-state physics. Here every electron is ascribed to a particular atom in the normal state, and excited states are created by ion formation (by the formation of "pairs" and "vacancies"). This picture is generally preferred by physical chemists and then frequently described somewhat misleadingly as a corpuscular picture. The considerations of Hund and Mulliken correspond to the band model in solid-state physics. Here even in the normal state every electron is distributed over all the atoms of the crystal. The normal state of the entire system is formed by the distribution of the electrons over the states of the one-electron approximation in accord with the Fermi distribution (any one state occupied by only two electrons). Quite incorrectly, the band model is frequently regarded as the only approach consistent with wave mechanics.

The relationships for the hydrogen molecule show us, however, that the atomistic picture has the drawback of a complete disregard of the polar states in the description of the normal state. The band model, on the other hand, exaggerates the importance of the polar states. Both pictures or models are thus equally imperfect and may be employed with the same justification, and the same care, supplementing each other mutually.[2] There is no analogy to a perturbation calculation with the broader formulation (VI.4.09) in solid-state theory.

Since the foregoing considerations proceed from the homopolar hydrogen molecule, they apply only for atomic lattices with atomic or valence bonds. However, if the difference between the atomistic picture and the band model is seen to rest in the fact that the atomistic picture ascribes the same state of charge to every building stone of the lattice without exception in the normal state, whereas the band model exaggerates the importance of charge transfers between the building stones of the lattice in the description of the normal state, the following extension to the ionic lattice appears appropriate:

In an ionic lattice the atomistic picture ascribes, in the normal state, the same state of charge to all building stones of a sublattice. Thus according to the atomistic picture, in an NaCl crystal all Na are positively charged and all Cl are negatively charged as long as the crystal

---

[1] See H. A. Bethe in Geiger and Scheel, *op. cit.*, vol. XXIV, part 1, p. 541.

[2] See F. Stöckmann, *Z. physik. Chem.*, **198**: 215 (1951).

remains in its normal state. Any deviation from this would correspond to an excited state of the crystal. The band model, on the other hand, would include deviations from the arrangement Na^+Cl^- even in the normal state and would, in fact, go much too far in this direction.

§5. Problems

1. Solve the Schrödinger equation in a one-dimensional delta function potential defined by

$$U(x) = -S \cdot \delta(x) \qquad (VI.5.01)$$

where S is a constant while

$$\delta(x) = \begin{cases} 0 \\ \infty \end{cases} \quad \text{for } \begin{matrix} x \neq 0 \\ x = 0 \end{matrix} \qquad (VI.5.02)$$

and

$$\int_{-\varepsilon}^{+\varepsilon} \delta(x)\, dx = 1 \qquad \text{for all } \varepsilon > 0 \qquad (VI.5.03)$$

For positive S values, there exist bound states which satisfy the boundary conditions

$$\psi(\pm \infty) = 0 \qquad (VI.5.04)$$

and which can be normalized

$$\int_{-\infty}^{+\infty} |\psi(x)|^2\, dx = 1 \qquad (VI.5.05)$$

Calculate the energy of these bound states as a function of S.

2. Write down the two normalized Heitler-London functions $\psi_\pm(x_1, x_2)$, for a "one-dimensional molecule" whose potential is given by two delta functions of the type described in Prob. 1:

$$U(x) = -S[\delta(x - d) + \delta(x + d)] \qquad (VI.5.06)$$

Give the mathematical expression for both functions and make a schematic drawing showing the probability distribution $|\psi|^2$ for *one* electron when the other electron is held fixed at the position of one of the two "atoms" and halfway between the two, that is, at $x = \pm d$ and at $x = 0$.

3. For the molecular potential of Eq. (VI.5.06), calculate the two Hund-Mulliken type one-electron wave functions which represent bound one-electron states in that molecule. Show that the energy values are the solutions of the transcendental equations

$$\varkappa[1 + \tanh \varkappa d] = \frac{2mS}{\hbar^2} \qquad \varkappa[1 + \coth \varkappa d] = \frac{2mS}{\hbar^2} \qquad (VI.5.07)$$

where

$$\varkappa = \sqrt{\frac{2m}{\hbar^2}(-E)} \qquad (VI.5.08)$$

Which of the two equations belongs to the symmetrical and the antisymmetrical function, respectively? Which function represents the ground state? Between what limits do the ground state and the excited state vary if the interatomic distance varies from zero to infinity?

From (VI.5.07) and (VI.5.08), derive explicitly approximation formulas for the energies of the two states as functions of d for large and for small d's, respectively.

CHAPTER VII

The Band Model

§1. Introduction

The band model results from approximation methods which represent an application of the method developed by Hund and Mulliken for ordinary molecules to the giant molecule of the crystal. Strictly the crystal, with N nuclei having m electrons apiece, constitutes an $(N + N \cdot m)$-body problem. If, to begin with, the mobility of the N nuclei is neglected, the problem is reduced to an $N \cdot m$-body problem, whose solution is again built up from solutions of a one-electron problem. The characteristic common trait of the procedure of Hund and Mulliken on the one hand and of the band model on the other rests in the choice of the one-electron problem and the manner in which the various solutions of the one-electron problem are combined.

If, in analogy to the procedure of Heitler and London, the motion of an electron in the field of a single atom core were chosen as the one-electron problem, we would obtain the atomistic picture.[1] For the band model we choose, instead, the behavior of an electron in the field of all atom cores and all remaining electrons as the one-electron problem. It is true that only the force actions of the atomic cores, regarded as immobile, are considered in greater detail. The force actions of the remaining $N \cdot m - 1$ mobile electrons are considered most inadequately only in so far as they screen, more or less, the fields of the atomic cores. Incidentally, these details play a role only as the band model is applied to specific substances.[2] The assumption that the electron

---

[1] See Fig. VI.2.1.

[2] J. C. Slater, *Phys. Rev.*, **45**: 794 (1934) (sodium). J. Millman, *Phys. Rev.*, **47**: 286 (1935) (lithium). F. Seitz, *Phys. Rev.*, **47**: 400 (1935) (lithium). H. M. Krutter, *Phys. Rev.*, **48**: 664 (1935) (copper). F. Hund and B. Mrowka, *Ber. Verhandl. sächs. Akad. Wiss. Leipzig, Math.-phys. Kl.*, **87**: 185 and 325 (1935) (diamond). G. E. Kimball, *J. Chem. Phys.*, **3**: 560 (1935) (diamond). W. Shockley, *Phys. Rev.*, **50**: 754 (1936) (NaCl). D. H. Ewing and F. Seitz, *Phys. Rev.*, **50**: 760 (1936) (LiF and LiH). C. Herring and A. G. Hill, *Phys. Rev.*, **58**: 132 (1940) (beryllium). F. G. von der Lage and H. A. Bethe, *Phys. Rev.*, **71**: 612 (1947) (sodium).

considered moves in a periodic field suffices for a series of very important general theorems.

It must be emphasized that this is an assumption. As already mentioned, a part of the force actions on the electron is exerted by the remaining electrons. These are mobile and influenced in their behavior by the reference electron, resulting, in turn, in changes in their force actions on the reference electron.[1] If we assume that the electrons dodge each other with infinite ease and that the space vacated by one electron is very rapidly occupied by another electron taking its place, an electron passing from one atomic core to the next meets identical force fields and the description by a fixed periodic potential appears sensible. This need not always be the case, and it is as yet an open question whether the peculiarities of the so-called open-band semiconductors result from an inadequacy of the assumption of a periodic potential in this instance.[2]

On the other hand, the same difficulties arise already in the treatment of a single atom with several or a large number of electrons. Here Hartree's method of the self-consistent field has demonstrated that stepwise approximations permit the determination of potential distributions which take account of the interactions of the electrons quite well, even in a one-electron treatment.

In the band model we proceed, in any case, from a one-electron problem describing the motion of an electron in a fixed periodic potential field.

Accordingly, we must seek those energy eigenvalues E of the Schrödinger equation

$$\left[-\frac{\hbar^2}{2m} \left(\frac{\partial^2}{\partial x^2} + \frac{\partial^2}{\partial y^2} + \frac{\partial^2}{\partial z^2} \right) + (-e) \cdot U(x, y, z) \right] \psi(x, y, z)$$
$$= E \cdot \psi(x, y, z) \quad \text{(VII.1.01)}$$

with the lattice-periodic potential $U(\mathbf{r} + l_1\mathbf{a}_1 + l_2\mathbf{a}_2 + l_3\mathbf{a}_3) \equiv U(\mathbf{r})$, for which the solution $\psi(\mathbf{r})$ remains finite throughout the crystal lattice. However, if we should regard a crystal with finite macro-

---

[1] Thus, strictly speaking, the reference electron does not move in a fixed potential, but in a force field such as occurs in the treatment of the image force in the emission of electrons from an incandescent solid. See, e.g., the article by W. Schottky in Wien and Harms, "Handbuch der Experimentalphysik," vol. XIII, part 2, p. 254, Akademische Verlagsgesellschaft, Leipzig, 1928.

[2] J. H. de Boer and E. J. W. Verwey, *Proc. Phys. Soc. (London)*, **49:** 59 (1935). W. Schottky, *Z. Elektrochem.*, **45:** 33 (1939), in particular p. 57. H. Dressnandt, *Z. Physik*, **115:** 369 (1940). C. Wagner, *Physik. Z.*, **36:** 721 (1935); reprinted in *Z. tech. Phys.*, **16:** 327 (1935). C. Wagner and E. Koch, *Z. physik. Chem.*, **B32:** 439 (1936). R. Peierls, *Proc. Phys. Soc. (London)*, **49:** 72 (1937).

scopic dimensions as an "entire" crystal lattice, we would introduce complexities in the solution which occur naturally at the crystal surface and have nothing to do with the behavior of the electron deep in the interior of the crystal. To dissect out neatly this behavior deep within the crystal, we apply an artifice also employed elsewhere in the theory of crystal lattices. We assume an infinite crystal and demand of ψ periodicity in an arbitrarily chosen fundamental domain G, which contains a large number of unit cells. This procedure is justified by the fact that it permits a large number of conclusions in which the arbitrary size of the fundamental domain does not enter.

There are certain specific formulations of the periodic potential $U(\mathbf{r})$ for which an exact solution of the problem under consideration is possible.[1] However, the approximation methods of Bloch and Brillouin, to be discussed next (§2 and §3), are more informative physically.[2]

In §4 we summarize the general properties, which do not depend on specific approximations, of the one-electron problem with periodic potential field and discuss briefly the cell method (Wigner and Seitz).

Then in §5 to §9 we outline additional properties of the one-electron approximation. In §5, momentum, velocity, and current contribution of an electron are discussed. In §6 and §7 we are concerned with the action of an external static field on an electron in a crystal, whereas §8 covers the case of an optical alternating field. Finally, in §9, we discuss the effect of material and thermal deviations of a real lattice from an ideally ordered lattice, leading to the concepts of mean free path, mean time between collisions, and mobility.

Up to this point we are still concerned with obtaining a one-electron approximation and familiarizing ourselves with it. The many-electron problem is first attacked in §10, though only in the relatively primitive manner corresponding to the approximation of Hund and Mulliken discussed in Chap. VI. It was shown there how the many-electron eigenfunction is built up as sum of products of solutions of the one-electron problem. Such a many-electron eigenfunction cannot tell

---

[1] R. de L. Kronig and W. G. Penney, *Proc. Roy. Soc.* (*London*), **130**: 499 (1931). P. M. Morse, *Phys. Rev.*, **35**: 1310 (1930). M. J. O. Strutt, "Lamésche, Mathieusche und verwandte Funktionen in Physik und Technik," Ergebnisse der Mathematik und ihrer Grenzgebiete, vol. 1, No. 3, Springer-Verlag OHG, Berlin, 1932.

[2] The situation is similar to the two-center–one-electron problem discussed in §1 of the preceding chapter. This can be solved exactly if the two centers are hydrogen nuclei with a simple coulomb potential. Nevertheless, we preferred an approximate solution, since it was more fruitful for a comparison with the procedure of Heitler and London.

more regarding a particular selected electron than the one-electron eigenfunction which pertains to the electron in question in the many-electron eigenfunction.   At this stage of the theory, the many-electron eigenfunction has really only formal significance and may be replaced by a statement regarding the distribution of the available electrons over the quantum states of the one-electron problem.   This makes it plausible why in many descriptions of the band model of solid-state theory the many-electron eigenfunctions (the so-called Slater determinants[1]) are not even written down and why, instead, the electrons are simply distributed over the band system of the one-electron problem.   We shall follow this example in §10 of this introductory representation.

In §11 we shall discuss, finally, the conclusions derived from the band model regarding the conductivity properties of a particular crystal.

§2. The Bloch Approximation for Strongly Bound Electrons

a. Construction of a Wave Function

In the method of Bloch,[2] an approximate solution of the one-electron problem (VII.1.01) just outlined is made possible by proceeding from the case of strongly bound electrons.   This has the following significance.   The energy of the electron under consideration is to be so low that, energetically, it lies deep within the funnel of potential energy created for an electron by an atom core of the lattice.   In order to pass over to a neighboring atom core, the electron must tunnel through a high potential hill (see Fig. VII.2.1). Such a transition will, hence, occur relatively rarely.   Under these circumstances, the ψ function of the electron will have approximately the same form in the neighbor-

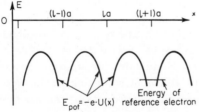

FIG. VII.2.1. Position of a strongly bound electron on the energy diagram.

hood of the lth atom core as though this core were completely isolated and the electron were the valence electron in the field of a single atom core.   In formulating these ideas mathematically, we shall restrict ourselves to a one-dimensional atomic lattice.   The essential relation-

[1] J. C. Slater, *Phys. Rev.*, **34**: 1293 (1929).

[2] F. Bloch, *Z. Physik.*, **52**: 555 (1929).

ships are brought out more clearly in this fashion.   The transfer of the results to the three-dimensional lattice will lead to no difficulties. We shall discuss molecular lattices toward the end (see page 182).

For $x \approx la$ with $l = 0, \pm 1, \pm 2, \ldots$ and a = lattice constant we obtain

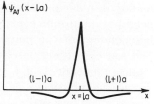

$$\psi(x) \approx \psi_{at}(x - la)   \text{(VII.2.01)}$$

The atomic eigenfunction $\psi_{at}(x - la)$ is centered about the lth lattice point and falls off rapidly with increasing distance from this lattice point (see Figs. VII.2.2 and VII.2.3).

Fig. VII.2.2. Concentration of an atomic eigenfunction ψ_{at} about the lth lattice point.

The relation (VII.2.01) will apply only in the neighborhood of the lth lattice point and cannot be extended to all of space.   Instead, in the neighborhood of another lattice point,

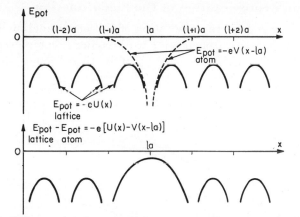

Fig. VII.2.3. Difference of the potential energy supplied by the lattice and that supplied by the lth atom.

the ψ function of the electron in question will be equal to the eigenfunction centered about this other lattice point.   Thus we are led to the formulation

$$\psi(x) = \sum_{l = -\infty}^{l = +\infty} c_l \psi_{at}(x - la)$$

Symmetry considerations alone make it possible to make a guess regarding the essential features of the coefficients c_l.   Since all atoms in the lattice are completely equivalent, the participation of a particular atomic eigenfunction cannot be larger or smaller than that of any other eigenfunction.   Accordingly, the coefficients c_l must all have the same absolute value:

$$c_l = c\, e^{j\varphi_l}$$

Furthermore, the regular arrangement of the lattice points in space makes it plausible that the phase difference $\varphi_{l+1} - \varphi_l$ between two neighboring atomic eigenfunctions $\psi_{at}(x - (l + 1)a)$ and $\psi_{at}(x - la)$ is independent of the point of the linear atom chain at which the two selected eigenfunctions happen to lie. Hence $\varphi_{l+1} - \varphi_l$ must have a value independent of l, which we can designate with ka. We shall discuss the physical meaning of the quantity k, which, for the present, may take on any real value, at a later point. We have thus arrived at the following form[1] for $\psi(x)$:

$$\psi(x) = \psi(x; k) = c \sum_{l=-\infty}^{l=+\infty} e^{jkla}\psi_{at}(x - la) \qquad (VII.2.02)$$

b. Graphic Representation of the Eigenfunction

We obtain a graphic representation of this eigenfunction if, at every point x of the linear atom chain, we imagine a complex plane perpendicular to the direction x and plot in these planes Re $\psi(x)$ and

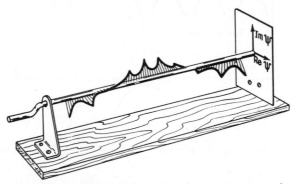

Fig. VII.2.4. Eigenfunction of an electron in a crystal.

Im $\psi(x)$ (see Fig. VII.2.4). We see that, in every unit cell, the total eigenfunction $\psi(x)$ corresponds to the atomic eigenfunction but that it is rotated progressively from unit cell to unit cell by a phase angle ka. The absolute value of $\psi(x)$ is thus the same in every unit cell, i.e., equal to the absolute value of the atomic eigenfunction ψ_{at} [apart from the as yet undetermined factor c in (VII.2.02)], so that the probability density is the same in all unit cells.

[1] The correctness of (VII.2.02) and (VII.2.03) will be further confirmed below, see p. 177.

c. Normalization of the Eigenfunctions in the Fundamental Domain

We utilize this remark for determining the undetermined factor c in (VII.2.02). The probability of finding the electron in the lth unit cell is

$$c^2 \cdot \int_{x=la-\frac{1}{2}a}^{x=la+\frac{1}{2}a} |\psi_{at}(x - la)|^2 \, dx$$

In the case here assumed of strongly bound electrons, the atomic eigenfunction $\psi_{at}(x - la)$ is concentrated about the point $x = la$. We may hence neglect the contributions of the regions $-\infty < x < la - \frac{1}{2}a$ and $la + \frac{1}{2}a < x < 1 + \infty$ to the "atomic" normalization integral

$$\int_{x=-\infty}^{x=+\infty} |\psi_{at}(x - la)|^2 \, dx = 1$$

and set

$$\int_{x=-\infty}^{x=+\infty} |\psi_{at}|^2 \, dx = \int_{x=+la-\frac{1}{2}a}^{x=+la+\frac{1}{2}a} |\psi_{at}|^2 \, dx$$

Then the probability of finding the electron in the lth unit cell becomes $c^2 \cdot 1$ and the probability of finding it in any of the G unit cells of the fundamental domain, $G \cdot c^2$. Since $\psi(x)$ is supposed to be normalized in the fundamental domain, we must put $G \cdot c^2 = 1$, so that $c = 1/\sqrt{G}$ and

$$\psi(x) = \psi(x; k) = \frac{1}{\sqrt{G}} \sum_{l=-\infty}^{l=+\infty} e^{jkla}\psi_{at}(x - la) \qquad \text{(VII.2.03)}$$

d. Fulfillment of the Requirement of Periodicity in the Fundamental Domain

Apart from the requirement of normalization, we must also fulfill the requirement of periodicity in the fundamental domain, as stated on page 165. In the one-dimensional case this takes the form

$$\psi\left(-\frac{G}{2}a\right) = \psi\left(+\frac{G}{2}a\right) \qquad \text{(VII.2.04)}$$

If we substitute (VII.2.03) in this equation, the strong concentration of the atomic eigenfunctions about their lattice point makes the term with $l = -G/2$ the only one of importance on the left and that with $l = +G/2$ the only one of importance on the right. Equation

(VII.2.04) thus reduces to

$$\frac{1}{\sqrt{G}} \, e^{jk\left(-\frac{G}{2}\right)a} \, \psi_{\mathrm{at}}(0) = \frac{1}{\sqrt{G}} \, e^{jk\left(+\frac{G}{2}\right)a} \, \psi_{\mathrm{at}}(0)$$

or

$$e^{jkGa} = 1$$

which is satisfied by

$$k = \frac{2\pi}{a} \cdot \frac{n}{G} \qquad n = \pm \text{ integer} \tag{VII.2.05}$$

One quantum state claims[1] a segment $2\pi/aG$ on the k scale.

e. Free and Reduced k Values

Of the values of k which are consistent with periodicity in the fundamental domain as given by (VII.2.05), $k = 0$ has the smallest absolute value. For it the eigenfunction $\psi(x) = \psi(x; 0)$ is real since the individual atomic eigenfunctions may be assumed to be real and since these are added without any phase rotation if $k = 0$:

$$\psi(x; 0) = \frac{1}{\sqrt{G}} \{ \cdots + \psi_{\mathrm{at}}(x + 2a) + \psi_{\mathrm{at}}(x + 1a) + \psi_{\mathrm{at}}(x)$$
$$+ \psi_{\mathrm{at}}(x - 1a) + \psi_{\mathrm{at}}(x - 2a) + \cdots \} \quad \text{(VII.2.06)}$$

For the next k values $\pm 2\pi/aG$, the ψ functions are no longer real since the individual atomic eigenfunctions are rotated by the angle $ka = \pm 2\pi/G$, which is finite though small.

For the next two k values $\pm 4\pi/aG$, the rotation $ka = \pm 4\pi/G$ is already twice as large and ψ is again complex. Then ψ becomes once again real only for the $(G/2)$th pair of values

$$k = \pm \frac{2\pi \, (G/2)}{aG} = \pm \frac{\pi}{a}$$

Here the rotation between successive atomic eigenfunctions is just $\pm \pi$, which, for the two cases $k = +\pi/a$ and $k = -\pi/a$, leads to one and the same eigenfunction

$$\psi\left(x; \pm \frac{\pi}{a}\right) = \frac{1}{\sqrt{G}} \{ \cdots + \psi_{\mathrm{at}}(x + 2a) - \psi_{\mathrm{at}}(x + 1a) + \psi_{\mathrm{at}}(x)$$
$$- \psi_{\mathrm{at}}(x - 1a) + \psi_{\mathrm{at}}(x - 2a) - \cdots \} \quad \text{(VII.2.07)}$$

[1] Here we have typical examples of statements which, by themselves, have no physical meaning since they contain the arbitrary number of cells G in the fundamental domain. In combination with other considerations they lead, however, to statements which no longer contain the arbitrary G and which are then of great physical significance. See, e.g., footnote 1 on p. 179, Eqs. (VII.10.07) to (VII.10.09) on p. 264, or the derivation of Eq. (VIII.1.07) on p. 286.

Altogether there are thus

$$1 + 2\left(\frac{G}{2} - 1\right) + 1 = 1 + G - 2 + 1 = G$$

different eigenfunctions in the k interval

$$-\frac{\pi}{a} < k \leq +\frac{\pi}{a} \qquad \text{(VII.2.08)}$$

This exhausts the totality of eigenfunctions. The next pair of values consistent with (VII.2.05), $k = \pm(\pi/a + 2\pi/aG)$, yields the phase rotations $\pm(\pi + 2\pi/G)$. These, however, are identical with

$$\pm\left(\pi + \frac{2\pi}{G} - 2\pi\right) = \mp\left(\pi - \frac{2\pi}{G}\right)$$

since in a phase rotation the addition or subtraction of a complete revolution 2π is immaterial. The two eigenfunctions with

$$k = \pm\left(\frac{\pi}{a} + \frac{2\pi}{aG}\right)$$

thus are identical with the two with $k = \mp(\pi/a - 2\pi/aG)$. However, the last two values occurred already as the pair preceding $k = \pm\pi/a$. We see thus that we can confine attention to the interval (VII.2.08) in the k values and may regard this as periodicity interval on the k scale, since outside this interval the eigenfunctions repeat themselves periodically. Thus, we obtain the same eigenfunctions for k and $k + 2\pi h/a$ with $h = \pm 1, \pm 2, \ldots$ If k is limited to the interval (VII.2.08) we also speak of a reduced k value.

f. The Interpretation of $\psi(x; k)$ as a Running Electron Wave Modulated with the Periodicity of the Lattice. The Special Cases of the Standing Waves $\psi(x; 0)$ and $\psi(x; \pm\pi/a)$

The special real cases (VII.2.06) and (VII.2.07) are particularly well suited for graphic representation (see Fig. VII.2.5). As we pass over to the time-dependent Schrödinger function

$$\psi(x, t) = \psi(x)\,e^{-iEt/\hbar} \qquad \text{(VII.2.09)}$$

we find that these real cases are, furthermore, distinguished by the fact that they represent standing waves. In general, however, the ψ function represents a running wave. We may obtain an idea of the nature of this wave by the following transformation of (VII.2.03) and (VII.2.09):

$$\psi(x,\, t) = \frac{1}{\sqrt{G}} \sum_{l=-\infty}^{l=+\infty} e^{jkla}\psi_{\mathrm{at}}(x - la) \cdot e^{-j\frac{E}{\hbar}t}$$

$$= \frac{1}{\sqrt{G}} \sum_{l=-\infty}^{l=+\infty} e^{-jk(x-la)}\psi_{\mathrm{at}}(x - la) \cdot e^{j\left(kx - \frac{E}{\hbar}t\right)}$$

$$\psi(x,\, t) = u(x;\, k) \cdot e^{j(kx-\omega t)} \tag{VII.2.10}$$

with
$$\omega = \frac{E}{\hbar} \tag{VII.2.11}$$

and
$$u(x;\, k) = \frac{1}{\sqrt{G}} \sum_{l=-\infty}^{l=+\infty} e^{-jk(x-la)}\psi_{\mathrm{at}}(x - la) \tag{VII.2.12}$$

If we compare (VII.2.10) with the usual representations of a plane wave

$$a\, e^{j(kx-\omega t)} = a\, e^{j2\pi\left(\frac{x}{\lambda} - ft\right)} = a\, e^{jk(x-ct)} \tag{VII.2.13}$$

we see that the amplitude of the electron wave in the periodic potential

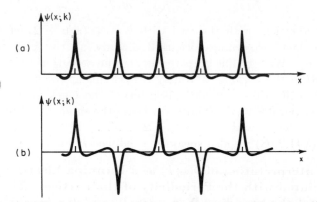

Fig. VII.2.5. The eigenfunctions are real at the band edges (in the one-dimensional atomic lattice). (a) $k = 0$: state at the lower edge of the band if the exchange integral is negative. (b) $k = \pi/a$: state at the upper edge of the band if the exchange integral is negative.

field is not independent of position, but is modulated with the periodicity of the lattice. Thus, (VII.2.12) shows that the amplitude $u(x;\, k)$ has the periodicity of the lattice

$$u(x + a;\, k) \equiv u(x;\, k) \tag{VII.2.14}$$

Equation (VII.2.14) is proved by substituting the definition of $u(x;\, k)$ given by (VII.2.12) and introducing a new summation index

$l' \equiv l - 1$. We see, furthermore, that the k values, which have been rather colorless so far, represent the wave number $k = 2\pi/\lambda$.

It was shown on page 171 that the two k values k and $k + 2\pi h/a$ lead to the same eigenfunction $\psi(x)$. This is possible only if the modulation factors with lattice periodicity $u(x; k)$ and $u(x; k + 2\pi h/a)$ are related by

$$u\left(x; k + 2\pi \frac{h}{a}\right) = u(x; k)\, e^{-j2\pi \frac{h}{a}x}$$

A check with (VII.2.12) confirms this. Although the substitution $k \to k + 2\pi h/a$ does not change the eigenfunction itself,[1] this does not apply to the modulation factor $u(x; k)$ by itself.

g. Perturbation Calculation

So far we have dealt in detail with the setting up and the character of an eigenfunction for an electron in a periodic potential field. However, since we have based the eigenfunction (VII.2.03) only on plausible considerations of symmetry, it is now high time to confirm the form (VII.2.03) by a perturbation calculation. Furthermore, only such a perturbation calculation can supply the energy eigenvalues which belong to the guessed eigenfunctions, and these eigenvalues are always of greatest importance in quantum-mechanical considerations.

The procedure which we shall employ for the approximate solution of the Schrödinger equation for an electron in a crystal

$$-\frac{\hbar^2}{2m}\frac{d^2}{dx^2}\psi - (E + e\overline{U}(x))\psi = 0 \qquad \text{(VII.1.01)}$$

will become plainer if we forget about our past considerations and start once again from the beginning.

Accordingly, we write for the unknown eigenfunction $\psi(x)$ of the electron in the crystal

$$\psi(x) = \sum_{l=-\infty}^{l=+\infty} c_l \psi_{\text{at}}(x - la)$$

and seek to determine the unknown coefficients c_l. Here we proceed just as though the atomic eigenfunctions $\psi_{\text{at}}(x - la)$ centered about the several lattice points constituted a complete orthogonal system or as in the determination of the Fourier coefficients in a Fourier expan-

---

[1] Nor does it change the energy eigenvalue E, as we shall deduce from Eq. (VII.2.22).

sion.[1] Thus we substitute the expansion in the Schrödinger equation (VII.1.01):

$$\sum_{l=-\infty}^{l=+\infty} c_l \left\{ -\frac{\hbar^2}{2m}\frac{d^2}{dx^2}\psi_{at}(x - la) - (E + eU(x))\psi_{at}(x - la) \right\} = 0$$

(VII.2.15)

Now the atomic eigenfunction $\psi_{at}(x - la)$ satisfies the Schrödinger equation of the isolated atom with the atomic eigenvalue E_{at} and the potential $V(x - la)$ of the lth atom core

$$-\frac{\hbar^2}{2m}\frac{d^2}{dx^2}\psi_{at}(x - la) - (E_{at} + eV(x - la))\psi_{at}(x - la) = 0 \quad \text{(VII.2.16)}$$

If this is utilized in (VII.2.15), we find

$$\sum_{l=-\infty}^{l=+\infty} c_l\{(E - E_{at})\psi_{at}(x - la) + e(U(x) - V(x - la))\psi_{at}(x - la)\} = 0$$

We now multiply with an arbitrary atomic eigenfunction $\psi_{at}^*(x - ra)$ and integrate over the fundamental domain $-Ga/2 < x < +Ga/2$:

$$\sum_{l=-\infty}^{l=+\infty} c_l \left\{ (E - E_{at}) \cdot \int_{x=-\frac{G}{2}a}^{x=+\frac{G}{2}a} \psi_{at}^*(x - ra)\psi_{at}(x - la)\, dx \right.$$

$$\left. + e \int_{x=-\frac{G}{2}a}^{x=+\frac{G}{2}a} \psi_{at}^*(x - ra)(U(x) - V(x - la))\psi_{at}(x - la)\, dx \right\} = 0 \quad \text{(VII.2.17)}$$

Bloch now puts

$$\int_{x=-\frac{G}{2}a}^{x=+\frac{G}{2}a} \psi_{at}^*(x - ra) \cdot \psi_{at}(x - la) \cdot dx \approx \delta_{rl} = \begin{cases} 1 & \text{for } r = l \\ 0 & \text{for } r \neq l \end{cases}$$

(VII.2.18)

since the factors in the integrand which are concentrated about the

---

[1] The deeper justification of this procedure rests in the fact that we obtain in this manner the best solution of a variation problem equivalent to the Schrödinger equation, as in the Ritz procedure. See, e.g., F. Hund in H. Geiger and K. Scheel, "Handbuch der Physik," vol. XXIV, part 1, p. 575, Springer-Verlag OHG, Berlin, 1933.

points $x = ra$ and $x = la$ coincide only for $r = l$ and since the integrand can attain appreciable values only in these cases. For $r \neq l$ one of the two factors has dropped to such a low value at every point x that no appreciable contributions can result. On the other hand, for $r = l$ the integral is practically[1] the normalization integral of the atomic eigenfunction ψ_{at}, and hence $= 1$. For the second type

of integral $\displaystyle\int_{x=-\frac{G}{2}a}^{x=+\frac{G}{2}a} \psi_{at}^*(x - ra)[U(x) - V(x - la)]\psi_{at}(x - la)\, dx$ in

(VII.2.17) Bloch retains the three cases $l = r + 1, l = r$, and $l = r - 1$ (see Fig. VII.2.6). He does not content himself with the case $l = r$

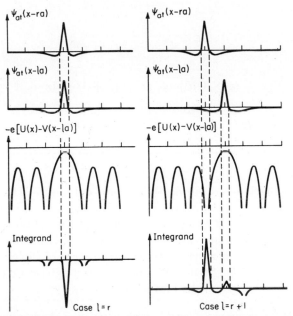

FIG. VII.2.6. Concerning the calculation of the "coulomb energy" and the "exchange integral."

since, although the factors $\psi_{at}(x - ra)$ and $\psi_{at}(x - la)$ coincide here, the central factor $[U(x) - V(x - la)]$ becomes very small in the very region $x \approx ra = la$ in which these two factors contribute materially (see Fig. VII.2.3). Hence the integrals with $l = r + 1$ and with

[1] In the ranges $-\infty < x < -Ga/2$ and $+Ga/2 < x < +\infty$ which are missing as compared with the normalization integral, the contributions are negligible because of the rapid falling off of $\psi_{at}(x)$.

$l = r - 1$ must be retained in addition to the integral with $l = r$, since in these two instances also at least two of the three factors in the integrand, namely, now $\psi_{\mathrm{at}}(x - ra)$ and $[U(x) - V(x - la)]$, are appreciably large in the region $x \approx ra$. Incidentally, the symmetry of the atomic eigenfunctions about "their" lattice point and the symmetry of the potential variations U and V lead to equal values for the integrals[1] with $l = r + 1$ and $l = r - 1$.

We put

$$-e \cdot \int_{x=-\frac{G}{2}a}^{x=+\frac{G}{2}a} \cdots dx \approx \int_{x=-\infty}^{x=+\infty} \psi_{\mathrm{at}}^*(x - ra)$$

$$\cdot (-e)[U(x) - V(x - ra)] \cdot \psi_{\mathrm{at}}(x - ra) = C \qquad \text{(VII.2.19)}$$

$$-e \cdot \int_{x=-\frac{G}{2}a}^{x=+\frac{G}{2}a} \cdots dx \approx \int_{x=-\infty}^{x=+\infty} \psi_{\mathrm{at}}^*(x - ra) \cdot (-e)$$

$$\cdot [U(x) - V(x - (r + 1)a)] \cdot \psi_{\mathrm{at}}(x - (r + 1)a)\, dx = A \qquad \text{(VII.2.20)}$$

$$-e \cdot \int_{x=-\frac{G}{2}a}^{x=+\frac{G}{2}a} \cdots dx \approx \int_{x=-\infty}^{x=+\infty} \psi_{\mathrm{at}}^*(x - ra) \cdot (-e)$$

$$\cdot [U(x) - V(x - (r - 1)a)] \cdot \psi_{\mathrm{at}}(x - (r - 1)a)\, dx = A$$

These designations are supposed to point out that (VII.2.19) represents the "coulomb energy" of the electron considered in the field of the perturbation $-e[U(x) - V(x - ra)]$ of the potential energy, whereas (VII.2.20) is the "exchange integral" (*Austauschintegral*) of this potential-energy perturbation for a transition of the electron from one atom core to its neighbor. We shall return to an intuitive interpretation of the exchange integral later (page 178).

[1] Figure VII.2.6 gives only a graphic representation of the reasoning of Bloch. We shall not discuss further whether the conditions in an actual case are such as to justify the argument quantitatively. A test of this question would lead to a rather difficult study of the variation of the lattice potential and would also, e.g., have to treat separately the case in which the reference electron is a valence electron in the outermost shell and that in which it is strongly bound in the inner shells. In the last instance in particular, it is questionable whether the approximation of Heitler and London is not to be preferred to the procedure of Hund and Mulliken.

It should be emphasized at this point that the Bloch approximation represents, historically, the first treatment of electrons in a crystal. Here qualitative traits are of primary importance; the results can scarcely be regarded as quantitatively significant.

With (VII.2.18), (VII.2.19), and (VII.2.20), Eq. (VII.2.17) leads to

$$\cdots +0 + 0 \cdots + c_{r-1}\{(E - E_{at}) \cdot 0 - A\} + c_r\{(E - E_{at}) \cdot 1 - C\}$$
$$+ c_{r+1}\{(E - E_{at}) \cdot 0 - A\} + 0 + \cdots = 0$$

or
$$-Ac_{r-1} + \{E - (E_{at} + C)\}c_r - Ac_{r+1} = 0 \qquad \text{(VII.2.21)}$$

Here the subscript r may be given any value $0, \pm 1, \pm 2, \ldots$ leading to an infinite number of linear Eqs. (VII.2.21) for the determination of an infinite number of unknowns c_r.

For their solution we may note the following: Since no terms occur which are free from the unknowns c_r, we are dealing with a homogeneous system of equations. A solution which is not identically equal to zero exists only if the determinant of this system of equations vanishes. This leads to an equation for determining the energy parameter E. If E is one of the roots of this secular equation, a nonvanishing solution becomes possible. It is determined except for a common factor which is fixed by the normalization requirement for

$$\psi(x) = \sum_{l=-\infty}^{l=+\infty} c_l \psi_{at}(x - la)$$

However, we shall not carry through a systematic solution of Eqs. (VII.2.21) but shall utilize instead the previously (pages 168 and 169) guessed values of the c_r, namely,

$$c_r = \frac{1}{\sqrt{G}} e^{jkra}$$

and shall verify that these satisfy the infinite system of linear equations (VII.2.21) if the energy parameter E has the value[1]

$$E = E_{at} + C + 2A \cos ka \qquad \text{(VII.2.22)}$$

For the left side of (VII.2.21), we obtain

$$-A \frac{1}{\sqrt{G}} e^{jk(r-1)a} + \{2A \cos ka\} \cdot \frac{1}{\sqrt{G}} e^{jkra} - A \frac{1}{\sqrt{G}} e^{jk(r+1)a}$$
$$= \frac{A}{\sqrt{G}} e^{jkra}[-e^{-jka} + 2 \cos ka - e^{jka}]$$

The bracketed term makes this in fact equal to zero independently of the running index r.

[1] It is of course decisive for the verification that the running index r no longer appears in the value (VII.2.22), i.e., that with a single value of E all equations of the infinite system (VII.2.21) can be satisfied by the system of values

$$c_r = \frac{1}{\sqrt{G}} e^{jkra} \qquad r = 0, \pm 1, \pm 2, \ldots$$

So far we have confirmed the values of the coefficients guessed previously as well as the form (VII.2.02) or (VII.2.03) of the eigenfunction $\psi(x)$ of the electron in the crystal. In addition to this, the energy spectrum of the electron in the crystal has been determined as given by (VII.2.22).

h. Physical Interpretation of the Formula for the Energy (VII.2.22)

The result (VII.2.22) is readily understood physically. The atomic eigenvalue E_{at} is changed first of all by the fact that the potential energy $-eV(x - la)$ of a single atom core is supplemented by a perturbation $-e[U(x) - V(x - la)]$. In the total energy there appears, accordingly, the mean value C of this potential-energy perturbation weighted with the probability density $|\psi_{at}(x - ra)|^2$. C is negative since, in the integrand of (VII.2.19), the central factor $-e[U(x) - V(x - ra)]$ is negative (see Fig. VII.2.3) and the product $|\psi_{at}(x - ra)|^2$ of the other two factors is always positive. The negative term C in (VII.2.22) thus corresponds to the stronger binding of the reference electron in the field of many atom cores as compared with the binding in the field of a single atom core.

The most important part of (VII.2.22) is, however, the third term $2A \cos ka$. This exchange energy arises from the fact that the reference electron does not remain at one atom core but tunnels through the potential hill to the neighboring atom from time to time and spends, on the average, an equal amount of time at every atom core.[1]

In the section Free and Reduced k Values (page 170) we have seen that there are G different eigenfunctions

$$\psi(x) = \psi(x; k) = \frac{1}{\sqrt{G}} \sum_{l=-\infty}^{l=+\infty} e^{jkla}\psi_{at}(x - la) \quad \text{(VII.2.03)}$$

which differ in the value of the wave number k,

$$k = \frac{2\pi}{a} \cdot \frac{n}{G} \qquad n = \pm \text{ integer} \qquad \text{(VII.2.05)}$$

In order to cover all the eigenfunctions, n had to traverse only the interval

$$-\frac{G}{2} < n \leq +\frac{G}{2}$$

---

[1] See, e.g., S. Flügge and H. Marschall, "Rechenmethoden der Quantentheorie," pp. 162–164, Springer-Verlag OHG, Berlin, 1947; or H. A. Bethe in Geiger and Scheel, *op. cit.*, vol. XXIV, part 1, p. 335. Here further details are also given concerning the relation between exchange energy and frequency of change of location.

k traversing at the same time the interval of the reduced wave numbers

$$-\frac{\pi}{a} < k \le +\frac{\pi}{a} \qquad \text{(VII.2.08)}$$

Outside this interval, the same eigenfunctions recurred periodically. Correspondingly, (VII.2.22) shows that also no new energy eigenvalues appear outside the periodicity interval (VII.2.08). Thus the atomic eigenvalue E_{at} splits up, through the simultaneous action of the G atoms of the fundamental domain, into $G/2$ twofold eigenvalues (VII.2.22), since the same eigenvalue E belongs to $k = +2\pi n/aG$ and to $k = -2\pi n/aG$. Since G is supposed to be a very large number, the bringing together of G separate atoms changes the atomic eigenvalue E_{at} into a quasi-continuous band of $G/2$ twofold eigenvalues or G

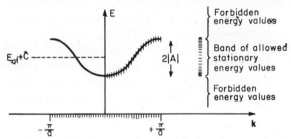

Fig. VII.2.7. Variation of the energy value E with the wave number k (for negative exchange integral, $A < 0$). It is a peculiarity of the linear atomic lattice that the density of states is least in the middle of the band and increases toward both band boundaries. The converse applies in general for actual three-dimensional lattices.

"states." [See Fig. VII.2.7. If we omit the limitation on k by (VII.2.08), we obtain Figs. VII.3.11 and VII.3.12 in §3. This representation will prove advantageous in §6 and §7.] According to the Pauli principle, every one of these states may be occupied by two electrons with opposite spins so that the band can accommodate $2(2G/2) = 2G$ electrons or two electrons per unit cell or per atom.[1] However, this remark oversteps the boundaries of this §2, in which we are not yet concerned with the many-electron problem,[2] but only with an approximate solution of the preliminary one-electron problem.

The boundaries of the band are formed by $ka = 0$ and $ka = \pm\pi$. These two values of the wave number have played a special role before, in so far as they led to the standing waves of Fig. VII.2.5. We

[1] In this form the statement becomes independent of the arbitrary number of cells G in the fundamental domain and becomes thus physically meaningful.

[2] This will first be taken up in §10.

conclude, hence, that standing waves correspond to the boundaries of the band for the linear atomic lattice here considered. At the edges of the band we have, furthermore,

$$\Delta E \sim (\Delta k)^2 \qquad \text{(VII.2.23)}$$

as follows from (VII.2.22) or Fig. VII.2.7.

i. Band Spectrum of a Crystal, Degenerate Atomic Eigenvalues, Application to Three-dimensional Lattices

So far we have been concerned with a single atomic eigenvalue E_{at}. However, the splitting up into a band of eigenvalues, as isolated atoms are brought together in a crystal, applies equally for all eigenvalues of the atom. Thus we obtain from the discrete spectrum of the atom a band spectrum of the crystal, in which bands of allowed and forbidden energy values alternate (see Fig. VII.2.8).

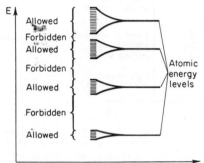

FIG. VII.2.8. The splitting of the discrete atomic spectrum into the band spectrum of the crystal.

Furthermore, it should be pointed out that it was assumed in the preceding considerations that only one atomic eigenfunction $\psi_{\mathrm{at}}(x)$ belonged to the selected atomic eigenvalue E_{at}, so that the atomic eigenvalue E_{at} was not degenerate. The rule that a band accommodates two electrons per unit cell was derived with this assumption. For degenerate atomic eigenvalues—and these are in fact the rule—the situation becomes different. However, we shall not discuss further at this point the number of available places in the band since for a three-dimensional lattice the circumstances can become quite complex (see, however, §11). We use this instead as a first indication that caution is advised in applying the several results to the three-dimensional lattice.

Thus we have, e.g., for the linear atomic lattice just treated two different eigenfunctions for one and the same eigenvalue E, namely, a wave running toward the right and one running toward the left. Already in the two-dimensional and particularly in the three-dimensional lattice, many electron waves running in all possible directions belong, in general, to a single eigenvalue. Furthermore, not all the eigenfunctions belonging to the lowest and highest energies, i.e., to the band boundaries, need be standing waves. For example, for a face-centered cubic lattice this is not so for the upper band boundary (for a negative exchange integral). Furthermore, the relation (VII.2.23) does not apply at this boundary.

In the three-dimensional case, the periodicity interval $-\pi/a < k \leq +\pi/a$ on the k scale found for the linear lattice is replaced by a periodicity polyhedron in $\mathbf{k}$-vector space. Outside this polyhedron, eigenvalues and eigenfunctions repeat themselves periodically. For example, the Bloch approximation yields for a quadratic point lattice an E surface above the $(\mathbf{k}_z, \mathbf{k}_y)$ plane subdivided into periodicity squares, as shown in Fig. VII.2.9. As already mentioned, this view

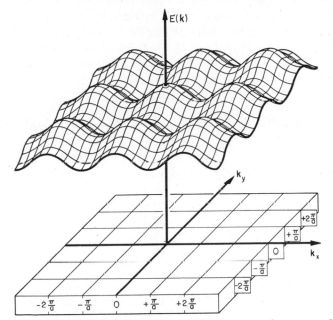

FIG. VII.2.9. Variation of the energy E with the wave number vector $\mathbf{k}$ for the two-dimensional case (quadratic point lattice).

of the $E(k)$ dependence will prove advantageous in §6 and §7. This periodicity polyhedron is frequently, and wrongly, identified with the so-called first Brillouin zone in $\mathbf{k}$ space, which will be discussed in §3. In §11, the diamond lattice will provide an example in which the Bloch periodicity polyhedron and the first Brillouin zone differ (see pages 273ff.).

In the one-dimensional case a quantum state claims a segment $2\pi/(aG)$ of the k scale, as we found on page 170. In the three-dimensional case, correspondingly, a volume $[2\pi/aG]^3$ of $\mathbf{k}$ space is ascribed to a quantum state. If we introduce the volume $V_{\text{fund}} = (Ga)^3$ of the

fundamental domain considered, the volume in **k** space ascribed to
one quantum state becomes simply $(2\pi)^3/V_{\text{fund.}}$[1]

In the three-dimensional lattice we must note, furthermore, whether
the atomic eigenvalue pertains to an s, a p, or a d term. Thus, in a
simple cubic lattice, an atomic p eigenvalue with its three p eigenfunctions splits up into three bands.[2]   Energetically these three bands
coincide completely, however, an extreme example of band overlap,
which will be mentioned repeatedly in §3.

Finally it should be pointed out that the form (VII.2.03) of the
eigenfunctions applies only for simple translation lattices.[3]   For lattices with a basis, such as molecular lattices,[3] $\psi(x)$ must be written as
a sum of several summations (VII.2.02)—one summation for each
sublattice.   The coefficients of the individual summations (VII.2.02)
must then be determined by the perturbation calculation.   This has
at times been overlooked in the literature.[4]

§3. Brillouin's Approximation for Weakly Bound Electrons

While even the strongly bound electrons considered in the Bloch
approximation (see Fig. VII.2.1)
do not remain permanently at one
atom because of the tunnel effect,
the electrons of high energy considered in the Brillouin approximation (see Fig. VII.3.1)[5] can fly
through the entire lattice almost
like free electrons.   Their eigenfunctions will be accordingly very
nearly plane waves $e^{j(\mathbf{k}\cdot\mathbf{r})}$.   We thus
face a problem very similar to that
of the bombardment of a crystal with X-rays or cathode rays.   The

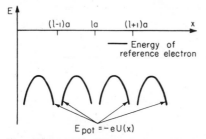

FIG. VII.3.1. Position of a quasi-free
electron in the energy diagram.

[1] To see how, in the application of this statement in Chap. VIII, §1, the volume
of the arbitrary fundamental domain drops out, see the derivation of Eq. (VIII.1.07)
on pp. 283 to 286.

[2] See, e.g., H. A. Bethe in Geiger and Scheel, *op. cit.*, vol. XXIV, part 2, pp.
401–404.

[3] For a further discussion of this concept, see pp. 269 to 271.

[4] H. A. Bethe gives in Geiger and Scheel, *op. cit.*, vol. XXIV, part 2, p. 397, a
formula (12.17) for the energy spectrum of a lattice with a basis in which apparently account has not been taken of the above-mentioned circumstance.

[5] See footnote 2, p. 192.

phenomena occurring in this instance are well known,[1] and we shall report on them first.   The results of Brillouin's perturbation calculation for weakly bound electrons then become highly plausible physically, so that we can omit the perturbation calculation itself.

a. Diffraction of a Three-dimensional Wave by a Linear Series of Points

We begin with the diffraction phenomenon resulting from the incidence of a plane wave on a linear series of points in a direction forming a direction cosine $\alpha = \cos \varphi$ with the row of points (see Fig. VII.3.2). Every lattice point emits a spherical wave.   There are then several directions in the plane of the drawing in which the diffracted spherical waves are superposed at infinite distance with the phase differences $\cdots -2 \cdot 2\pi,\ -1 \cdot 2\pi,\ 0,\ +1 \cdot 2\pi,$ $+2 \cdot 2\pi \cdots$ and hence reinforce each other.   In these directions, which form the direction cosines $\alpha_{-2},\ \alpha_{-1},\ \alpha_0,\ \alpha_{+1},\ \alpha_{+2}$ with the row of points, the diffracted beams of

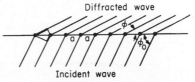

Diffracted wave

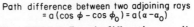

Incident wave

Path difference between two adjoining rays
$= a\,(\cos \phi - \cos \phi_0) = a\,(\alpha - \alpha_0)$

Fig. VII.3.2. Laue's diffraction condition, $a(\alpha - \alpha_0) = h\lambda$.

-2d, -1st, 0, $+1$st, $+2$d order are observed.   Figure VII.3.2 yields Laue's interference condition

$$a(\alpha_{h_1} - \alpha) = h_1\lambda \qquad h_1 = 0,\ \pm 1,\ \pm 2,\ \cdots \qquad (\text{VII.3.01})$$

For the direction α_{h_1} of the diffracted beam of the order h_1, we obtain therefore

$$\alpha_{h_1} = \alpha + h_1 \frac{\lambda}{a} \qquad h_1 = 0,\ \pm 1,\ \pm 2,\ \ldots \qquad (\text{VII.3.02})$$

Since, however, $|\alpha_{h_1}|$, as a direction cosine, cannot exceed unity, not all solutions (VII.3.02) are physically meaningful, but only a limited number of them, up to a certain positive and a certain negative limit of h_1, depending on the smallness of λ/a.   We see thus that for an arbitrary, but sufficiently small, wavelength there is a finite number of diffracted beams if we limit ourselves to the plane of the drawing of Fig. VII.3.2, i.e., to the plane of incidence.   This is, however, not at all necessary.   The interference condition (VII.3.01) for the in-phase superposition of the diffracted spherical waves can be fulfilled equally well for directions which do not lie in the plane of incidence.   The only

---

[1] We refer here to the excellent presentations of P. P. Ewald, "Kristalle und Röntgenstrahlen," Springer-Verlag OHG, Berlin, 1923, and in Geiger and Scheel, *op. cit.*, vol. XXIII, part 2.

thing that matters is the angle φ_{h_1} between the diffracted beam and the direction of the linear point lattice. We thus see that all diffracted beams of the same, e.g., of the second order,[1] lie on a cone with a half-aperture angle φ_2 (Fig. VII.3.3).

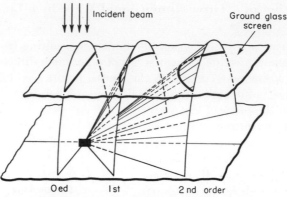

FIG. VII.3.3. The diffraction cones of the linear lattice, for an incident beam perpendicular to the lattice axis. (From P. P. Ewald, "Kristalle und Röntgen-strahlen," p. 43, Springer-Verlag OHG, Berlin, 1923.)

In summary, a one-dimensional point lattice in three-dimensional space will diffract an infinite number of beams from an incident plane wave of arbitrary direction and arbitrary (though sufficiently small) wavelength. All beams of any one order lie on an interference cone whose axis coincides with the direction of the point lattice.

b. Diffraction of a Three-dimensional Plane Wave by a Two-dimensional Point Lattice

We now pass over to a two-dimensional, e.g., quadratic, point lattice in three-dimensional space. Again, in the direction of a diffracted beam, the spherical waves diffracted by all lattice points must be superposed in phase. If this is checked first for the lattice points which form a linear point lattice in the direction of the x axis, we arrive again at Laue's condition (VII.3.01), where α_{h_1} and α are now the direction cosines with respect to the x axis. Hence, once again, cones of order 0, ± 1, ± 2, . . . would be diffracted from a wave of arbitrary direction of incidence and arbitrary (though sufficiently small) wavelength. However, it is here not at all certain that the effects proceeding from parallel series of points 1, 2, 3 (see Fig. VII.3.4) will also be in phase and hence reinforce each other.

We can also state that a gathering of the points of the quadratic

[1] That is, $h_1 = +2$.

lattice in the point series 1', 2', 3' parallel to the y axis is equally as valid as their previous grouping in the point series 1, 2, 3 . . . parallel to the x axis and that with the former grouping diffraction cones of the order 0, ±1, ±2, . . . about the y axis are obtained if a Laue condition

$$a(\beta_{h_2} - \beta) = h_2\lambda \qquad (VII.3.03)$$

for the direction cosines β_{h_2} and β with respect to the y axis is fulfilled.

A cooperation of all lattice points in a particular direction α_{h_1}, β_{h_2} will take place only if both condition (VII.3.01) and condition (VII.3.03) are fulfilled.   Geometrically, this means that the direction of diffraction of the order h_1, h_2 must lie both on the h_1th diffraction cone about the x axis and the h_2th diffraction cone about the y axis.   Thus the only directions of diffraction remaining for the two-dimensional point lattice in three-dimensional space for arbitrary direction and wavelength of the incident waves are given by the two straight lines of intersection of the h_1th cone about the x axis and the h_2th cone about the y axis.   Algebraically this is expressed by the fact that (VII.3.01) and (VII.3.03) are two equations for the two unknowns α_{h_1} and β_{h_2}, which are herewith completely determined.   It is true that, to fix a direction in space completely, three direction cosines are required; the third direction cosine γ is obtained from the equation

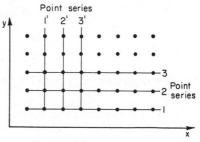

FIG. VII.3.4. The diffraction problem at a quadratic point lattice.

$$\alpha^2 + \beta^2 + \gamma^2 = 1 \qquad (VII.3.04)$$

which applies for the direction cosines for orthogonal axes.[1]

Since this prescribes a value only to γ^2, not to γ itself, the sign of γ is still undetermined, so that the two Laue conditions (VII.3.01) and (VII.3.03) select two directions in space for the diffracted beam.

c. Diffraction of a Three-dimensional Plane Wave by a Three-dimensional Point Lattice

In similar fashion we must demand of the diffracted beams of a three-dimensional point lattice in three-dimensional space that they be

---

[1] For nonorthogonal axes we would obtain a general condition

$$a\alpha^2 + b\beta^2 + c\gamma^2 + 2d\alpha\beta + 2e\beta\gamma + 2f\gamma\alpha = 1$$

instead of the condition (VII.3.04), which may be regarded as "transformed to principal axes."

the intersections of three cones, e.g., about the x, the y, and the z axis. Since, however, in general, three cones do not intersect in a common straight line, we can conclude that for a three-dimensional point lattice in three-dimensional space an incident wave of arbitrary direction and arbitrary wavelength will not give rise to any diffracted beams.

Algebraically this circumstance is expressed by the fact that a third Laue condition

$$a(\gamma_{h_3} - \gamma) = h_3\lambda \tag{VII.3.05}$$

is added to (VII.3.01) and (VII.3.03) and that, then, (VII.3.01), (VII.3.03), and (VII.3.05) represent three equations for the three unknowns $\alpha_{h_1}, \beta_{h_2}, \gamma_{h_3}$. These equations always have solutions. However, these solutions will satisfy the necessary side condition

$$\alpha_{h_1}^2 + \beta_{h_2}^2 + \gamma_{h_3}^2 = 1 \tag{VII.3.06}$$

for the direction cosines with orthogonal axes[1] only in rare discrete cases.

We can summarize our review of the diffraction phenomena of point lattices as follows: A one-dimensional point lattice in three-dimensional space diffracts an infinite number of beams of a particular order for arbitrary direction and arbitrary (though sufficiently small) wavelength of the incident wave; a two-dimensional point lattice in three-dimensional space produces under the same circumstances only two diffracted beams; and a three-dimensional point lattice in three-dimensional space produces in general, i.e., for arbitrary direction and arbitrary wavelength of the incident wave, no diffracted beams whatever.

d. The Subdivision of k Space into the Brillouin Zones

The so-called Brillouin zone construction is a means of seeing quickly under what circumstances, i.e., for what directions of incidence and what wavelengths, a three-dimensional point lattice produces a diffracted beam. To arrive at this construction we first write the three Laue conditions (VII.3.01), (VII.3.03), and (VII.3.05) in the following form:

$$\frac{1}{2\pi}\left(\frac{2\pi}{\lambda}\alpha' - \frac{2\pi}{\lambda}\alpha\right) = h_1 \cdot \frac{1}{a_1} + h_2 \cdot 0 + h_3 \cdot 0 \tag{VII.3.07}$$

$$\frac{1}{2\pi}\left(\frac{2\pi}{\lambda}\beta' - \frac{2\pi}{\lambda}\beta\right) = h_1 \cdot 0 + h_2 \cdot \frac{1}{a_2} + h_3 \cdot 0 \tag{VII.3.08}$$

$$\frac{1}{2\pi}\left(\frac{2\pi}{\lambda}\gamma' - \frac{2\pi}{\lambda}\gamma\right) = h_1 \cdot 0 + h_2 \cdot 0 + h_3 \cdot \frac{1}{a_3} \tag{VII.3.09}$$

[1] See footnote on page 185.

Here we have designated the direction cosines α_{h_1}, β_{h_2}, γ_{h_3} of the diffracted beam simply with α', β', γ'. Furthermore, we shall base the following treatment right away on the general translation lattice with three oblique axes $\mathbf{a}_1$, $\mathbf{a}_2$, $\mathbf{a}_3$.

In (VII.3.07), (VII.3.08), and (VII.3.09), $2\pi\alpha/\lambda$, $2\pi\beta/\lambda$, $2\pi\gamma/\lambda$ are the perpendicular projections of the wave vector $\mathbf{k}$ of the incident wave on the three translation axes $\mathbf{a}_1$, $\mathbf{a}_2$, $\mathbf{a}_3$. The same applies for $2\pi\alpha'/\lambda$ . . . with reference to the wave vector $\mathbf{k}'$ of the diffracted wave. Furthermore, we introduce, in view of the right side of Eqs. (VII.3.07) to (VII.3.09), the three vectors $\mathbf{b}_1$, $\mathbf{b}_2$, $\mathbf{b}_3$ by the requirement that, e.g., the perpendicular projections of the vector $\mathbf{b}_1$ with reference to the three translation axes $\mathbf{a}_1$, $\mathbf{a}_2$, $\mathbf{a}_3$ be equal to $1/a_1$, 0, 0.[1] Thus $\mathbf{b}_1$ must satisfy the three equations

$$\mathbf{b}_1 \cdot \frac{\mathbf{a}_1}{a_1} = \frac{1}{a_1} \qquad \mathbf{b}_1 \cdot \frac{\mathbf{a}_2}{a_2} = 0 \qquad \mathbf{b}_1 \cdot \frac{\mathbf{a}_3}{a_3} = 0$$

or
$$\mathbf{b}_1 \cdot \mathbf{a}_1 = 1 \qquad \mathbf{b}_1 \cdot \mathbf{a}_2 = 0 \qquad \mathbf{b}_1 \cdot \mathbf{a}_3 = 0 \qquad \text{(VII.3.10)}$$

Correspondingly, $\mathbf{b}_2$ and $\mathbf{b}_3$ must fulfill

$$\mathbf{b}_2 \cdot \mathbf{a}_1 = 0 \qquad \mathbf{b}_2 \cdot \mathbf{a}_2 = 1 \qquad \mathbf{b}_2 \cdot \mathbf{a}_3 = 0 \qquad \text{(VII.3.11)}$$
$$\mathbf{b}_3 \cdot \mathbf{a}_1 = 0 \qquad \mathbf{b}_3 \cdot \mathbf{a}_2 = 0 \qquad \mathbf{b}_3 \cdot \mathbf{a}_3 = 1 \qquad \text{(VII.3.12)}$$

The factors of h_1 in (VII.3.07), (VII.3.08), and (VII.3.09) are also the perpendicular projections of $\mathbf{b}_1$ on the three axes $\mathbf{a}_1$, $\mathbf{a}_2$, $\mathbf{a}_3$. The same applies for the factors of h_2 and h_3 with respect to the vectors $\mathbf{b}_2$ and $\mathbf{b}_3$. Hence we can combine the three Laue conditions in the vector equation

$$\frac{1}{2\pi}(\mathbf{k}' - \mathbf{k}) = h_1\mathbf{b}_1 + h_2\mathbf{b}_2 + h_3\mathbf{b}_3 = \mathbf{h} \qquad \begin{aligned} h_1 &= 0, \pm 1, \pm 2, \ldots \\ h_2 &= 0, \pm 1, \pm 2, \ldots \\ h_3 &= 0, \pm 1, \pm 2, \ldots \end{aligned}$$

$$\text{(VII.3.13)}$$

It is true that this vectorial Laue condition has for arbitrary $\mathbf{k}$ a solution

$$\frac{1}{2\pi}\mathbf{k}' = \frac{1}{2\pi}\mathbf{k} + \mathbf{h} \qquad \text{(VII.3.14)}$$

However, in order that $\mathbf{k}'$ may be the wave vector of a diffracted wave, its absolute value $|\mathbf{k}'| = 2\pi/\lambda$ must be equal to the absolute value $|\mathbf{k}| = 2\pi/\lambda$ since the wavelength of the diffracted wave must be equal

[1] $\mathbf{b}_1$, $\mathbf{b}_2$, and $\mathbf{b}_3$ form the so-called reciprocal lattice.

to that of the incident wave. Thus (VII.3.14) has the side condition

$$|\mathbf{k}'| = |\mathbf{k}| \qquad (VII.3.15)$$

which corresponds to the earlier side condition (VII.3.04). A diffracted wave of order h_1, h_2, h_3 exists only when both Eqs. (VII.3.14) and (VII.3.15) are satisfied by the one unknown $\mathbf{k}'$.

We shall now rephrase the question of page 186, namely, for what directions of incidence and what wavelengths a three-dimensional point lattice forms a diffracted beam, in the more restricted form, under what circumstances a beam of a particular order h_1, h_2, h_3 is produced. Then the vector $\mathbf{h}$ in the Laue condition (VII.3.13) is fixed. The addition of the side condition (VII.3.15) requires now that $\mathbf{k}'/(2\pi)$ and

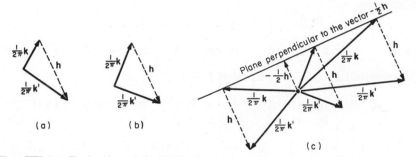

Fig. VII.3.5. Derivation of the Brillouin zone construction. (a) Consideration of Laue's diffraction condition alone, $\dfrac{1}{2\pi}\mathbf{k}' = \dfrac{1}{2\pi}\mathbf{k} + \mathbf{h}$. (b) Added consideration of the side condition $|\mathbf{k}'| = |\mathbf{k}|$. (c) The end point of $\mathbf{k}/(2\pi)$ must lie in the plane perpendicular to $-\mathbf{h}/2$ if diffraction is to take place.

$\mathbf{k}/(2\pi)$ form an isosceles triangle with the vector $\mathbf{h}$ (see Fig. VII.3.5a and b). It follows from this (see Fig. VII.3.5c) that for changing direction of incidence the wavelength determined by $|\mathbf{k}| = 2\pi/\lambda$ must vary in such a manner that the end point of $\mathbf{k}$ always lies on the perpendicular plane through the end point of the vector $-\tfrac{1}{2}\mathbf{h}$.

Herewith we have already answered the restricted question: Which plane waves $e^{j\mathbf{k}\cdot\mathbf{r}}$ lead to a diffracted beam of the order h_1, h_2, h_3? They are all those waves whose wave vectors divided by 2π end on the perpendicular plane through the end point of the vector $-\tfrac{1}{2}\mathbf{h}$.

As we return to the more general question of page 186, under what circumstances a plane wave $e^{j\mathbf{k}\cdot\mathbf{r}}$ produces a diffracted beam of any order, we must recall that both the vector $-\mathbf{h}$ and the vector $+\mathbf{h}$ are vectors of the reciprocal lattice, since (VII.3.13) defined the vector $\mathbf{h}$ as follows:

$$\mathbf{h} = h_1\mathbf{b}_1 + h_2\mathbf{b}_2 + h_3\mathbf{b}_3 \qquad \left.\begin{array}{c} h_1 \\ h_2 \\ h_3 \end{array}\right\} = 0, \pm 1, \pm 2, \pm 3, \ldots \quad \text{(VII.3.16)}$$

Thus, if we draw the reciprocal lattice for the translation lattice under consideration and construct the bisecting perpendicular plane for every lattice vector of the reciprocal lattice, then a diffracted wave $e^{j\mathbf{k}\cdot\mathbf{r}}$ occurs if and only if the end point of $\mathbf{k}/2\pi$ lies on one of the bisecting perpendicular planes.

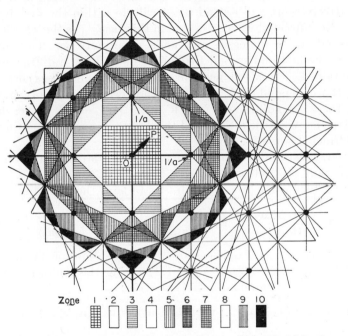

Fɪɢ. VII.3.6. Brillouin zones for the quadratic two-dimensional lattice.   Strong Bragg reflection occurs if the end point of $\mathbf{k}/(2\pi)$ lies on one of the continuous lines. (From L. Brillouin, "Quantenstatistik," Springer-Verlag OHG, Berlin, 1931.)

The construction of the bisecting perpendicular planes in the reciprocal lattice is designated as Brillouin zone construction.   The cubic lattice offers, of course, the simplest example for the carrying out of this construction.   Here the three vectors $\mathbf{a}_1$, $\mathbf{a}_2$, and $\mathbf{a}_3$ are mutually orthogonal and all of equal length, namely, equal to the lattice constant a.   By (VII.3.10) the vector $\mathbf{b}_1$ must be perpendicular to $\mathbf{a}_2$ and $\mathbf{a}_3$ and coincides hence in direction with $\mathbf{a}_1$.   Also by (VII.3.10), its length is equal to $1/a$.   The same applies for $\mathbf{b}_2$ and $\mathbf{b}_3$, so that the reciprocal lattice is in the present instance a cubic lattice with the lattice constant $1/a$. Figure VII.3.6 shows the ($\mathbf{b}_1$, $\mathbf{b}_2$) plane of this reciprocal lattice and the carrying out of the Brillouin zone construction within this plane. The bisecting perpendicular planes of the reciprocal lattice vectors $h_1\mathbf{b}_1 + h_2\mathbf{b}_2 + 0 \cdot \mathbf{b}_3$ in this ($\mathbf{b}_1$, $\mathbf{b}_2$) plane intersect this plane in the lightly drawn straight lines. We see, therefore, how the reciprocal lattice is subdivided into the Brillouin zones.

If a plane wave with the wave vector $\mathbf{k}$ is incident from any direction on the cubic point lattice with the lattice constant a, $\mathbf{k}/2\pi$ must be entered on the reciprocal lattice. For large wavelength λ, $\mathbf{k}/2\pi$ will be relatively short and its end point will lie within the first Brillouin zone. No diffracted wave $\mathbf{k}'$ occurs in this case. As the wavelength λ is reduced, $\mathbf{k}/2\pi$ increases and ends eventually on the boundary between the first and second Brillouin zone. Then a diffracted wave $\mathbf{k}'$ is obtained. As λ is reduced further and $\mathbf{k}/2\pi$ increases correspondingly, the end point of $\mathbf{k}/2\pi$ lies in the second Brillouin zone[1] and, again, there is no diffracted wave $\mathbf{k}'$ until the vector $\mathbf{k}/2\pi$ reaches the boundary between the second and third Brillouin zone, resulting again in a diffracted wave $\mathbf{k}'$, etc.

For carrying out the construction for complex lattices, it is important to note that the determining equations (VII.3.10), (VII.3.11), and (VII.3.12) for the reciprocal axes $\mathbf{b}_1$, $\mathbf{b}_2$, $\mathbf{b}_3$ have the following solution:

$$\mathbf{b}_1 = \frac{\mathbf{a}_2 \times \mathbf{a}_3}{(\mathbf{a}_1\mathbf{a}_2\mathbf{a}_3)} \qquad \mathbf{b}_2 = \frac{\mathbf{a}_3 \times \mathbf{a}_1}{(\mathbf{a}_1\mathbf{a}_2\mathbf{a}_3)} \qquad \mathbf{b}_3 = \frac{\mathbf{a}_1 \times \mathbf{a}_2}{(\mathbf{a}_1\mathbf{a}_2\mathbf{a}_3)} \quad \text{(VII.3.17)}$$

Its correctness may be checked by substitution of (VII.3.17) in (VII.3.10), (VII.3.11), and (VII.3.12), noting the following relations for the common denominator of (VII.3.17):

$$(\mathbf{a}_1\mathbf{a}_2\mathbf{a}_3) = \mathbf{a}_1 \cdot (\mathbf{a}_2 \times \mathbf{a}_3) = \mathbf{a}_2 \cdot (\mathbf{a}_3 \times \mathbf{a}_1) = \mathbf{a}_3 \cdot (\mathbf{a}_1 \times \mathbf{a}_2) \quad \text{(VII.3.18)}$$

e. Interpretation of the Diffraction Phenomenon as Bragg Reflection at a Family of Lattice Planes

For a physical interpretation it may be worth while to note that the planes perpendicular to $\mathbf{h}$ (and hence of course also to $-\tfrac{1}{2}\mathbf{h}$) are the families of lattice planes with the Miller indices[2] h_1, h_2, h_3. This may be seen in the following manner. According to the definition of the Miller indices, one of the lattice planes has the intercepts on the axes $\mathbf{a}_1/h_1$, $\mathbf{a}_2/h_2$, $\mathbf{a}_3/h_3$. The vectors $(\mathbf{a}_1/h_1 - \mathbf{a}_2/h_2)$ and $(\mathbf{a}_1/h_1 - \mathbf{a}_3/h_3)$

---

[1] Or, in special cases, the fourth zone.

[2] A very clear introduction to the Miller indices is given by Ewald, *op. cit.*, pp. 20 and 26.

thus lie in this lattice plane, and their vector product is perpendicular to it.   For this vector product, we find

$$\left(\frac{1}{h_1}\,\mathbf{a}_1 - \frac{1}{h_2}\,\mathbf{a}_2\right) \times \left(\frac{1}{h_1}\,\mathbf{a}_1 - \frac{1}{h_3}\,\mathbf{a}_3\right)$$

$$= \frac{1}{h_1^2}\,\mathbf{a}_1 \times \mathbf{a}_1 - \frac{1}{h_2 h_1}\,\mathbf{a}_2 \times \mathbf{a}_1 - \frac{1}{h_1 h_3}\,\mathbf{a}_1 \times \mathbf{a}_3 + \frac{1}{h_2 h_3}\,\mathbf{a}_2 \times \mathbf{a}_3$$

$$= 0 + \frac{(\mathbf{a}_1\mathbf{a}_2\mathbf{a}_3)}{h_1 h_2 h_3}\left\{ + h_3\,\frac{\mathbf{a}_1 \times \mathbf{a}_2}{(\mathbf{a}_1\mathbf{a}_2\mathbf{a}_3)} + h_2\,\frac{\mathbf{a}_3 \times \mathbf{a}_1}{(\mathbf{a}_1\mathbf{a}_2\mathbf{a}_3)} + h_1\,\frac{\mathbf{a}_2 \times \mathbf{a}_3}{(\mathbf{a}_1\mathbf{a}_2\mathbf{a}_3)}\right\}$$

$$= \frac{(\mathbf{a}_1\mathbf{a}_2\mathbf{a}_3)}{h_1 h_2 h_3}\,\{h_1\mathbf{b}_1 + h_2\mathbf{b}_2 + h_3\mathbf{b}_3\}$$

$$= \frac{(\mathbf{a}_1\mathbf{a}_2\mathbf{a}_3)}{h_1 h_2 h_3}\,\mathbf{h}$$

Thus the vector $(\mathbf{a}_1/h_1 - \mathbf{a}_2/h_2) \times (\mathbf{a}_1/h_1 - \mathbf{a}_3/h_3)$ which is perpendicular to the lattice plane (h_1, h_2, h_3) is also parallel to $\mathbf{h}$.   Hence the planes perpendicular to $\mathbf{h}$ are the lattice planes with the Miller indices h_1, h_2, h_3.

We recall here Bragg's interpretation of the diffraction process at the point lattice.   If, in Fig. VII.3.5, a parallel displacement of the

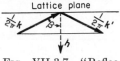

FIG. VII.3.7. "Reflection" at the lattice plane with the Miller indices (h_1, h_2, h_3).

FIG. VII.3.8. For reflection at a lattice plane "adjoining" rays have no path difference.

diffracted wave vector $\mathbf{k}'/2\pi$ is carried out, we see from Fig. VII.3.7 that the incident wave $\mathbf{k}/2\pi$ is in effect "reflected" at the lattice plane (h_1, h_2, h_3).   The spherical waves diffracted by the lattice points of one plane are in phase because of the symmetrical position of $\mathbf{k}$ and $\mathbf{k}'$ and, consequently, reinforce each other (see Fig. VII.3.8).   The fact that the waves reflected by two adjoining lattice planes do not annul each other by destructive interference but, instead, reinforce each other is assured by the relation

$$\cos \beta = \frac{\frac{1}{2}|\mathbf{h}|}{\frac{1}{2\pi}\,|\mathbf{k}|}$$

which may be read off from Fig. VII.3.7.   Since $|\mathbf{k}| = 2\pi/\lambda$, we may deduce from this

$$2\,\frac{1}{|\mathbf{h}|}\,\cos \beta = \lambda \qquad\qquad (\text{VII.3.19})$$

Furthermore,

$$\frac{1}{|\mathbf{h}|} = \frac{1}{n|\mathbf{h}^*|} = \frac{1}{n} d_{h_1^* h_2^* h_3^*}$$

where n is the largest common denominator of the Miller indices $h_1 = nh_1^*$, $h_2 = nh_2^*$, $h_3 = nh_3^*$ and where the absolute value of the vector $\mathbf{h}^* = h_1^*\mathbf{b}_1 + h_2^*\mathbf{b}_2 + h_3^*\mathbf{b}_3$ formed with the reduced Miller indices h_1^*, h_2^*, h_3^* is equal to the reciprocal of the separation $d_{h_1^* h_2^* h_3^*}$ of

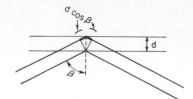

FIG. VII.3.9. For reflection at two adjoining lattice planes the path difference is $2d \cos \beta$.

two adjoining lattice planes.[1] Thus (VII.3.19) becomes the well-known Bragg reflection condition

$$2 \cdot d_{h_1^* h_2^* h_3^*} \cdot \cos \beta = n\lambda \qquad (VII.3.20)$$

for a reflection of nth order at the lattice planes (h_1, h_2, h_3). This condition assures a path difference $n\lambda$ and hence mutual reinforcement between the beams reflected at two successive lattice planes (see Fig. VII.3.9).

f. The Results of the Brillouin Approximation for Weakly Bound Electrons

We have discussed in some detail the diffraction phenomena at a three-dimensional point lattice and will now compare our results with those of Brillouin's approximation for weakly bound electrons.[2] Brillouin finds:

[1] For a proof see, e.g., Ewald, *op. cit.*, pp. 249–250. For a theorem of number theory used by Ewald without proof, see, e.g., B. L. van der Waerden, "Moderne Algebra," part 1, p. 61, Springer-Verlag OHG, Berlin, 1937, or Arnold Scholz, "Einführung in die Zahlentheorie," vol. 1131, p. 22, Sammlung Göschen, 1939.

[2] At the beginning of §3 and in Fig. VII.3.1, we have indicated that Brillouin's approximation is concerned with electrons of high total energy. Since, however, an electron in a region of potential energy which is constant in space behaves like a free electron, the characteristic properties of bound electrons result from spatial variations of potential energy. Accordingly, weakly bound electrons are electrons in a nearly constant potential field. In fact, the decisive assumption in Brillouin's approximation is that the variable part of the potential energy may be regarded as a small perturbation.

1. The eigenfunction of a weakly bound electron is, in general, practically a plane wave $e^{jk \cdot r}$.

2. The energy $E(k)$ depends on the wave vector k practically in the same manner as for a free electron, i.e., according to the law[1]

$$E(\mathbf{k}) = \frac{\hbar^2}{2m} |\mathbf{k}|^2 = \frac{\hbar^2}{2m} (k_x^2 + k_y^2 + k_z^2)$$

See Fig. VII.3.10a.

3. The perturbation by the variable part of the potential energy provides the plane wave $e^{jk \cdot r}$ with a modulation factor $u(\mathbf{r}; \mathbf{k})$ with the periodicity of the lattice. If the wave vector k of the free electron[2] is used, this modulation factor has small amplitudes unless k has a value for which considerations of wave optics indicate a Bragg reflection. For such k values the eigenfunction is represented no longer simply by a plane wave $e^{jk \cdot r}$, but by a superposition of the incident and the diffracted or "reflected" wave. Thus the eigenfunction assumes the character of a standing wave in a direction perpendicular to the reflecting lattice plane. In case k is perpendicular to the reflecting lattice plane, the eigenfunction becomes a standing wave entirely.

4. The modification of the variation of $E(k)$ by the variable part of the potential energy is, in general, slight. The change with respect to Fig. VII.3.10a is small. For k values leading to a Bragg reflection (i.e., for the Brillouin zone boundaries), discontinuities occur in the otherwise continuous variation $E(k)$ (see Fig. VII.3.10b). This arises from the fact that the incident and the reflected waves $e^{jk \cdot r}$ and $e^{jk' \cdot r}$ have the same wavelength, so that $|k| = |k'|$ and that hence the unper-

---

[1] This dependence is found immediately if the formula $\psi(x) = A e^{jk \cdot r}$ is substituted in the Schrödinger equation

$$-\frac{\hbar^2}{2m} \Delta\psi - E\psi = 0$$

of the free electron:

$$-\frac{\hbar^2}{2m} \cdot j^2 \cdot (k_x^2 + k_y^2 + k_z^2)A\ e^{jk \cdot r} - EA\ e^{jk \cdot r} = 0$$

$$E = +\frac{\hbar^2}{2m} |\mathbf{k}|^2 = \frac{\hbar^2}{2m} (k_x^2 + k_y^2 + k_z^2)$$

[2] It is of course also permissible to employ instead of k a wave vector $k + 2\pi h$, where h is a vector of the reciprocal lattice [see p. 187, in particular footnote 1, and Eq. (VII.3.13)]. In the one-dimensional case, this corresponds to a transition from k to $k + 2\pi h/a$ with $h = \pm 1, \pm 2, \ldots$ The modulation factor then changes over into a modulation factor

$$u(\mathbf{r}; \mathbf{k} + 2\pi\mathbf{h}) = u(\mathbf{r}; \mathbf{k})\ e^{-j 2\pi\mathbf{h} \cdot \mathbf{r}}$$

(see also p. 173).

turbed energy eigenvalues $\hbar^2|\mathbf{k}|^2/(2m)$ and $\hbar^2|\mathbf{k}'|^2/(2m)$ are equal to each other. The incident and reflected waves are hence degenerate, and the common unperturbed eigenvalue is split when the perturbation by the variable part of the potential energy is considered. The perturbation produces a forbidden band in the gap-free continuum of the unperturbed energy values. The calculation teaches the following regarding the magnitude of the splitting. In view of its periodicity with the lattice constant a, the lattice potential $U(\mathbf{r})$ may be expanded in a Fourier series

$$U(x) = \sum_{h=-\infty}^{h=+\infty} U_h \, e^{j2\pi\frac{h}{a}x} \qquad\qquad (VII.3.21)$$

[For a three-dimensional lattice, (VII.3.21) is replaced by a threefold

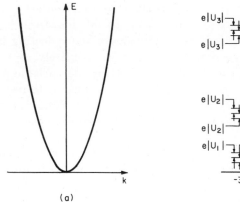

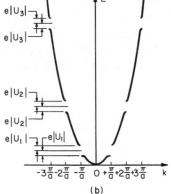

(a)   (b)

FIG. VII.3.10a. The variation of the energy with the wave number k for the free electron.

FIG. VII.3.10b. The development of forbidden energy regions as result of Bragg reflections.

Fourier expansion.] The split-up energy values are grouped symmetrically about the unperturbed energy value at a distance which is equal to $e|U_h|$ (see Fig. VII.3.10b). This makes it particularly plain that the deviation of the electron in a crystal from a free electron results from the variable components in the lattice potential.

5. If the Brillouin approximation is carried out one-dimensionally, i.e., for a linear point lattice with lattice constant a in one-dimensional space, the forbidden energy regions occur at the points $k = \pm\pi/a$, $\pm 2\pi/a$ . . . (see Fig. VII.3.10b). We may refer in this one-dimensional case to Fig. VII.3.6, provided that we limit ourselves to the horizontal axis of this figure and to the vertical zone boundaries. Since the zone boundaries occur at $\pm 1/2a$, $\pm 2/2a$, $\pm 3/2a$ . . . ,

Bragg reflections occur if

$$\frac{1}{2\pi} k = \pm h \cdot \frac{1}{2}\frac{1}{a}$$

or

$$k = \pm h \frac{\pi}{a}$$

We see particularly clearly from this simple example that the Brillouin zones constitute a complete subdivision of the range of variation of the independent variable k, whereas the expression "energy bands" directs attention to the existence of forbidden bands or gaps in the range of variation of the dependent variable E.

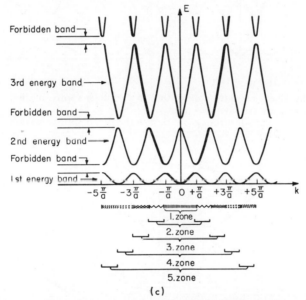

FIG. VII.3.10c. Energy spectrum according to the Brillouin approximation.

6. We have already mentioned, in footnote 2, page 193, that we may employ, in place of the wave number k of the free electron, one of the equivalent wave numbers $k + 2\pi h/a$ with $h = \pm 1, \pm 2, \ldots$. This leaves the eigenfunction $u(x; k)\, e^{jkx}$ and the eigenvalue E unaltered, although the modulation factor with lattice periodicity, $u(x; k)$, changes over into $u(x; k)\, e^{-2\pi jhx/a}$. Hence the variation of $E(k)$ may also be plotted as in Fig. VII.3.10c. This even becomes the natural course when carrying out consistently the degeneracy perturbation calculation required in the neighborhood of a Brillouin zone boundary.[1]

[1] To arrive at the representation in Fig. VII.3.10b, it is necessary to suppress one of the eigenvalues supplied by the perturbation calculation at a time, which is really not at all justified.

The comparison with the Bloch approximation to be given at a later point (page 198) is also facilitated hereby.

We turn once more to the Brillouin approximation for a quadratic point lattice in order to describe the phenomenon of band overlap, which is so important for the theory of the metals with a valence of 2 (see §11).   We choose this two-dimensional example, because **k** space may then be represented in Fig. VII.3.13 as a horizontal (k_x, k_y) plane

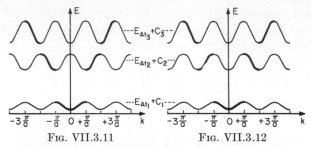

FIG. VII.3.11   FIG. VII.3.12

FIG. VII.3.11. Energy spectrum according to the Bloch approximation.   Exchange integrals alternately positive and negative.

FIG. VII.3.12. Energy spectrum according to the Bloch approximation.   Exchange integrals all negative.

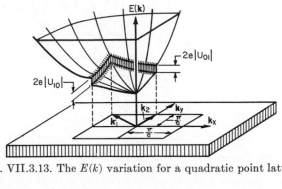

FIG. VII.3.13. The $E(k)$ variation for a quadratic point lattice.

above which, in a perpendicular direction, the energy $E(\mathbf{k}) = E(k_x, k_y)$ may be plotted.   The first Brillouin zone

$$-\frac{\pi}{a} \leq k_x \leq +\frac{\pi}{a} \qquad -\frac{\pi}{a} \leq k_y \leq +\frac{\pi}{a}$$

is marked out particularly in the horizontal **k** plane.   The $E(\mathbf{k})$ surface of a free electron would be a paraboloid of revolution:

$$E(\mathbf{k}) = \frac{\hbar^2}{2m} |\mathbf{k}|^2 = \frac{\hbar^2}{2m} (k_x^2 + k_y^2)$$

The left rear quarter of this paraboloid has been drawn,[1] and it is shown how the paraboloid is cut apart along the two boundaries $k_x = -\pi/a$ and $k_y = +\pi/a$ of the first Brillouin zone. The edges are bent horizontally, so that at the cut there is a gap twice as large as the corresponding Fourier coefficient of the lattice potential (see page 193, item 4).

The two edges of the cut in the energy surface $E(\mathbf{k})$ are represented in Fig. VII.3.14 by drawing the (k_x, E) plane $k_y = +\pi/a$. It is seen here that the highest value of the first band lies, for not too large $|U_{01}|$, higher than the lowest energy value of the second band. The bands overlap. It is true that, according to Fig. VII.3.13, the highest value

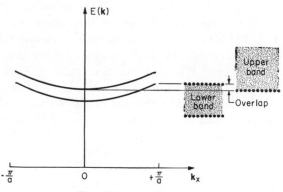

Fig. VII.3.14. Band overlap.

of the first band corresponds to the wave vector $\mathbf{k}_1 = (-\pi/a, +\pi/a)$, whereas the lowest value of the second band corresponds to another wave vector, namely, $\mathbf{k}_2 = (0, +\pi/a)$. Different wave vectors, and consequently different directions of the electron waves, belong in general to the same energy values in the first and the second band. Thus, in the case of band overlap, the electron can pass from one energy band to the next higher one without energy uptake. At the same time, it must change its direction. This, however, happens at any rate very frequently as the result of thermal collisions (see Chap. VII, §9).

[1] Our spatial representation of this two-dimensional example thus corresponds to Fig. VII.3.10b of the one-dimensional case. However, this should not lead to the erroneous conclusion that the possibility of the representation in Fig. VII.3.10c is a peculiarity of the one-dimensional case. It was pointed out already on p. 181 and in Fig. VII.2.9 that the transition from the wave vector $\mathbf{k}$ to a wave vector $\mathbf{k} + 2\pi\mathbf{h}$, without change in the eigenfunction or eigenvalue, is possible also in multidimensional cases.

g. Comparison of the Bloch and Brillouin Approximations. Reduced and Free Wave Vector

We return to Fig. VII.2.7 and retrace it in completed form in Figs. VII.3.11 and VII.3.12. In doing this, we do not reduce the wave number k to the interval $-\pi/a < k \leq +\pi/a$ and draw, furthermore, the variation $E(k)$ for several successive atomic eigenvalues E_{at}. In Fig. VII.3.11 it is assumed that the exchange integrals belonging to the eigenfunctions of successive atomic states are alternately negative and positive. With these—rather artificial—assumptions, the variation $E(k)$ according to Bloch (Fig. VII.3.11) attains a certain similarity with the results of the Brillouin approximation (Fig. VII.3.10c). This is not the case for Fig. VII.3.12, where all the exchange integrals have been assumed to be negative. Under certain circumstances (e.g., in the case of Fig. VII.3.11) it can thus be advantageous to replace the wave vector reduced to the first Brillouin zone with a free wave vector with unlimited range. We then obtain, turning back from Fig. VII.3.10c to Fig. VII.3.10b, an ordering of the permitted states by the wave number k alone, whereas the use of the reduced wave number demands an added index denoting the number of the band. A comparison of the Bloch and Brillouin approximations shows that in both instances a strengthening of binding narrows the allowed bands and widens the forbidden energy bands. Loosening of the binding leads, vice versa, to broader allowed and narrower forbidden energy bands. In the Bloch approximation, the width of the allowed bands is determined by the exchange integral, which becomes small in absolute value when, as a result of strong binding, the atomic eigenfunctions are concentrated closely about the atomic cores. In the Brillouin approximation, the widths of the forbidden energy bands are closely related to the Fourier amplitudes of the potential (see page 193, item 4). As we have pointed out in a footnote on page 192, the binding of the electrons is determined by the variable component of the potential. Thus, strong binding demands large alternating amplitudes of the periodic potential, and these large Fourier amplitudes lead to wide forbidden bands.

A comparison of Figs. VII.3.10c and VII.3.11 shows that the Bloch and Brillouin approximations lead to the same subdivision of the k axis in the one-dimensional case. This is true also for many more complex three-dimensional lattices. Thus, for the face-centered cubic and the body-centered cubic lattices, Bloch's periodicity polyhedron and the first Brillouin zone are identical. We will see, however, at a later point (§11) from a lattice with basis, the diamond lattice, that this identity is by no means universal.

§4. General Statements about the Eigenfunctions and the Energy Spectrum of an Electron in the Periodic Potential Field

a. Agreements in the Results of Bloch and Brillouin

In the last two paragraphs we have treated the special cases of strongly bound electrons and nearly free electrons by approximation methods. In spite of quantitative differences, we arrived at a number of qualitative results common to both cases. In fact, the most important qualitative properties of the eigenfunction and of the energy spectrum follow simply from the periodicity of the potential energy. They are summarized below.

1. The solutions $\psi(\mathbf{r})$ of the Schrödinger equation

$$-\frac{\hbar^2}{2m}\Delta\psi - (E + eU(\mathbf{r}))\psi(\mathbf{r}) = 0 \qquad \text{(VII.4.01)}$$

with a potential energy $U(\mathbf{r})$ with lattice periodicity can always be written in the form

$$\psi(\mathbf{r}; \mathbf{k}) = u(\mathbf{r}; \mathbf{k})\, e^{j\mathbf{k}\cdot\mathbf{r}} \qquad \text{(VII.4.02)}$$

where the function $u(\mathbf{r}; \mathbf{k})$ has lattice periodicity.[1]

2. The energy scale is broken up into a number of allowed bands, which are separated by forbidden bands. If E lies in an allowed band, the corresponding ψ has a real $\mathbf{k}$ value. ψ then represents a plane wave with an amplitude modulated with lattice periodicity. $\mathbf{k}$ attains the meaning of a wave number and indicates the number of wavelengths λ in a distance 2π:

$$|\mathbf{k}| = \frac{2\pi}{\lambda} \qquad \text{(VII.4.03)}$$

If E lies in a forbidden band, the corresponding ψ has a complex $\mathbf{k}$ value. ψ then increases or decreases exponentially. The fulfillment of periodic boundary conditions is not possible.[2]

3. A wave vector $\mathbf{k} + 2\pi\mathbf{h}$ leads to the same eigenfunction and hence the same energy E as the wave vector $\mathbf{k}$. $\mathbf{h}$ is here a vector of the reciprocal lattice (see page 187, in particular footnote 1). On the basis of this fact we obtain a subdivision of $\mathbf{k}$ space (or the $\mathbf{k}$ plane or $\mathbf{k}$ axis for two- and one-dimensional problems) into zones within which the eigenfunctions ψ and the eigenvalues E repeat themselves periodically (see, e.g., Figs. VII.2.9, VII.3.10c, VII.3.11, VII.3.12).

[1] G. Floquet, *Ann. école norm.*, **12:** 47 (1883).

[2] H. A. Kramers, *Physica*, **2:** 483 (1935).

4. Frequently, but not always, the energy shows a variation of the type

$$E = E_{\text{bound}} \mp \text{const} \cdot |\mathbf{k} - \mathbf{k}_{\text{bound}}|^2 \qquad \text{(VII.4.04)}$$

at the upper and the lower boundaries of the energy band.

5. An energy value E, which is forbidden for a particular direction of propagation $\mathbf{k}$, may be allowed for another direction of propagation $\mathbf{k}'$. Thus, if we pass from a consideration of a particular direction of propagation to a consideration of all directions of propagation, the width of the forbidden bands is reduced. This effect can go so far that an energy band forbidden for a particular direction of propagation vanishes when all directions of propagation are considered. We then speak of band overlap.

6. Increasing the binding of the electrons to the atomic cores broadens the forbidden and narrows the allowed energy bands. Weakening of the binding, vice versa, broadens the allowed and narrows the forbidden energy bands.

These are statements which follow quite generally simply from the lattice periodicity of the potential energy $-eU(\mathbf{r})$. It would of course be valuable if, for given $U(\mathbf{r})$, these general statements could be extended, e.g., by indicating in (VII.4.02) the amplitude modulation $u(\mathbf{r};\mathbf{k})$ or, in (VII.4.04), the values of E_{bound} and of const. Neither the Bloch nor the Brillouin approximation has proved suitable for this in cases of physical interest. The electrons responsible for conduction phenomena in actual solid bodies are neither strongly bound nor almost free, but lie just midway between these two cases. For the attainment of quantitative statements, the cellular method of Wigner and Seitz[1] has proved most successful so far.

b. The Cellular Method of Wigner and Seitz

Wigner and Seitz treat the potential fields about the individual atomic cores as spherically symmetric. They can also adduce a series of reasons why this assumption does not depart greatly from reality. They then subdivide space within the lattice into polyhedral cells about each atomic core by erecting bisecting perpendicular planes on the lines joining an atom core to its nearest neighbors and eventually also to its next-to-nearest neighbors. Within one such cell the spherically symmetrical potential variation is obtained from experimental data or from Hartree tabulations, the Schrödinger equation is separated in spherical coordinates, and the radial part of the eigenfunction is determined by numerical methods.

[1] E. Wigner and F. Seitz, *Phys. Rev.*, **43**: 804 (1933).

For the isolated atom the boundary conditions follow from the requirement that the eigenfunction must not become infinitely large either at the origin or at infinite distance. For the atom in the lattice, only the boundary condition at the origin remains unaltered. The boundary condition at infinity is replaced by the requirement that the eigenfunction must pass over continuously into the next cell at the cell boundary. To permit the practical realization of the procedure, this boundary condition is fulfilled only at the centers of the polyhedral faces bounding the cell.

The cellular method, particularly as perfected by Slater,[1] has had remarkable success with monovalent metals. The difficulties increase rapidly if there are several valence electrons per atom. Further efforts have been made to extend the method for this purpose.[2] However, no results which are reliable quantitatively as well as qualitatively have become available up to the present for the valence lattices of the diamond type with four valence electrons per atom (C, Si, Ge, Sn), which are of particular interest for semiconductor physics.[3] Also for lattices with two kinds of atoms the quantitative results are not comparable with those obtained for monovalent and divalent metals.[4]

§5. Mean Momentum, Mean Velocity, and Mean Current of an Electron in a Crystal

The Schrödinger functions

$$\psi(\mathbf{r}; \mathbf{k}) = u(\mathbf{r}; \mathbf{k})\, e^{j\mathbf{k}\cdot\mathbf{r}} \tag{VII.5.01}$$

are eigenfunctions of the operator $-\hbar^2\Delta/(2m) + E_{\mathrm{pot}}$ of the total energy. Since the momentum operator

$$\mathbf{p}_{\mathrm{op}} = \frac{\hbar}{j}\,\mathrm{grad} = \frac{\hbar}{j}\left\{\frac{\partial}{\partial x}, \frac{\partial}{\partial y}, \frac{\partial}{\partial z}\right\}$$

does not, in general, commute with the operator of the total energy, they cannot at the same time be eigenfunctions of the momentum.[5]

[1] J. C. Slater, *Phys. Rev.*, **45**: 794 (1934).

[2] C. Herring and A. G. Hill, *Phys. Rev.*, **58**: 132 (1940).

[3] For a summary and bibliography of more recent work in this field, see F. Herman, *Proc. IRE*, **43**: 1703 (1955).

[4] See footnote 2, p. 163.

[5] As such, they would have to be pure exponentials $e^{j\mathbf{k}\cdot\mathbf{r}}$. The factor $u(\mathbf{r}; \mathbf{k})$ with lattice periodicity is thus here in the way. Only for a free electron we have $u(\mathbf{r}; \mathbf{k}) = \mathrm{const} = A$, so that $\psi(\mathbf{r}) = A\, e^{j\mathbf{k}\cdot\mathbf{r}}$ is an eigenfunction of both the total

Thus, an electron represented by (VII.5.01) possesses a sharply defined total energy $E(\mathbf{k})$, but no sharply defined momentum. Accordingly, only a quantum-mechanical average of the momentum can be given, which must be calculated by the rule

$$\mathbf{p} = \int_{V_{\text{fund}}} \psi^*(\mathbf{r}; \mathbf{k}) \mathbf{p}_{\text{op}} \psi(\mathbf{r}; \mathbf{k}) \, dV = \frac{\hbar}{j} \int_{V_{\text{fund}}} \psi^*(\mathbf{r}; \mathbf{k}) \text{ grad } \psi(\mathbf{r}; \mathbf{k}) \, dV$$

$$(VII.5.02)$$

The evaluation of (VII.5.02) requires an explicit knowledge of the eigenfunctions (VII.5.01). Fortunately, however, it is possible to transform (VII.5.02) into

$$\mathbf{p} = \frac{m}{\hbar} \text{ grad}_k E(\mathbf{k}) \qquad (VII.5.03)$$

or $\qquad p_x = \dfrac{m}{\hbar} \dfrac{\partial}{\partial k_x} E(k_x, k_y, k_z) \qquad p_y = \dfrac{m}{\hbar} \dfrac{\partial}{\partial k_y} E(k_x, k_y, k_z)$

$$p_z = \frac{m}{\hbar} \frac{\partial}{\partial k_z} E(k_x, k_y, k_z)$$

Herewith the mean momentum can be computed simply from the variation of the energy E with the wave number $\mathbf{k}$. This variation $E(\mathbf{k})$ is at least qualitatively known (see, e.g., Figs. VII.3.10c, VII.3.11, and VII.3.12), so that qualitative statements regarding the mean momentum belonging to a state (VII.5.01) are possible.

The derivation of (VII.5.03) from (VII.5.02) demands, unfortunately, a certain amount of calculation. We shall make it somewhat more general than is required for the present purpose.[1] The point of departure is the Schrödinger equation (VII.1.01)

$$\left[-\frac{\hbar^2}{2m} \Delta - eU(\mathbf{r}) - E(\mathbf{k}) \right] \psi(\mathbf{r}; \mathbf{k}) = 0 \qquad (VII.5.04)$$

---

energy and the momentum. This is possible in this special case because for the free electron, with $E_{\text{pot}} = \text{const}$, the operators of the total energy and of the momentum commute. For a free electron a state of sharply defined total energy also happens to be a state of sharply defined momentum. See in this connection, e.g., E. Fues in Wien and Harms, "Handbuch der Experimentalphysik, Ergänzungswerk," p. 212, Akademische Verlagsgesellschaft, Leipzig, 1935, and H. A. Kramers, "Die Grundlagen der Quantentheorie" in Eucken and Wolf, "Hand- und Jahrbuch der Chemischen Physik," pp. 138 and 162, Akademische Verlagsgesellschaft, Leipzig, 1938.

[1] The general formula (VII.5.08) is employed, e.g., at the very top of p. 186 in W. V. Houston, *Phys. Rev.*, **57**: 184 (1940).

which is differentiated with respect to k_x:

$$\left[-0 + 0 - \frac{\partial}{\partial k_x} E \right] \psi(\mathbf{r}; \mathbf{k}) + \left[-\frac{\hbar^2}{2m} \Delta - eU(\mathbf{r}) - E(\mathbf{k}) \right] \frac{\partial}{\partial k_x} \psi(\mathbf{r}; \mathbf{k}) = 0$$

Application of (VII.5.01) leads to

$$-\frac{\partial E}{\partial k_x} \psi(\mathbf{r}; \mathbf{k}) + \left[-\frac{\hbar^2}{2m} \Delta - eU(\mathbf{r}) - E(\mathbf{k}) \right]$$
$$\cdot \left[jxu(\mathbf{r}; \mathbf{k}) \, e^{j\mathbf{k} \cdot \mathbf{r}} + \frac{\partial u(\mathbf{r}; \mathbf{k})}{\partial k_x} e^{j\mathbf{k} \cdot \mathbf{r}} \right] = 0$$

We now multiply from the left with $\psi^*(\mathbf{r}; \mathbf{k}')$ and integrate over the fundamental domain[1]

$$-\frac{\partial E}{\partial k_x} \int_{V_{\text{fund}}} \psi^*(\mathbf{r}; \mathbf{k}') \psi(\mathbf{r}; \mathbf{k}) \, dV$$
$$+ \int_{V_{\text{fund}}} \psi^*(\mathbf{r}; \mathbf{k}') \left[-\frac{\hbar^2}{2m} \Delta - eU(\mathbf{r}) - E(\mathbf{k}) \right]$$
$$\cdot \left[jx\psi(\mathbf{r}; \mathbf{k}) + \frac{\partial u(\mathbf{r}; \mathbf{k})}{\partial k_x} \cdot e^{j\mathbf{k} \cdot \mathbf{r}} \right] dV = 0$$

In the first integral we utilize the orthogonality of the eigenfunctions. The second integral is split into two integrals:

$$-\frac{\partial E}{\partial k_x} \cdot \delta_{kk'}$$
$$+ \int_{V_{\text{fund}}} \psi^*(\mathbf{r}; \mathbf{k}') \left[-\frac{\hbar^2}{2m} \Delta - eU(\mathbf{r}) - E(\mathbf{k}) \right] jx\psi(\mathbf{r}; \mathbf{k}) \, dV$$
$$+ \int_{V_{\text{fund}}} \psi^*(\mathbf{r}; \mathbf{k}') \left[-\frac{\hbar^2}{2m} \Delta - eU(\mathbf{r}) - E(\mathbf{k}) \right] \frac{\partial u(\mathbf{r}; \mathbf{k})}{\partial k_x} e^{j\mathbf{k} \cdot \mathbf{r}} \, dV$$

$$= \left\{ \begin{array}{c} \mathrm{I} \\ +\mathrm{II} \\ +\mathrm{III} \end{array} \right\} = 0 \quad \text{(VII.5.05)}$$

We first treat the third term of the sum, in which we can

---

[1] Of course, $\mathbf{k}$ and $\mathbf{k}'$ do not pertain to an incident and diffracted wave, as in §3, but are arbitrary wave vectors. After all, there is no diffracted wave for arbitrary $\mathbf{k}$.

make use of the Hermitian character of the operator of the total energy $[-\hbar^2\Delta/(2m) - eU(\mathbf{r}) - E(\mathbf{k})]$, since both $\psi^*(\mathbf{r}; \mathbf{k})$ and $[\partial u(\mathbf{r}; \mathbf{k})/\partial k_x]\, e^{j\mathbf{k}\cdot\mathbf{r}}$ are periodic in the fundamental domain:[1]

$$\text{III} = \int_{V_{\text{fund}}} \frac{\partial u(\mathbf{r}; \mathbf{k})}{\partial k_x}\, e^{j\mathbf{k}\cdot\mathbf{r}}\left[-\frac{\hbar^2}{2m}\Delta - eU(\mathbf{r}) - E(\mathbf{k}) \right]\psi^*(\mathbf{r}; \mathbf{k'})\, dV$$

With the Schrödinger equation (VII.5.04), with $\mathbf{k'}$ replacing $\mathbf{k}$, we obtain

$$\text{III} = \int_{V_{\text{fund}}} \frac{\partial u(\mathbf{r}; \mathbf{k})}{\partial k_x}\, e^{j\mathbf{k}\cdot\mathbf{r}}[E(\mathbf{k'}) - E(\mathbf{k})]\psi^*(\mathbf{r}; \mathbf{k'})\, dV$$

and, furthermore, with Eq. (VII.5.01) in which, again, $\mathbf{k}$ has been replaced by $\mathbf{k'}$,

$$\text{III} = \int_{V_{\text{fund}}} \frac{\partial u(\mathbf{r}; \mathbf{k})}{\partial k_x}\, e^{j\mathbf{k}\cdot\mathbf{r}}[E(\mathbf{k'}) - E(\mathbf{k})]u^*(\mathbf{r}; \mathbf{k'})\, e^{-j\mathbf{k'}\cdot\mathbf{r}}\, dV \quad \text{(VII.5.06)}$$

We now turn to the second term in (VII.5.05). Since $jx\psi(\mathbf{r}; \mathbf{k})$ is not periodic in the fundamental domain, we cannot make use of the Hermitian character of the operator $[-\hbar^2\Delta/(2m) - eU(\mathbf{r}) - E(\mathbf{k})]$. We note instead that

$$\Delta(x \cdot \psi(\mathbf{r}; \mathbf{k})) = x \cdot \Delta\psi(\mathbf{r}; \mathbf{k}) + 2 \cdot 1 \cdot \frac{\partial}{\partial x}\, \psi(\mathbf{r}; \mathbf{k}) + 0$$

---

[1] It is not always noted that the validity of the commutation rule for a Hermitian operator depends on certain properties of the commuted functions. Thus the momentum operator $p_{\text{op}} = (\hbar/j)d/dx$ is Hermitian. However, the relation

$$\int f^* p_{\text{op}} g\, dx = \int g p_{\text{op}}^* f^*\, dx$$

rests on an integration by parts

$$\int_{x=x_1}^{x=x_2} f^*\frac{\hbar}{j}\frac{d}{dx}\, g\, dx = \frac{\hbar}{j}\, [f^*g]_{x=x_1}^{x=x_2} + \int_{x=x_1}^{x=x_2} g\left(\frac{\hbar}{-j}\frac{d}{dx}f^* \right) dx$$

It applies in the simple form here employed only if $[f^*(x_2)g(x_2) - f^*(x_1)g(x_1)]$ vanishes. This is true in most quantum-mechanical problems, since we consider here only functions f and g which vanish at the limits x_1 and x_2. In problems with a periodic potential field, this difference vanishes for a different reason, namely, the periodicity in the fundamental domain $x_1 = -Ga/2$, $x_2 = +Ga/2$:

$$f(x_2) = f\left(+\frac{G}{2}a \right) = f\left(-\frac{G}{2}a \right) = f(x_1)$$

$$g(x_2) = g\left(+\frac{G}{2}a \right) = g\left(-\frac{G}{2}a \right) = g(x_1)$$

$$f^*(x_2)g(x_2) - f^*(x_1)g(x_1) = 0$$

and hence

$$\left[-\frac{\hbar^2}{2m} \Delta - eU(\mathbf{r}) - E(\mathbf{k}) \right] x\psi(\mathbf{r}; \mathbf{k})$$

$$= x \cdot \left[-\frac{\hbar^2}{2m} \Delta - eU(\mathbf{r}) - E(\mathbf{k}) \right] \psi(\mathbf{r}; \mathbf{k}) - \frac{\hbar^2}{2m} \cdot 2 \frac{\partial}{\partial x} \psi(\mathbf{r}; \mathbf{k})$$

$$= x \cdot \qquad\qquad 0 \qquad\qquad - \frac{\hbar^2}{m} \frac{\partial}{\partial x} \psi(\mathbf{r}; \mathbf{k})$$

The last is obtained with the aid of (VII.5.04). If we use this simple expression in the integrand of II, we find

$$\text{II} = \int\limits_{V_{\text{fund}}} \psi^*(\mathbf{r}; \mathbf{k}') j \left(-\frac{\hbar^2}{m} \frac{\partial}{\partial x} \psi(\mathbf{r}; \mathbf{k}) \right) dV$$

$$= \frac{\hbar}{m} \int\limits_{V_{\text{fund}}} \psi^*(\mathbf{r}; \mathbf{k}') \frac{\hbar}{j} \frac{\partial}{\partial x} \psi(\mathbf{r}; \mathbf{k}) \, dV$$

$$= \frac{\hbar}{m} \int\limits_{V_{\text{fund}}} \psi^*(\mathbf{r}; \mathbf{k}') p_{x_{\text{op}}} \psi(\mathbf{r}; \mathbf{k}) \, dV = \frac{\hbar}{m} p_{x\mathbf{k}'\mathbf{k}} \qquad \text{(VII.5.07)}$$

Here $p_{x\mathbf{k}'\mathbf{k}}$ is the so-called matrix element of the x component of the momentum operator (VII.5.02).

Equations (VII.5.05), (VII.5.06), and (VII.5.07) together yield

$$-\frac{\partial E}{\partial k_x} \cdot \delta_{\mathbf{k}\mathbf{k}'} + \frac{\hbar}{m} p_{x\mathbf{k}'\mathbf{k}} + [E(\mathbf{k}') - E(\mathbf{k})] \cdot$$

$$\int\limits_{V_{\text{fund}}} u^*(\mathbf{r}; \mathbf{k}') \frac{\partial u(\mathbf{r}; \mathbf{k})}{\partial k_x} \, e^{j(\mathbf{k}-\mathbf{k}')\cdot\mathbf{r}} \, dV = 0 \qquad \text{(VII.5.08)}$$

For the present occasion, we need only this equation for $\mathbf{k} = \mathbf{k}'$. It then yields immediately

$$-\frac{\partial E}{\partial k_x} + \frac{\hbar}{m} p_{x\mathbf{k}\mathbf{k}} + 0 = 0$$

i.e., the x component of the desired relation (VII.5.03)

$$p_x = p_{x\mathbf{k}\mathbf{k}} = \frac{m}{\hbar} \frac{\partial E}{\partial k_x}$$

Herewith the valuable relation (VII.5.03) has been proved. We shall now proceed to its physical evaluation.

In general, the total energy E will depend on a wave vector component, such as k_x, in the manner shown by Figs. VII.3.10c to VII.3.12. Hence, we deduce from (VII.5.03) that the mean value of the cor-

responding momentum component vanishes at the band edges.[1] The
fact, represented in Fig. VII.2.5, that the wave function becomes here
a standing wave—at least in the x direction—is in agreement with this.

The curve of the energy shows its steepest inclination near the
centers of the bands. These states have, therefore, by (VII.5.03), the
largest momentum values.

The mean momentum **p** is related to the mean velocity **v** by

$$\mathbf{v} = \frac{1}{m}\,\mathbf{p} \qquad\qquad (\text{VII.5.09})$$

since the velocity operator $\hbar/jm$ grad and the momentum operator
$\hbar/j$ grad differ only by the factor $1/m$. Thus we find from (VII.5.03)
for the mean velocity

$$\mathbf{v} = \frac{1}{\hbar}\,\mathrm{grad}_{\mathbf{k}}\,E(\mathbf{k}) \qquad\qquad (\text{VII.5.10})$$

This rather abstract discussion attains a certain graphic significance
from the identity of the mean velocity **v** for a state (VII.5.01) with the
group velocity of a wave packet formed by neighboring states centered
about the state (VII.5.01). This identity may be demonstrated with
the aid of (VII.5.10). The time factor for a state (VII.5.01) is
$e^{-(j/\hbar)E(\mathbf{k})\cdot t}$, so that the frequency $(1/h)E(\mathbf{k})$ is no longer simply proportional to the wave number **k**. There is, hence, dispersion.[2] In a
one-dimensional example the group velocity is then

$$\frac{\partial\omega}{\partial k} = \frac{1}{\hbar}\frac{d}{dk}E$$

By (VII.5.10) this is identical with the quantum-mechanical mean
value

$$\frac{1}{m}\mathbf{p} = \frac{1}{m}\int_{V_{\text{fund}}} \psi^*(\mathbf{r};\,\mathbf{k})\frac{\hbar}{j}\,\mathrm{grad}\,\psi(\mathbf{r};\,\mathbf{k})\,dV$$

[1] Since we are dealing with a quantum-mechanical mean value, any particular
measurement can yield a value for the momentum component in question which
differs from zero even for a state at the band edge. On the average, for many
measurements, however, equally large positive and negative values must occur
with equal frequency. The quantum-mechanical mean value of the kinetic energy
for a state at the band edge is, on the other hand, by no means zero. Here measured values of p_x^2 are averaged, whereas for the momentum measurements p_x
itself is averaged so that positive and negative values can compensate each other.
These circumstances are related to the fact that the ψ function which becomes a
standing wave at the band edge may be represented by a superposition of equal
numbers of plane waves running to the right and to the left.

[2] A. Sommerfeld, "Atombau und Spektrallinien," vol. II, p. 8, Eq. (14), Vieweg-
Verlag, Brunswick, Germany, 1944. See also W. Shockley, "Electrons and Holes
in Semiconductors," p. 160, Fig. 6.2, D. Van Nostrand Company, Inc., Princeton,
N.J., 1950.

All this is familiar for the plane waves of a free electron; however, the validity, here demonstrated, for the lattice-modulated waves of an electron in a crystal is by no means obvious.

To obtain, finally, an expression for the current density corresponding to an electron in a crystal with the eigenfunction

$$\psi(\mathbf{r}; \mathbf{k}) = u(\mathbf{r}; \mathbf{k}) \, e^{j\mathbf{k}\cdot\mathbf{r}}$$

we proceed from the familiar expression[1]

$$\frac{\hbar}{2jm} (\psi^* \text{ grad } \psi - \psi \text{ grad } \psi^*)$$

for the flux of probability density of an electron with normalized eigenfunction ψ. Multiplication with the charge $-e$ leads to the current density

$$-\frac{\hbar}{2j} \frac{e}{m} (\psi^* \text{ grad } \psi - \psi \text{ grad } \psi^*)$$

For the stationary solution $\psi(\mathbf{r}; \mathbf{k})$ with a probability density $\psi^*(\mathbf{r}; \mathbf{k})\psi(\mathbf{r}; \mathbf{k})$ independent of time which we shall substitute in this expression, the divergence of the current density vanishes according to the continuity equation.[2] In the one-dimensional case, the current density must hence be constant in space. In two- and three-dimensional cases a solenoidal component may be added, which, however, must have lattice periodicity since the wave factors $e^{j\mathbf{k}\cdot\mathbf{r}}$ and $e^{-j\mathbf{k}\cdot\mathbf{r}}$, which are periodic in the fundamental domain but do not have lattice periodicity, cancel each other in the foregoing expression for the current density. Such solenoidal portions of the current density, which are repeated from unit cell to unit cell, obviously arise from electron orbits about the atom cores if they exist at all. They are of no interest for the macroscopic current density produced by an electron in a crystal. If we cause them to vanish by taking a space average, we get for the mean current density i_{single} of a single electron in a crystal

$$i_{single} = -\frac{\hbar}{2j} \frac{e}{m} \frac{1}{V_{fund}} \int_{V_{fund}} (\psi^* \text{ grad } \psi - \psi \text{ grad } \psi^*) \cdot dV \quad \text{(VII.5.11)}$$

By a transformation we obtain

$$i_{single} = -\frac{e}{m} \frac{1}{V_{fund}} \cdot \frac{1}{2} \cdot \int_{V_{fund}} \left(\psi^* \cdot \frac{\hbar}{j} \text{ grad } \psi + \psi \frac{\hbar}{-j} \text{ grad } \psi^*\right) \cdot dV$$

[1] See, e.g., E. Fues in Wien and Harms, "Handbuch der Experimentalphysik, Ergänzungswerk," p. 150, Eq. (5.6).
[2] *Ibid.*, p. 149, Eq. (5.5).

and, furthermore, if we utilize the momentum operator and its Hermitian character,

$$\mathbf{i}_{single} = -\frac{e}{m} \cdot \frac{1}{V_{fund}} \cdot \frac{1}{2}\left[\int\limits_{V_{fund}} \psi^* \cdot \mathbf{p}_{op}\psi \, dV + \int\limits_{V_{fund}} \psi\mathbf{p}_{op}^*\psi^* \, dV \right]$$

$$\mathbf{i}_{single} = -\frac{e}{m} \cdot \frac{1}{V_{fund}} \cdot \int\limits_{V_{fund}} \psi^*\mathbf{p}_{op}\psi \, dV$$

According to Eq. (VII.5.02), the integral is equal to the quantum-mechanical mean value $\mathbf{p}$ of the momentum. We obtain, therefore,

$$\mathbf{i}_{single} = -\frac{e}{m} \cdot \frac{1}{V_{fund}} \cdot \mathbf{p} \qquad (VII.5.12)$$

If, finally, we make use of (VII.5.09) and (VII.5.10), we obtain

$$\mathbf{i}_{single} = -\frac{e}{V_{fund}} \cdot \mathbf{v} = -\frac{e}{V_{fund}} \frac{1}{\hbar} \operatorname{grad}_k E(\mathbf{k}) \qquad (VII.5.13)$$

If we recall that

$$\rho = -\frac{e}{V_{fund}}$$

is the charge density for uniform distribution of the electron charge $-e$ over the volume V_{fund} of the fundamental domain, we find complete analogy with the classical formula

Current density = charge density · velocity of convection

The same formula could have been derived with the aid of wave packets, for which the velocity of the center of gravity equals the group velocity $\mathbf{v}$ of the $\psi(\mathbf{r}; \mathbf{k})$ waves. Such a derivation would, however, fit in with corpuscular notions. We prefer to give, in §9, pages 246 to 247, a derivation of the equation

$$\mathbf{i}_{single} = -\frac{e}{V}\mathbf{v}$$

from a completely corpuscular standpoint.

§6. The Effect of an External Field on an Electron in a Crystal and the Effective Mass of an Electron in a Crystal

Conductivity questions require a clarification of the action of an added external force on an electron in a crystal. We shall treat this matter first for a free electron.

a. The Free Electron under the Influence of an External Force F

If an electron is accelerated by a force $\mathbf{F}$, its energy E increases with time. Hence, the determination of the law of acceleration is not facilitated by a derivation of the stationary states from the time-free Schrödinger equation with the aid of some boundary conditions, a course which is appropriate in a great majority of quantum-mechanical problems. Instead, we must proceed from the time-dependent Schrödinger equation

$$- \frac{\hbar^2}{2m} \Delta\psi + E_{\text{pot}}\, \psi = j\hbar \frac{\partial\psi}{\partial t} \qquad (\text{VII.6.01})$$

and follow the evolution in time $\psi(\mathbf{r}, t)$ of a given initial state $\psi(\mathbf{r}, 0)$.

If the free electron is subject to no external force, its potential energy is constant in space:

$$E_{\text{pot}} = -eU \qquad (\text{VII.6.02})$$

and (VII.6.01) is solved by the plane wave

$$\psi(\mathbf{r}, t) = \psi(\mathbf{r}; \mathbf{k}) \cdot e^{-\frac{j}{\hbar}Et} = A\, e^{j\left[\mathbf{k}\cdot\mathbf{r} - \frac{1}{\hbar}Et\right]} \qquad (\text{VII.6.03})$$

We may check this by substitution of (VII.6.03) in (VII.6.01) and will then find for the dependence of the energy E on the wave number

$$E(\mathbf{k}) = -eU_0 + \frac{\hbar^2}{2m} |\mathbf{k}|^2 \qquad (\text{VII.6.04})$$

Let, now, the electron be subject to an external force $\mathbf{F}$ which, for the sake of convenience, we shall assume to be constant in space. It is hence derived as a negative space gradient from a potential $-\mathbf{F} \cdot \mathbf{r}$[1] so that the potential energy E_{pot} is given by

$$E_{\text{pot}} = -eU_0 - \mathbf{F} \cdot \mathbf{r} \qquad (\text{VII.6.05})$$

instead of by (VII.6.02). Equation (VII.6.01) therefore assumes the

---

[1] Thus, in component notation we have

$$F_x = -\frac{\partial}{\partial x}\left(-F_x \cdot x - F_y \cdot y - F_z \cdot z\right)$$

$$F_y = -\frac{\partial}{\partial y}\left(-F_x \cdot x - F_y \cdot y - F_z \cdot z\right)$$

$$F_z = -\frac{\partial}{\partial z}\left(-F_x \cdot x - F_y \cdot y - F_z \cdot z\right)$$

or, in a single vector equation,

$$\mathbf{F} = -\operatorname{grad}\,(-\mathbf{F} \cdot \mathbf{r})$$

form

$$-\frac{\hbar^2}{2m}\Delta\psi - eU_0\psi - \mathbf{F}\cdot\mathbf{r}\psi = j\hbar\frac{\partial\psi}{\partial t} \qquad \text{(VII.6.06)}$$

We shall see that this equation is solved by the following formula:

$$\psi(\mathbf{r},\,t) = \psi(\mathbf{r};\,\mathbf{k}(t))\cdot\exp\left[-\frac{j}{\hbar}\int_{\tau=0}^{\tau=t}E(\mathbf{k}(\tau))\,d\tau\right]$$

$$= A\cdot\exp j\left[\mathbf{k}(t)\cdot\mathbf{r} - \frac{1}{\hbar}\int_{\tau=0}^{\tau=t}E(\mathbf{k}(\tau))\cdot d\tau\right] \qquad \text{(VII.6.07)}$$

Here the wave number $\mathbf{k}$ is assumed to have the following time dependence:

$$\mathbf{k}(t) = \mathbf{k}(0) + \frac{1}{\hbar}\mathbf{F}t \qquad \text{or} \qquad \dot{\mathbf{k}}(t) = \frac{1}{\hbar}\mathbf{F} \qquad \text{(VII.6.08)}$$

By definition, we understand by $E(\mathbf{k}(t))$ the same functional dependence of the energy on the wave vector $\mathbf{k}$ as for the absence of an external force. Hence, also by definition, Eq. (VII.6.04)

$$E(\mathbf{k}(t)) = -eU_0 + \frac{\hbar^2}{2m}|\mathbf{k}(t)|^2 \qquad \text{(VII.6.04)}$$

continues to be valid for a $\mathbf{k}(t)$ varying with time. We shall verify the formula (VII.6.07) by substitution in (VII.6.06).

Before this, some of our readers may welcome a somewhat more concrete description of the physical situation expressed by the formulas (VII.6.05), (VII.6.06) and the solution (VII.6.07), (VII.6.08), which up to now has been presented in purely mathematical and hence rather abstract terms.

We have assumed the force to be constant in space, so that there exists a constant force field throughout infinite space. The picture contains neither the origin of the lines of force at some surface charge nor their ending at some other surface charge. The solenoidal electrical field in the accelerating tube of a betatron may serve as an example for such a field. The field is produced by the time variation of a central magnetic flux. Its lines of force are therefore circles. They do not originate at or end on electrical charges, but form closed loops. If the accelerating tube has a very large radius, we can forget about its curvature, and we have an unbounded, though not infinite, space in which the same force $\mathbf{F}$ prevails everywhere—at least in the direction of the field—as soon as the central magnetic flux has begun

to change.   If, at the instant $t = 0$, even before the "switching on" of
the force **F**, electrons are traveling in the accelerating tube, they will
be represented by a wave with an appropriate wave vector **k** (see Fig.
VII.6.1).   Solution (VII.6.07), in combination with (VII.6.08), tells
us that the electrons in the accelerating tube are represented also after
the switching on of the force by an unlimited "plane" wave whose

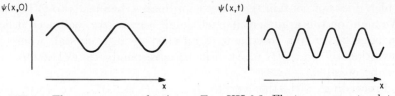

FIG. VII.6.1. Electron wave at the time   FIG. VII.6.2. Electron wave at a later
$t = 0$.   time $t > 0$, a force F having acted since
                                               $t = 0$.

wavelength remains constant in space, but becomes uniformly smaller
with time (see Fig. VII.6.2).

We now proceed to the verification of the solution (VII.6.07),
(VII.6.08) and obtain first from (VII.6.07) by differentiation

$$\frac{\partial}{\partial x} \psi(\mathbf{r}, t) - jk_x(t) \cdot \psi(\mathbf{r}, t)$$

$$\frac{\partial^2}{\partial x^2} \psi(\mathbf{r}, t) = -k_x^2(t) \cdot \psi(\mathbf{r}, t)$$

$$-\frac{\hbar^2}{2m} \Delta\psi(\mathbf{r}, t) = +\frac{\hbar^2}{2m} \cdot |\mathbf{k}(t)|^2 \cdot \psi(\mathbf{r}, t)$$

From this we obtain with the aid of (VII.6.04)

$$-\frac{\hbar^2}{2m} \Delta\psi(\mathbf{r}, t) = [E(\mathbf{k}(t)) + eU_0] \cdot \psi(\mathbf{r}, t)$$

or $$-\frac{\hbar^2}{2m} \Delta\psi(\mathbf{r}, t) - eU_0\psi(\mathbf{r}, t) = E(\mathbf{k}(t)) \cdot \psi(\mathbf{r}, t)   \quad (VII.6.09)$$

We could have written down Eq. (VII.6.09) even without calcula-
tion, since, by definition, $\psi(\mathbf{r}; \mathbf{k}) = A\,e^{j\mathbf{k}\cdot\mathbf{r}}$ satisfies the stationary
Schrödinger equation in the absence of an external force:

$$-\frac{\hbar^2}{2m} \Delta\psi(\mathbf{r}; \mathbf{k}) - eU_0\psi(\mathbf{r}; \mathbf{k}) = E(\mathbf{k})\psi(\mathbf{r}; \mathbf{k})$$

If **k**, instead of being constant, varies with a parameter which does not
occur in the stationary equation, namely, time, this does not detract
from the fulfillment of the stationary Schrödinger equation provided

only that the value $E(\mathbf{k}(t))$ pertaining to the moment of time in question is substituted for the energy $E(\mathbf{k})$. The addition of the time factor

$$\exp\left[-\frac{j}{\hbar} \int\limits_{\tau=0}^{\tau=t} E(\mathbf{k}(\tau))\, d\tau \right]$$

which does not contain the space coordinates then leads to (VII.6.09). We mention this argument in such detail because we shall need it later on page 213 in the treatment of an electron in a crystal, where the deviation of Eq. (VII.6.13), which corresponds to (VII.6.09), will not be possible.

Proceeding with the verification of (VII.6.07), we form from (VII.6.07), making use of (VII.6.08),

$$j\hbar \frac{\partial}{\partial t}\psi(\mathbf{r},\, t) = j\hbar \cdot j \cdot \left[\dot{\mathbf{k}}(t) \cdot \mathbf{r} - \frac{1}{\hbar} E(\mathbf{k}(t)) \right] \psi(\mathbf{r},\, t)$$

$$= -\hbar \cdot \left[\frac{1}{\hbar}\mathbf{F} \cdot \mathbf{r} - \frac{1}{\hbar} E(\mathbf{k}(t)) \right] \psi(\mathbf{r},\, t)$$

$$= -[\mathbf{F} \cdot \mathbf{r} - E(\mathbf{k}(t))]\psi(\mathbf{r},\, t)$$

which is substituted on the right side of (VII.6.06). On the left side we substitute the first two terms from (VII.6.09). We then obtain an identity, namely,

$$E(\mathbf{k}(t))\psi(\mathbf{r},\, t) - \mathbf{F} \cdot \mathbf{r} \cdot \psi(\mathbf{r},\, t) = -[\mathbf{F} \cdot \mathbf{r} - E(\mathbf{k}(t))]\psi(\mathbf{r},\, t)$$

which demonstrates the fulfillment of (VII.6.06) by formulas (VII.6.07) and (VII.6.08).

b. The Electron in a Crystal under the Influence of an External Force F

We now claim that the behavior of an electron in a crystal under the influence of an external force may be described, just as that of a free electron, by letting the wave number $\mathbf{k}$ in the wave function

$$\psi(\mathbf{r};\, \mathbf{k}) = u(\mathbf{r};\, \mathbf{k})\, e^{j\mathbf{k}\cdot\mathbf{r}}$$

of the unperturbed problem depend on time in accordance with the law (VII.6.08). A simple attempt at verification will show that this does not apply with complete rigor.

The statement just made signifies that the time-dependent Schrödinger equation of an electron in a crystal under the influence of an external force

$$-\frac{\hbar^2}{2m}\,\Delta\psi(\mathbf{r},\,t)-(eU(\mathbf{r})+\mathbf{F}\cdot\mathbf{r})\psi(\mathbf{r},\,t)=j\hbar\,\frac{\partial}{\partial t}\,\psi(\mathbf{r},\,t)\quad\text{(VII.6.10)}$$

has the solution

$$\psi(\mathbf{r},\,t)=\psi(\mathbf{r};\,\mathbf{k}(t))\cdot\exp\left[-\frac{j}{\hbar}\int_{\tau=0}^{\tau=t}E(\mathbf{k}(\tau))\,d\tau\right]$$

$$=u(\mathbf{r};\,\mathbf{k}(t))\exp j\left[\mathbf{k}(t)\cdot\mathbf{r}-\frac{1}{\hbar}\int_{\tau=0}^{\tau=t}E(\mathbf{k}(\tau))\,dt\right]\quad\text{(VII.6.11)}$$

with

$$\mathbf{k}(t)=\mathbf{k}+\frac{1}{\hbar}\,\mathbf{F}t\quad\text{or}\quad\dot{\mathbf{k}}(t)=\frac{1}{\hbar}\,\mathbf{F}\qquad\text{(VII.6.12)}$$

$\psi(\mathbf{r};\,\mathbf{k}(t))=u(\mathbf{r};\,\mathbf{k}(t))\,e^{j\mathbf{k}\cdot\mathbf{r}}$ is here any solution of the stationary Schrödinger equation

$$-\frac{\hbar^2}{2m}\,\Delta\psi-eU(\mathbf{r})\psi=E\psi$$

Correspondingly, the energy E in the exponent of the time-dependent factor of (VII.6.11) is assumed to depend on the time-dependent wave vector $\mathbf{k}(t)$ in the same manner as on the constant wave number $\mathbf{k}$ for an electron in a crystal with lattice potential $U(\mathbf{r})$ without external force. Examples are provided by Figs. VII.2.9, VII.3.10c, and VII.3.12, as well as by Eq. (VII.2.22) for the specific case of the Bloch approximation.

This remark immediately leads to[1]

$$-\frac{\hbar^2}{2m}\,\Delta\psi(\mathbf{r};\,\mathbf{k}(t))-eU(\mathbf{r})\psi(\mathbf{r};\,\mathbf{k}(t))=E(\mathbf{k}(t))\cdot\psi(\mathbf{r};\,\mathbf{k}(t))$$

so that, with the addition of the time factor

$$\exp\left[-\frac{j}{\hbar}\int_{\tau=0}^{\tau=t}E(\mathbf{k}(\tau))\,d\tau\right]$$

we have

$$-\frac{\hbar^2}{2m}\,\Delta\psi(\mathbf{r},\,t)-eU(\mathbf{r})\psi(\mathbf{r},\,t)=E(\mathbf{k}(t))\cdot\psi(\mathbf{r},\,t)\quad\text{(VII.6.13)}$$

This is the first step in a verification of (VII.6.11). To carry it further,

[1] The reasoning is the same as that employed for Eq. (VII.6.09).

we must form

$$\frac{\partial}{\partial t}\psi(\mathbf{r},\,t) = \frac{\partial}{\partial t}\left\{u(\mathbf{r};\,\mathbf{k}(t))\cdot\exp j\left[\mathbf{k}(t)\cdot\mathbf{r}-\frac{1}{\hbar}\int\limits_{\tau=0}^{\tau=t}E(\mathbf{k}(\tau))\,d\tau\right]\right\}$$

$$= j\left[\dot{\mathbf{k}}(t)\cdot\mathbf{r}-\frac{1}{\hbar}E(\mathbf{k}(t))\right]\psi(\mathbf{r},\,t)+\left(\frac{\partial u(\mathbf{r};\,\mathbf{k}(t))}{\partial k_x}\cdot\dot{k}_x(t)\right.$$

$$\left.+\frac{\partial u(\mathbf{r};\,\mathbf{k}(t))}{\partial k_y}\,\dot{k}_y(t)+\frac{\partial u(\mathbf{r};\,\mathbf{k}(t))}{\partial k_z}\,\dot{k}_z(t)\right)\exp j[\,\cdots\,]$$

$$\frac{\partial}{\partial t}\psi(\mathbf{r},\,t) = j\left[\dot{\mathbf{k}}(t)\cdot\mathbf{r}-\frac{1}{\hbar}E(\mathbf{k}(t))\right]\psi(\mathbf{r},\,t)+\mathrm{grad_k}\,u(\mathbf{r};\,\mathbf{k}(t))\cdot\dot{\mathbf{k}}(t)$$

$$\cdot\exp j\left[\mathbf{k}(t)\cdot\mathbf{r}-\frac{1}{\hbar}\int\limits_{\tau=0}^{\tau=t}E(\mathbf{k}(\tau))\,d\tau\right]$$

With (VII.6.12) we then find

$$j\hbar\frac{\partial}{\partial t}\psi(\mathbf{r},\,t) = -(\mathbf{F}\cdot\mathbf{r})\psi(\mathbf{r},\,t)+E(\mathbf{k}(t))\psi(\mathbf{r},\,t)+j\mathbf{F}\cdot\mathrm{grad_k}\,u(\mathbf{r};\,\mathbf{k}(t))$$

$$\cdot\exp j\left[\mathbf{k}(t)\cdot\mathbf{r}-\frac{1}{\hbar}\int\limits_{\tau=0}^{\tau=t}E(\mathbf{k}(\tau))\,d\tau\right]\quad\text{(VII.6.14)}$$

A combination of (VII.6.13) and (VII.6.14) then shows that (VII.6.11) almost satisfies the Schrödinger equation (VII.6.10). The term $j\mathbf{F}\cdot\mathrm{grad_k}\,u(\mathbf{r};\,\mathbf{k}(t))\cdot\exp j[\,\cdots\,]$ on the right side of (VII.6.10) remains uncompensated, however.

We shall now show that this failure of the assumption (VII.6.12) arises from the fact that it does not take account of transitions of the electron into higher bands which may take place under the influence of the added force $\mathbf{F}$. To this end, we shall try to improve on formula (VII.6.11). It appears reasonable to replace the simple expression (VII.6.11) by a sum of such expressions with initially unknown amplitudes A:

$$\psi(x,\,t) = \sum_{N'=1}^{\infty}\sum_{n'=-\frac{G}{2}}^{n'=+\frac{G}{2}-1}A_{N'n'}\psi_{N'}\left(x;\,k_{n'}+\frac{1}{\hbar}Ft\right)$$

$$\cdot\exp\left[-\frac{j}{\hbar}\int\limits_{\tau=0}^{\tau=t}E_{N'}\left(k_{n'}+\frac{1}{\hbar}F\tau\right)d\tau\right]\quad\text{(VII.6.15)}$$

For the sake of simplicity we have passed over to the one-dimensional case. Hence Eq. (VII.2.05) gives for the individual wave-number values

$$k_n = \frac{2\pi}{a} \cdot \frac{n}{G}$$

The summation over n' in (VII.6.15) thus encompasses all G eigenfunctions of a band, the summation over N', the several bands. Even this extended formula, however, does not lead closer to the goal, since now we have on the right side of Eq. (VII.6.10) a sum of uncompensated terms

$$j A_{N'n'} F \frac{\partial}{\partial k} u_{N'} \left(x; k_{n'} + \frac{1}{\hbar} Ft \right) \exp j[\cdots]$$

Compensation becomes possible only if we let the amplitudes $A_{N'n'}$ depend on the time

$$A_{N'n'} = A_{N'n'}(t)$$

Substitution of (VII.6.15) now leads to additional terms on the right side of (VII.6.10):

$$j\hbar \dot{A}_{N'n'}(t)\psi_{N'} \left(x; k_{n'} + \frac{1}{\hbar} Ft \right) \exp\left[-\frac{j}{\hbar} \int_{\tau=0}^{\tau=t} E_{N'} \left(k_{n'} + \frac{1}{\hbar} F\tau \right) d\tau \right]$$

and the fulfillment of (VII.6.10) leads to the requirement

$$0 = \begin{cases} \sum_{N'=1}^{\infty} \sum_{n'=-\frac{G}{2}}^{n'=+\frac{G}{2}-1} j\hbar \dot{A}_{N'n'}(t)\psi_{N'} \left(x; k_{n'} + \frac{1}{\hbar} Ft \right) \\[2em] \qquad\qquad \cdot \exp\left[-\frac{j}{\hbar} \int_{\tau=0}^{\tau=t} E_{N'} \left(k_{n'} + \frac{1}{\hbar} F\tau \right) d\tau \right] \\[2em] + \sum_{N'=1}^{\infty} \sum_{n'=-\frac{G}{2}}^{n'=+\frac{G}{2}-1} j A_{N'n'}(t) \cdot F \cdot \frac{\partial}{\partial k} u_{N'} \left(x; k_{n'} + \frac{1}{\hbar} Ft \right) \\[2em] \qquad\qquad \cdot \exp j\left[\left(k_{n'} + \frac{1}{\hbar} Ft \right) \cdot x - \frac{1}{\hbar} \int_{\tau=0}^{\tau=t} E_{N'} \left(k_{n'} + \frac{1}{\hbar} F\tau \right) d\tau \right] \end{cases}$$

$$(VII.6.16)$$

To determine what are in principle an infinite number of unknowns $A_{N'n'}$, we multiply (VII.6.16) by

$$\psi_N^*\left(x; k_n + \frac{1}{\hbar}Ft\right)\exp\left[+\frac{j}{\hbar}\int\limits_{\tau=0}^{\tau=t} E_N\left(k_n + \frac{1}{\hbar}F\tau\right)d\tau\right]$$

and integrate over the fundamental domain of the crystal.

As solutions of the stationary problem, the $\psi_N(x; k_n + Ft/\hbar)$ are orthogonal and normalized. We therefore obtain

$$0 = \begin{cases} + \displaystyle\sum_{N'=1}^{\infty}\sum_{n'=-\frac{G}{2}}^{n'=+\frac{G}{2}-1} j\hbar\dot{A}_{N'n'}(t)\cdot\delta_{NN'}\delta_{nn'} \\[2ex] \qquad\cdot\exp\left[-\frac{j}{\hbar}\int\limits_{\tau=0}^{\tau=t}\left[E_{N'}\left(k_{n'}+\frac{1}{\hbar}F\tau\right)-E_N\left(k_n+\frac{1}{\hbar}F\tau\right)d\tau\right]\right. \\[2ex] + \displaystyle\sum_{N'=1}^{\infty}\sum_{n'=-\frac{G}{2}}^{n'=+\frac{G}{2}-1} jA_{N'n'}(t)\int\limits_{V_{\text{fund}}} u_N^*\left(x; k_n+\frac{1}{\hbar}Ft\right) \\[2ex] \qquad\cdot F\cdot\frac{\partial}{\partial k}u_{N'}\left(x; k_{n'}+\frac{1}{\hbar}Ft\right) \\[2ex] \qquad\cdot\exp j\left[\left(k_{n'}+\frac{1}{\hbar}Ft\right)x - \frac{1}{\hbar}\int\limits_{\tau=0}^{\tau=t}E_{N'}\left(k_{n'}+\frac{1}{\hbar}F\tau\right)d\tau\right. \\[2ex] \qquad\left.\left. -\left(k_n+\frac{1}{\hbar}Ft\right)x + \frac{1}{\hbar}\int\limits_{\tau=0}^{\tau=t}E_N\left(k_n+\frac{1}{\hbar}F\tau\right)d\tau\right]\cdot dV\right. \end{cases}$$

or

$$\dot{A}_{Nn}(t) = -\sum_{N'=1}^{\infty}\sum_{n'=-\frac{G}{2}}^{n'=+\frac{G}{2}-1} A_{N'n'}\frac{1}{\hbar}F\int\limits_{V_{\text{fund}}} u_N^*\left(x; k_n+\frac{1}{\hbar}Ft\right)e^{j(k_{n'}-k_n)x}$$

$$\cdot\frac{\partial}{\partial k}u_{N'}\left(x; k_{n'}+\frac{1}{\hbar}Ft\right)dV$$

$$\cdot\exp\left\{+\frac{j}{\hbar}\int\limits_{\tau=0}^{\tau=t}\left[E_N\left(k_n+\frac{1}{\hbar}F\tau\right)-E_{N'}\left(k_{n'}+\frac{1}{\hbar}F\tau\right)\right]d\tau\right\}$$

We now find that the summation over n' in (VII.6.15) is superfluous.

For every arbitrary but fixed point of time

$$u_N^*\left(x; k_n + \frac{1}{\hbar}Ft\right) \cdot \frac{\partial}{\partial k} u_{N'}\left(x; k_{n'} + \frac{1}{\hbar}Ft\right)$$

is a function with lattice periodicity. We can hence apply the theorem derived in Appendix I, page 381, to the effect that the integral of the product of a function $f(x)$ with lattice periodicity and a factor $e^{j(k-k')x}$ over the fundamental domain vanishes unless $k = k'$. Thus the summation over n' in the last equation for $\dot{A}_{Nn}(t)$ drops out and we obtain

$$\dot{A}_{Nn}(t) = -\frac{1}{\hbar}F \sum_{N'=1}^{\infty} A_{N'n}(t) \int_{V_{\text{fund}}} u_N^*\left(x; k_n + \frac{1}{\hbar}Ft\right)$$

$$\cdot \frac{\partial}{\partial k} u_{N'}\left(x; k_n + \frac{1}{\hbar}Ft\right) \cdot dV \qquad \text{(VII.6.17)}$$

$$\exp\left\{+\frac{j}{\hbar}\int_{\tau=0}^{\tau=t}\left[E_N\left(k_n + \frac{1}{\hbar}F\tau\right) - E_{N'}\left(k_n + \frac{1}{\hbar}F\tau\right)\right]d\tau\right\}$$

The dropping out of the summation over n' indicates in particular that for an electron which at the time $t = 0$ is represented by a function $\psi_N(x; k_n)$ no other wave numbers $k_{n'}$ play a role. More precisely, the action of the added force F changes the wave number k in accord with the time variation (VII.6.12), and the simple assumption (VII.6.11) would describe the behavior of the electron completely if states with equal $k(t) = k_n + Ft/\hbar$ were not excited in other bands $N' \neq N$ in the course of time. Equation (VII.6.17) teaches in effect that, even if at $t = 0$ only a single coefficient A_{N_0n} differed from zero and the electron occupied accordingly only the state k_n in the band N_0, all other coefficients $A_{N'n}$ will, in principle, be different from zero after a time t, so that the added force F effects transitions into every other band $N' \neq N_0$ with a certain probability. This probability is measured by the square of the absolute value of $A_{N'n}$. Carrying the treatment of the system of differential equations (VII.6.17) for the infinite number of coefficients $A_{N'n}$ further should indicate with what frequency transitions of the electron into another band occur for a given magnitude of the force F.[1] However, we shall be able to answer this

[1] We would use Eq. (VII.6.17) for this purpose. The preceding presentation follows W. V. Houston, *Phys. Rev.*, **57**: 184 (1940). We should also mention in this connection F. Bloch, *Z. Physik*, **52**: 555 (1928); R. Peierls, *Z. Physik*, **53**: 255 (1929); H. A. Bethe in Geiger and Scheel, *op. cit.*, vol. XXIV, part 2, p. 507; H. Jones and C. Zener, *Proc. Roy. Soc. (London)*, **144**: 101–117 (1934); J. C. Slater, *Revs. Mod. Phys.*, **6**: 209 (1934), particularly p. 259; and A. H. Wilson, "The Theory of

question more simply in another manner in §7. We shall see here also that only extraordinarily large forces can effect the transition of electrons into other bands with appreciable frequency. For forces of ordinary magnitude we can state simply that the electron is represented continuously by one[1] solution $\psi(\mathbf{r}; \mathbf{k})$ of the stationary Schrödinger equation in the absence of an external force, the variation of the wave vector with time being given by

$$\dot{\mathbf{k}} = \frac{1}{\hbar} \mathbf{F} \qquad \text{(VII.6.12)}$$

Equation (VII.6.12) has very important physical consequences, which we shall discuss next.

c. The Effective Mass of an Electron in a Crystal

Equation (VII.6.12) together with (VII.5.10) lead to an analogy for the equation for a free electron

$$\dot{\mathbf{v}} = \frac{1}{m} \mathbf{F} \qquad \text{(VII.6.18)}$$

For the sake of simplicity and to obtain a general view of the situation, we proceed from the variation $E(\mathbf{k})$ (VII.4.04) which is commonly assumed for the neighborhood of the band edges and which we shall now write in the form[2]

$$E = E_{\text{bound}} + \tfrac{1}{2}E''(|\mathbf{k}_{\text{bound}}|)[(k_x - k_{x\text{bound}})^2 + (k_y - k_{y\text{bound}})^2 + (k_z - k_{z\text{bound}})^2] \quad \text{(VII.6.19)}$$

In this particular variation of $E(\mathbf{k})$ with the wave vector $\mathbf{k}$, the second derivative $E''(\mathbf{k}_{\text{bound}})$ with respect to the absolute value of the wave

---

Metals," Cambridge University Press, London, 1935. The books of Fröhlich, Seitz, and Mott and Jones give a very simple proof for (VII.6.12) with the aid of an energy theorem. We fear, however, that in this very simple proof a very important part of the matter to be proved—namely, the continuous representation of an electron in the crystal by the solution $\psi(\mathbf{r}; \mathbf{k})$ of the stationary Schrödinger equation in the absence of an external force—is implicit in the formulation of the energy theorem so that the further deductions only give a more precise picture of the nature of the time dependence of $\mathbf{k}$. For a further objection to this argument, see Shockley, op. cit., pp. 424–425. With regard to this whole series of questions, see also D. Pfirsch and E. Spenke, Z. Physik, **137**: 309 (1954).

[1] More recently it has been found, however, that inc ertain problems (related to Ehrenfest's theorem) transitions to higher bands must be considered even for weak forces [see D. Pfirsch and E. Spenke, Z. Physik, **137**: 309 (1954)].

[2] The replacement of "const" in Eq. (VII.4.04) by $\tfrac{1}{2}E''$ $(|\mathbf{k}_{\text{bound}}|)$ is obtained from a Taylor expansion of the function $E(\mathbf{k})$ about the point $\mathbf{k} = \mathbf{k}_{\text{bound}}$.

vector $\mathbf{k}$ might equally well be replaced by one of the second derivatives of E with respect to one of its components k_x, k_y, or k_z.

For the special case (VII.6.19), the evaluation of (VII.5.10) yields an equation

$$\mathbf{v} = \frac{1}{\hbar} \cdot E''(|\mathbf{k}_{\text{bound}}|) \cdot (\mathbf{k} - \mathbf{k}_{\text{bound}}) \qquad \text{(VII.6.20)}$$

Differentiation with respect to time results in

$$\dot{\mathbf{v}} = \frac{1}{\hbar} \cdot E''(|\mathbf{k}_{\text{bound}}|) \cdot \dot{\mathbf{k}} \qquad \text{(VII.6.21)}$$

which, with (VII.6.12), leads to

$$\dot{\mathbf{v}} = \frac{1}{\hbar^2} \cdot E''(|\mathbf{k}_{\text{bound}}|) \cdot \mathbf{F} \qquad \text{(VII.6.22)}$$

Comparison of this relation (VII.6.22) for an electron in a crystal with Eq. (VII.6.18) for a free electron shows that for an electron in a crystal the electron mass is replaced, in acceleration processes, by an effective mass

$$m_{\text{eff}} = \frac{\hbar^2}{E''(|\mathbf{k}_{\text{bound}}|)} \qquad \text{(VII.6.23)}$$

Before turning to the important physical consequences of this equation, we shall consider the case of a more general variation $E(\mathbf{k})$.

To this end we differentiate, e.g., the x component of (VII.5.10) with respect to time

$$\dot{v}_x = \frac{1}{\hbar} \frac{d}{dt} \left[\frac{\partial}{\partial k_x} E(k_x, k_y, k_z) \right] = \frac{1}{\hbar} \left[\frac{\partial^2 E}{\partial k_x^2} \dot{k}_x + \frac{\partial^2 E}{\partial k_x \, \partial k_y} \dot{k}_y + \frac{\partial^2 E}{\partial k_x \, \partial k_z} \dot{k}_z \right]$$

and combine this equation with the corresponding ones for $\dot{v}_y$ and $\dot{v}_z$ in the vector equation

$$\dot{\mathbf{v}} = \frac{1}{\hbar} \left(\frac{\partial^2 E}{\partial k_l \, \partial k_m} \right) \cdot \dot{\mathbf{k}} \qquad \text{(VII.6.24)}$$

where the symbol $\partial^2 E / \partial k_l \, \partial k_m$ denotes the tensor

$$\left(\frac{\partial^2 E}{\partial k_l \, \partial k_m} \right) = \begin{bmatrix} \dfrac{\partial^2 E}{\partial k_x^2} & \dfrac{\partial^2 E}{\partial k_x \, \partial k_y} & \dfrac{\partial^2 E}{\partial k_x \, \partial k_z} \\[2ex] \dfrac{\partial^2 E}{\partial k_y \, \partial k_x} & \dfrac{\partial^2 E}{\partial k_y^2} & \dfrac{\partial^2 E}{\partial k_y \, \partial k_z} \\[2ex] \dfrac{\partial^2 E}{\partial k_z \, \partial k_x} & \dfrac{\partial^2 E}{\partial k_z \, \partial k_y} & \dfrac{\partial^2 E}{\partial k_z^2} \end{bmatrix} \qquad \text{(VII.6.25)}$$

From (VII.6.24) and (VII.6.12) we now obtain as the desired analogue to (VII.6.18) the equation

$$\dot{\mathbf{v}} = \frac{1}{\hbar^2} \left(\frac{\partial^2 E}{\partial k_l \, \partial k_m} \right) \cdot \mathbf{F} \tag{VII.6.26}$$

We see that, in general, the reciprocal effective mass of an electron in a crystal has the character of a tensor. By the choice of suitable axial directions x, y, z, such a tensor may be transformed to principal axes or, in other words, the nondiagonal terms $\partial^2 E / \partial k_x \, \partial k_y$, $\partial^2 E / \partial k_y \, \partial k_z$, etc., can be made to vanish. Equation (VII.6.26) can then be replaced by three component equations

$$\dot{v}_x = \frac{1}{\hbar^2} \frac{\partial^2 E}{\partial k_x^2} \cdot F_x \qquad \dot{v}_y = \frac{1}{\hbar^2} \frac{\partial^2 E}{\partial k_y^2} \cdot F_y \qquad \dot{v}_z = \frac{1}{\hbar^2} \frac{\partial^2 E}{\partial k_z^2} \cdot F_z$$

$$\dot{v}_x = \frac{1}{m_{x\,\text{eff}}} F_x \qquad \dot{v}_y = \frac{1}{m_{y\,\text{eff}}} F_y \qquad \dot{v}_z = \frac{1}{m_{z\,\text{eff}}} F_z \tag{VII.6.27}$$

We see, then, that three effective masses determine the acceleration in the directions of the three principal axes

$$m_{x\,\text{eff}} = \frac{\hbar^2}{\dfrac{\partial^2 E}{\partial k_x^2}} \qquad m_{y\,\text{eff}} = \frac{\hbar^2}{\dfrac{\partial^2 E}{\partial k_y^2}} \qquad m_{z\,\text{eff}} = \frac{\hbar^2}{\dfrac{\partial^2 E}{\partial k_z^2}} \tag{VII.6.28}$$

For a force $\mathbf{F}$ pointing in an arbitrary direction, the acceleration $\dot{\mathbf{v}}$ will thus, in general, no longer have the same direction as the force $\mathbf{F}$.

What are now the physical consequences of Eqs. (VII.6.22) and (VII.6.23) and (VII.6.26) and (VII.6.28)? The most striking feature of these relations is perhaps that Eqs. (VII.6.23) and (VII.6.28) lead to a negative effective mass at the upper edge of the band, where $E(\mathbf{k})$ has a maximum[1] (see Figs. VII.3.10 to VII.3.12), so that the second derivative of the energy with respect to the wave number becomes negative. For a force acting in the direction of motion, an electron energetically close to the upper band edge is hence decelerated instead of accelerated.[2]

[1] This apparently so obvious statement does not apply with such generality. In three-dimensional lattices, the relations at the band edges can become very complex. We mentioned this already on p. 180 with reference to the face-centered cubic lattice.

[2] We should note that the transition from positive effective masses in the lower part of the band to negative effective masses in the upper part of the band does not take place by way of $m_{\text{eff}} = 0$, but by way of $m_{\text{eff}} = \infty$. This applies, however, only for one coordinate direction at a time, e.g., the x direction. In the three-dimensional case an electron with the particular energy pertaining hereto will fail to react only to a force acting purely in the x direction because of $m_{\text{eff}} = \infty$, whereas for the y and z directions the effective masses will remain finite. Thus,

This statement ceases to be objectionable as soon as it is remembered what almost absurd procedure was followed in defining the effective mass. An electron in a crystal is subject, first of all, to very strong forces exerted by the lattice. In defining the effective mass by the equation $\dot{\mathbf{v}} = \mathbf{F}/m_{\text{eff}}$, we in effect disregard the lattice forces and act as though the added external force $\mathbf{F}$ alone were present. It must not surprise us if, in this procedure, strange values are obtained for the effective mass, since the lattice forces disregarded in the equation of definition $\dot{\mathbf{v}} = \mathbf{F}/m_{\text{eff}}$ express themselves in these anomalous values.

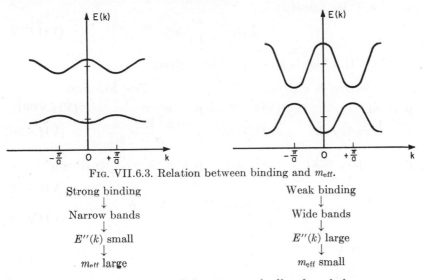

FIG. VII.6.3. Relation between binding and m_{eff}.

Strong binding · Weak binding
↓ · ↓
Narrow bands · Wide bands
↓ · ↓
$E''(k)$ small · $E''(k)$ large
↓ · ↓
m_{eff} large · m_{eff} small

In particular, for an electron lying energetically close below an upper edge of a band, the circumstances are such that a force acting in the direction of motion further increases the energy, so that the electron is brought still closer to the band edge. As a result, its eigenfunction becomes still more nearly a standing wave by increased Bragg reflection of the lattice and the mean velocity of the electron decreases. It is seen clearly how the action of the lattice, which is disregarded in the equation of definition $\dot{\mathbf{v}} = \mathbf{F}/m_{\text{eff}}$, is responsible for the seemingly strange behavior of the electron.

We had noted on page 200, item 6, that strong binding of the electrons to the atomic cores leads to narrow allowed energy bands. Now Fig. VII.6.3 shows that for narrow energy bands $E''(\mathbf{k})$ is small and

the uppermost electrons of a half-filled band will never fail to react to forces of arbitrary direction; their inability to change their velocity exists at most for specific directions.

that for wide energy bands $E''(\mathbf{k})$ is large. Thus Eq. (VII.6.23) leads to large effective masses for strong binding and small effective masses for weak binding, a very plausible result.

d. Summary

At the close of this section we shall collect once more the relations between mean momentum $\mathbf{p}$, mean velocity $\mathbf{v}$, wave number $\mathbf{k}$, and force $\mathbf{F}$ which have been obtained in the last two paragraphs. The simplifications obtained for the case of the free electron, for which the variation $E(\mathbf{k})$, namely,

$$E(\mathbf{k}) = \frac{\hbar^2}{2m}|\mathbf{k}|^2 \qquad\qquad \text{(VII.6.29)}$$

(see Fig. VII.3.10a) is known, are also given.

Electron in a Crystal		Free Electron	
$\mathbf{p} = m\mathbf{v}$	(VII.5.09)	$\mathbf{p} = m \cdot \mathbf{v}$	(VII.5.09)
$\mathbf{v} = \dfrac{1}{\hbar}\operatorname{grad}_\mathbf{k} E(\mathbf{k})$	(VII.5.10)	$\mathbf{v} = \dfrac{\hbar \cdot \mathbf{k}}{m} = \dfrac{h}{m\lambda}$	(VII.6.30)
$\mathbf{p} = \dfrac{m}{\hbar}\operatorname{grad}_\mathbf{k} E(\mathbf{k})$	(VII.5.03)	$\mathbf{p} = \hbar \cdot \mathbf{k} = \dfrac{h}{\lambda}$ (de Broglie)	
			(VII.6.31)
$\mathbf{F} = \hbar\,\dot{\mathbf{k}}$	(VII.6.12)	$\mathbf{F} = \hbar\dot{\mathbf{k}} = \dot{\mathbf{p}}$ (Newton)	
			(VII.6.32)

$$m_{x\text{eff}} = \frac{\hbar^2}{\dfrac{\partial^2 E}{\partial k_x^2}}$$

$$m_{y\text{eff}} = \frac{\hbar^2}{\dfrac{\partial^2 E}{\partial k_y^2}} \qquad \text{(VII.6.28)} \qquad m_{\text{eff}} = \frac{\hbar^2}{\dfrac{\hbar^2}{2m}\cdot 2} = m \qquad \text{(VII.6.33)}$$

$$m_{z\text{eff}} = \frac{\hbar^2}{\dfrac{\partial^2 E}{\partial k_z^2}}$$

$$\dot{v}_x = \frac{1}{m_{x\text{eff}}}F_x$$

$$\dot{v}_y = \frac{1}{m_{y\text{eff}}}F_y \qquad \text{(VII.6.27)} \qquad \dot{\mathbf{v}} = \frac{1}{m}\mathbf{F} \qquad \text{(VII.6.34)}$$

$$\dot{v}_z = \frac{1}{m_{z\text{eff}}}F_z$$

Remarks: 1. Equation (VII.5.09) applies for the quantum-mechanical mean values $\mathbf{p}$ and $\mathbf{v}$ of the momentum operator $\hbar/j\,\operatorname{grad}$ and the velocity operator $\hbar/jm$ grad and is hence a simple consequence of the difference in the factor m of the two operators. For the sake of graphic interpretation, the quantum-mechanical mean value $\mathbf{v}$ of the velocity operator may then be identified with the group velocity both for the electron in a crystal and for a free electron.

2. From the analogy of Eqs. (VII.6.12) and (VII.6.32) we see that for an electron in a crystal the so-called lattice momentum $\hbar\mathbf{k}$ plays the same role as the ordinary momentum $\mathbf{p}$ for the free electron. In general, $\mathbf{p} = \hbar\mathbf{k}$ applies only for the free electron.

3. Equations (VII.6.27) and (VII.6.28) apply in this simple form only when the tensor $\partial^2 E/k_l\,\partial k_m$ [see Eq. (VII.6.25)] has already been transformed to principal axes.

§7. The Transitions of an Electron into the Next Higher Band Effected by an External Force F

In §6 we have seen that the stationary solutions

$$\psi(\mathbf{r};\,\mathbf{k}) = u(\mathbf{r};\,\mathbf{k})\,e^{j\mathbf{k}\cdot\mathbf{r}} \qquad\qquad \text{(VII.7.01)}$$

of the force-free problem have a certain significance also for the behavior of an electron under the influence of an external force $\mathbf{F}$. It was shown that even when acted upon by an external force $\mathbf{F}$ the electron was represented at any instance by a ψ function as given by (VII.7.01). At the same time, the wave vector $\mathbf{k}$ did not remain constant, but varied according to the law

$$\dot{\mathbf{k}} = \frac{1}{\hbar}\,\mathbf{F} \qquad\qquad \text{(VII.6.12)}$$

In treating, here, the transitions of an electron into another band under the influence of an external force $\mathbf{F}$ in a manner originally employed by Zener,[1] we utilize another significance which the stationary solutions of the force-free problem retain in the transition to the problem with an external force. To explain this significance we recall the well-known wave-mechanical calculations on the transmission of an electron through a potential barrier (tunnel effect). Here the potential barrier is not treated as an external force, and there is no attempt to seek solutions varying with time of the force-free problem; instead, a stationary solution is obtained of the problem with potential barrier. The solution in front of the barrier is then composed of two stationary solutions of the force-free problem, which may be

[1] C. Zener, *Proc. Roy. Soc.* (*London*), **A145**: 523 (1934).

interpreted as incident and reflected waves and thus represent electrons which are moving toward the potential barrier and have been reflected by it, respectively.[1] In the space beyond the potential barrier the solution is identical with one stationary solution of the force-free problem and is interpreted as a transmitted wave. The desired probability of transmission of the electrons through the barrier is the ratio of the squares of the amplitudes of the transmitted and the incident wave, i.e., of two stationary solutions of the force-free problem.

Zener utilizes this significance of the stationary solutions of the force-free problem for the problem with an external force—a significance entirely different from that in Houston's procedure—for the treatment of the transition of electrons into another band. Just as in the treatment of the tunnel effect, we first obtain a stationary solution of the problem with external force. In one part of space this solution is identified with electrons in the lower band, in another part of space, on the other hand, with electrons which have passed over into the upper band.

Zener obtains the stationary solution of the problem with external force[2] $\mathbf{F}$

$$ -\frac{\hbar^2}{2m}\,\psi''(x) - (eU(x) + F\cdot x)\psi(x) = \mathbf{E}\psi(x) \qquad \text{(VII.7.02)} $$

by the following consideration: Even field strengths of the order of the breakdown field strengths (e.g., 10^5 to 10^6 volts cm^{-1}) produce potential differences of only $3\cdot 10^{-3}$ to $3\cdot 10^{-2}$ volt within a lattice constant (e.g., $3\cdot 10^{-8}$ cm). On the other hand, the variations in the lattice potential U resulting from the atom cores within a lattice constant are of the order of 10 volts.[3] We see hence that in (VII.7.02) the term $F\cdot x$ is practically constant, as compared to the lattice potential $U(x)$,

---

[1] It should be recalled that an unlimited plane wave of finite amplitude is interpreted most simply, in view of normalization difficulties in infinite space, as a representation of a beam of many electrons of equal velocity rather than as a representation of a single electron. The square of the amplitude of this wave is then a measure for the intensity of this "cathode-ray beam."

[2] For simplicity we consider the one-dimensional problem. For the reason for employing $\mathbf{E}$ in place of E, see p. 226.

[3] Along a straight line along which there lies a row of atom cores the variations of potential are even infinitely large since the potential energy of an electron becomes negatively infinite when it approaches the nucleus of an atom core arbitrarily closely. Since the valence electrons, which are here of interest, remain at a certain distance from the nuclei of the atom cores, the ionization potentials give a reasonable order of magnitude for the potential variations in question. These are, however, of the order of 10 volts. The Fourier coefficients of the threefold periodic function $U(x, y, z)$ are of the same order of magnitude. See H. A. Bethe in Geiger and Scheel, *op. cit.*, vol. XXIV, part 2, p. 423.

over a range of many lattice constants (see Fig. VII.7.1). For this reason, Zener claims that

$$\psi(x) = u(x; k(x)) \, e^{j \int_{x=0}^{x} k(x)dx} \qquad (VII.7.03)$$

is a good approximate solution of (VII.7.02). Here the wave number $k(x)$ is now a function of x in so far as it depends in the same manner on $E + Fx$ as on E in the force-free case, i.e., as in Figs. VII.3.10 to

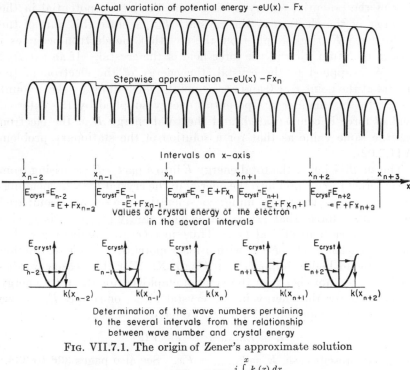

Actual variation of potential energy $-eU(x) - Fx$

Stepwise approximation $-eU(x) - Fx_n$

Intervals on x-axis

Values of crystal energy of the electron in the several intervals

Determination of the wave numbers pertaining to the several intervals from the relationship between wave number and crystal energy

FIG. VII.7.1. The origin of Zener's approximate solution

$$\psi(x) = u(x; k(x)) \, e^{j \int_{x=0}^{x} k(x) \, dx}$$

VII.3.12.[1] This is seen most simply by subdividing the x axis into intervals $x_1, x_2, \ldots x_n, x_{n+1}, \ldots$ and approximating Eq. (VII.7.02) within an interval $x_n < x < x_{n+1}$ covering several lattice constants by

$$-\frac{\hbar^2}{2m} \psi''(x) - eU(x)\psi(x) = E_{\text{crystal}} \psi(x) \qquad (VII.7.04)$$

[1] So far Figs. VII.3.10 to VII.3.12 have always been regarded as representations of the dependence of the energy in the crystal E on the wave number k. In quite the same manner they represent the inverse function, i.e., the dependence of the wave number k on the energy in the crystal E_{crystal}.

with $E_{\text{crystal}} = E + Fx_n$, i.e., by the force-free Schrödinger equation with the value $E + Fx_n$ for the energy of the electron in the crystal.

To explain the concept of the energy of the electron in the crystal E_{crystal}, we note that the energy of the electron in the crystal is in part kinetic, in part potential in nature. In the potential energy we can again distinguish between the part which arises from the lattice potential $U(x)$ and the part which arises from the external force F. We now combine the kinetic energy of the electron in the crystal with the portion of the potential energy arising from the lattice potential in the "energy of the electron in the crystal" E_{crystal}, since this part of the total energy E arises simply from the fact that the electron occupies a certain quantum state in the force field of the crystal. If an external force F is applied to the crystal, the energy of the electron in the crystal at the point $x = 0$ and at the point x must differ by the amount $F \cdot x$. In this manner the potential energy supplied by the external field of force is compensated, and the total energy E of the electron has the same value as that for a solution of the stationary problem (VII.7.02).

The subdivision of the total energy E into a part $-F \cdot x$ arising from the external force F and into the energy in the crystal E_{crystal} is meaningful only because the forces under consideration are so small compared to the lattice forces that $-F \cdot x$ varies very slowly in comparison with the rapid variations of $-eU(x)$. Thus, in $U(x)$ we are dealing with a micropotential, in $(1/e)F \cdot x$, with a macropotential. This distinction will be found highly important in Chap. X. For this reason we distinguish even now between the symbol employed for the total energy E and that for the energy in the crystal E_{crystal} or simply E. If we denote the macropotential by $V(x)$, we have

$$E = E_{\text{crystal}} + (-e) \cdot V(x)$$

or, in the present case, $E = E_{\text{crystal}} - Fx$. See also pages 336 to 338.

Zener's formulation (VII.7.03) may also be written in the form

$$\psi(x) = u(x; k(x)) \cdot e^{j\left[\int_{x=0}^{x_n} k(x)dx + \int_{x=x_n}^{x} k(x)dx\right]}$$

$$= u(x; k(x)) \cdot e^{j\int_{x=0}^{x=x_n} k(x)dx} \cdot e^{j\int_{x=x_n}^{x} k(x)dx}$$

In the interval considered this becomes, because of $k(x) \approx k(x_n)$,

$$\psi(x) = u(x; k(x_n)) \cdot e^{j\int_{x=0}^{x=x_n} k(x)dx} \cdot e^{jk(x_n)(x-x_n)}$$

$$\psi(x) = \text{const} \cdot u(x; k(x_n)) \cdot e^{jk(x_n)x} \tag{VII.7.05}$$

This, however, is the solution of the substitute force-free problem[1] (VII.7.04) introduced for the interval $x_n < x < x_{n+1}$.

As long as the value $E + F \cdot x$ of the energy of the electron in the crystal falls into an allowed energy band of the force-free problem (VII.7.04) (see Fig. VII.7.2), the wave number k is real and (VII.7.03) has the usual character of a lattice-modulated plane wave, though with a wave number which is slowly variable in space. This applies, e.g., up to the point $x = x_B$. For a further increase in x, the value $E + F \cdot x$

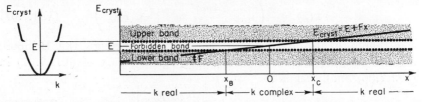

FIG. VII.7.2. The regions of real and complex wave number in the passage of an electron through a forbidden band.

of the energy of the electron in the crystal enters a forbidden band, the wave number k becomes complex, and (VII.7.03) falls off exponentially [see page 199, item 2, also Eq. (VII.7.05)]. As, for further increase in x, the value $E + F \cdot x$ of the energy of the electron in the crystal finally enters the next band, e.g., at $x = x_C > x_B$, the wave number k becomes once more real and (VII.7.03) assumes again the character of a lattice-modulated wave. As for the tunnel effect, the transmission probability w of the electron through the forbidden band is given by the ratio $|\psi(x_C)|^2/|\psi(x_B)|^2$. With (VII.7.03) this leads to

$$
w = \left(\frac{|\psi(x_C)|}{|\psi(x_B)|}\right)^2 = \left(\frac{|u(x_C; k(x_C))| \cdot e^{-\int_0^{x_C} \mathrm{Im}\, k(x)\, dx}}{|u(x_B; k(x_B))| \cdot e^{-\int_0^{x_B} \mathrm{Im}\, k(x)\, dx}}\right)^2
$$

$$
= \left(\frac{|u(x_C; k(x_C))|}{|u(x_B; k(x_B))|} \cdot e^{-\int_{x_B}^{x_C} \mathrm{Im}\, k(x)\, dx}\right)^2
$$

Zener writes, by way of approximation,

$$
w \approx e^{-2 \int_{x_B}^{x_C} \mathrm{Im}\, k(x)\, dx} \tag{VII.7.06}
$$

[1] Similar reasoning might justify the solution $u(x; k(x))\, e^{ik(x) \cdot x}$. As compared with Zener's formula (VII.7.03), this solution would have the drawback that the phase rotation between, e.g., an arbitrary point $x = x_I$ and the point $x = 0$ would

assuming that the lattice-periodic modulation factors $u(x_C; k(x_C))$ and $u(x_B; k(x_B))$ are immaterial for an estimate of the order of magnitude.[1]

To evaluate (VII.7.06), an explicit formulation of the dependence of the wave number k on the energy of the electron in the crystal E_{crystal} is required. Zener here utilizes papers by Hill and specializes Hill's results for a lattice potential $U(x) = 2V_1 \cos 2\pi(x/a)$ with a small amplitude V_1, thus coming within the range of the Brillouin approximation. The result given by him[2]

$$k(x) = \frac{\pi}{a}\left(1 \pm j\frac{4ma^2}{h^2}\sqrt{V_1^2 - (Fx)^2}\right) \qquad (\text{VII.7.07})$$

can therefore also be obtained by carrying through the Brillouin approximation. Substitution of the imaginary part of (VII.7.07) in (VII.7.06) finally leads to

$$w = \exp\left[-\frac{\pi^2}{h^2}\frac{maE_{CV}^2}{F}\right] \qquad (\text{VII.7.08})$$

Here $E_{CV} = 2V_1$ is the energy gap between the conduction band C and the valence band V, i.e., the width of the forbidden band traversed.[3]

---

be determined by the wave vector at one point only, namely, $x = x_I$. In the Zener approximation (VII.7.03), the integral form of the exponent

$$\left[\int_{x=0}^{x_I} k(x)\,dx\right]$$

takes care that the wave vector appropriate to any one point of the interval $0 \cdots x_I$ enters into the progression of the phase at this point.

Apart from this, Zener's approximate solution is the proper application to the electron in the crystal of the method of Wentzel, Kramers, and Brillouin (W.K.B. method). Zener's solution corresponds to the zero step in the W.K.B. method. With regard to the W.K.B. method, see, e.g., W. Weizel, "Lehrbuch der theoretischen Physik," vol. II, p. 1010, Springer-Verlag OHG, Berlin, 1950.

[1] This has led to a criticism by F. Cernuschi, *Proc. Cambridge Phil. Soc.*, **32**: 276 (1936).

[2] Zener gives for the factor ahead of the root mistakenly $8ma^2/h^2$. Zener's final result is again correct, however.

[3] It was noted already on p. 217 that Houston's approach, as presented in §6, when carried further must also answer the question of Zener transitions. Houston himself has obtained in this manner a result which deviates from (VII.7.08) by the factor $(2\pi)^2$. In fact, this approach yields Zener's result (VII.7.08) except for the entirely immaterial factor $(\pi/3)^2$. This is particularly satisfying because Zener's calculation is not wholly convincing in several respects. Thus Zener's formula (VII.7.03), unlike Houston's formulas in §6, does not pass over into an exact solution in the transition to the limit from an electron in a crystal to a free electron (amplitude of the potential variations $\rightarrow 0$). An attempt at verification shows this immediately. The fact that, in Zener's considerations, a wave reflected at the upper band edge does not occur may be related to this.

This is, thus, the probability that an electron striking the upper edge of the band passes through the forbidden band into the next higher band. How often in unit time does an electron acted upon by the force F strike the upper edge of the band in which it happens to be? In §6 we saw that the wave number k changes at the rate $\dot{k} = F/\hbar$ under the influence of F. In this process the electron oscillates energetically back and forth between the upper and the lower band edge, as indicated by Figs. VII.3.10 to VII.3.12. A k interval $2\pi/a$ must be traversed for a full cycle from the upper band edge to the lower band edge and back to the upper band edge. At a rate $\dot{k} = F/\hbar$ this requires a time $(2\pi/a)/(F/\hbar) = h/aF$. Thus the electron strikes the upper band edge aF/h times in unit time.

The number of transitions per second into the upper band is thus given by

$$\frac{aF}{h} w = \frac{aF}{h} \exp\left[-\frac{\pi^2}{h^2}\frac{maE_{CV}^2}{F}\right] \qquad \text{(VII.7.09)}$$

In Fig. VII.7.3 this equation has been evaluated for $a = 3 \cdot 10^{-8}$ cm and three different widths E_{CV} of the forbidden band. We see that the effect is completely negligible up to a certain, very high, field strength $|E| = F/e$ and sets in here quite abruptly. This confirms the statement in §6 that, for normal field strengths, Zener transitions of a lattice electron into the next higher band are entirely negligible.

To complete the picture, it should be noted that the oscillation in energy of the electron is accompanied by an oscillation in space. Thus, for the states with $0 < k < +\pi/a$ we have in the lowest band of Fig. VII.3.10 and according to (VII.5.10) positive velocities $v = E'(k)/\hbar$, whereas for the states $+\pi/a < k < +2\pi/a$ the velocities are negative, etc. For the distance of oscillation we obtain, therefore,

$$l_{osc} = \int_{t\,\text{bottom}}^{t\,\text{top}} v\, dt = \int_{k=0}^{k=+\frac{\pi}{a}} \frac{1}{\hbar} E'(k) \cdot \frac{dt}{dk} \cdot dk$$

$$l_{osc} = \int_{k=0}^{k=+\frac{\pi}{a}} E'(k) \cdot \frac{dk}{\hbar\dot{k}}$$

With (VII.6.12) this becomes

$$l_{osc} = \int_{k=0}^{k=+\frac{\pi}{a}} E'(k) \cdot \frac{dk}{F}$$

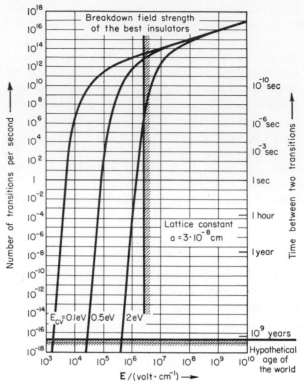

Fɪɢ. VII.7.3. Number of transitions per second of an electron in the crystal into the next band.

$$E_{CV} = \text{width of forbidden band}$$
$$\mathbf{E} = \text{field strength}$$

Based on Eq. (VII.7.09) or (VII.7.13) with

$$m_{\text{eff}} = m \, \frac{2ma^2 E_{CV}}{h^2} \text{ (Brillouin approximation)}$$

and furthermore, because of the constancy of F in time and space,

$$l_{\text{osc}} = \frac{1}{F} \int_{k=0}^{k=+\frac{\pi}{a}} E'(k) \, dk = \frac{E_{\text{top}} - E_{\text{bottom}}}{F} \qquad \text{(VII.7.10)}$$

If the external force F arises from an electrical field $\mathbf{E}$, we have

$$l_{\text{osc}} = \frac{\frac{1}{e} \, (E_{\text{top}} - E_{\text{bottom}})}{|\mathbf{E}|} \qquad \text{(VII.7.11)}$$

With the aid of this equation we shall show on pages 257 to258 that, for normal field strengths **E**, a full realization of this oscillation is prevented by collisions of the electron with phonons and lattice defects.

Further discussion is needed to settle whether this remark is applicable to valence electrons. To begin with, it can be applied with safety only to the excess electrons in the conduction band and to the holes in the valence band. For a valence band which is fully occupied by electrons, it becomes meaningless to speak of collision processes. Since all states are occupied, a collision process could consist only of an exchange of states between two electrons; in view of the indistinguishability of the electrons, this cannot be regarded as a real effect. (The Schrödinger function for a many-electron system is a Slater determinant and merely changes its sign for an exchange of two rows.) By the same reasoning, only a formal significance can be attached to the oscillation of the valence electrons in the fully occupied valence band. We shall not discuss the question further to what extent the thermal loosening of the occupation of the valence band alters the situation and to what extent it may be meaningful, after all, to speak of thermal collisions in connection with the valence electrons at the upper edge of the valence band, i.e., just before the Zener transition into the next higher band.

In any case, we have here arrived at a point where we have the impression that the band model, with its electrons in various energy states (in the valence band) spread over the entire crystal, is no longer adequate to the facts. In viewing the totality of valence electrons in a germanium crystal, with two electrons accommodated in each of the tetrahedrally arranged valence bonds, we can scarcely escape the impression that the atomistic approach is more appropriate.

The atomistic treatment of the Zener effect could be carried out to a rough approximation by treating the liberation by a strong field through tunneling of an electron bound in a potential well. The work required to free the electron classically, i.e., without tunnel effect, would be, just as in the band model, E_{CV}; for, in such a liberation, a valence electron is converted into a conduction electron. We can get an idea of the results to be expected from the papers of W. Franz,[1] which, however, must be modified somewhat in detail. In any case, we obtain in this manner a law in which the exponential factor takes the form

$$\exp\left[-\frac{4}{3}\frac{\sqrt{2m_{\text{eff}}}}{\hbar F}(E_{CV})^{3/2} \right] \qquad \text{(VII.7.12)}$$

[1] W. Franz, *Ergeb. exakt. Naturw.*, **27**: 16, Eq. (34) (1953).

A corresponding variation with

$$\exp\left[-\frac{4}{3}\frac{\sqrt{2m}}{\hbar F}(\Delta E)^{3/2} \right]$$

is obtained also for the field emission of electrons from cold metallic surfaces.[1]

It may seem at first sight that there are material differences between these variations and the Zener formula (VII.7.08). The occurrence of the bandwidth E_{CV} in the second power in the Zener formula, as contrasted with the $3/2$ power in the field emission laws, is particularly striking.

However, we can separate out, in the exponents of (VII.7.08) and (VII.7.09), the factor

$$2^{1/2}\frac{ma E_{CV}^{1/2}}{h} = \sqrt{\frac{2m^2a^2 E_{CV}}{h^2}}$$

and interpret it as $\sqrt{m_{\text{eff}}}$, where m_{eff} is the effective mass obtained in carrying through the Brillouin approximation.[2] Equation (VII.7.09) then takes on the following form:

$$\frac{\text{Number of transitions}}{\text{Number of valence electrons} \cdot \text{unit time}}$$

$$= \frac{aF}{h}\exp\left[-\frac{\pi^2}{h}\left(\frac{m_{\text{eff}}}{2}\right)^{1/2}\frac{E_{CV}^{3/2}}{F} \right]$$

$$= \frac{aF}{h}\exp\left[-\frac{\pi}{4}\frac{\sqrt{2m_{\text{eff}}}}{\hbar F}(E_{CV})^{3/2} \right] \quad (VII.7.13)$$

In this form (VII.7.13) of the Zener formula (VII.7.09), the exponential factor is in fact very similar to that of the field emission laws. Thus, compared with (VII.7.12), the only difference in the exponent is the difference between the factors $4/3$ and $\pi/4$. The form (VII.7.13) is preferred by several authors[3] as being less tied to details and peculiar-

---

[1] See H. A. Bethe in Geiger and Scheel, *op. cit.*, vol. XXIV, part 2, p. 439, Eqs. (19.12) and (19.13).

[2] H. Fröhlich, "Elektronentheorie der Metalle," bottom of p. 44, Eq. (24), Springer-Verlag OHG, Berlin, 1936.

[3] See, e.g., K. B. McAfee, E. J. Ryder, W. Shockley, and M. Sparks, *Phys. Rev.*, **83:** 650 (1951). In Eq. (1) of this paper the exponent is too large by a factor 2. This seems to be simply a printer's error, however, since in the numerical equation (3) of the same paper the exponent has again the right value.

ities of the Brillouin approximation than (VII.7.09). Hence we plot in Fig. VII.7.4 the results obtained from an evaluation of Eq. (VII.7.13) for the same data as those employed with Eq. (VII.7.09) in Fig. VII.7.3. We see that the principal characteristic of the effect, namely, the abrupt onset at a field strength of the order of 10^4 to 10^6 volts cm^{-1}, remains unaltered.

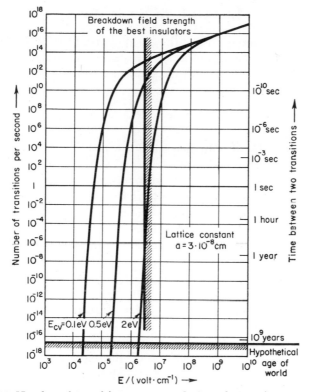

FIG. VII.7.4. Number of transitions per second of an electron in a crystal into the next band. E_{CV} = width of the forbidden band. E = field strength. Based on Eq. (VII.7.13) with $m_{eff} = m$.

Finally, we note that Zener himself was inclined to believe that the effect under consideration was of importance for the breakdown of insulators.[1] At present, there is some question as to whether break-

[1] We have seen on pp. 12 and 16 that an insulating crystal has a fully occupied and hence nonconducting valence band and empty conduction band (see also pp. 263 and 296). The insulating crystal can be made conducting only by introducing electrons into the empty conduction band. This could occur through the

down may not set in at lower field strengths as a result of other effects. However, the interest in the Zener effect has been materially increased recently, since McAfee, Ryder, Shockley, and Sparks have related to it the failure of rectifiers at high reverse voltages.[1]

§8. The Effect of an Optical Alternating Field on an Electron in a Crystal

In §6 and §7 we have studied the effect of an added force, constant in time, and more particularly of an electrostatic field, on an electron in a crystal. It was found that an electron in a crystal is accelerated in accord with the law[2]

$$\hbar \dot{\mathbf{k}} = \mathbf{F} \qquad\qquad (VII.8.01)$$

Transitions into the next higher band are possible only at very high field strengths, of the order of the breakdown field strength. The electron then passes over into that state of the next higher band which has the same reduced wave vector $\mathbf{k}$ as the original state. However, such transitions are completely negligible for field strengths which lie a power of 10 below the breakdown field strength. The acceleration process (VII.8.01) is then confined entirely to the same energy band.

We now claim that the action of an optical alternating field is, conversely, such that transitions of the electron into that state of the next higher band are excited for which the reduced wave vector $\mathbf{k}$ is the same as for the original state, whereas transitions within the same band are forbidden.

At first sight this statement may seem somewhat strange. We might well expect that the effects of the electrostatic field would follow from those of the electromagnetic alternating field in passing to

---

Zener effect above certain field strengths. Since the effect sets in very suddenly as the field strength is increased (Fig. VII.7.3), the crystal would suddenly become very highly conducting above a certain field strength, i.e., exhibit the phenomenon of "breakdown."

[1] See also G. K. McKay and K. B. McAfee, *Phys. Rev.*, **91**: 1079 (1953); and G. K. McKay, *Phys. Rev.*, **94**: 877 (1954).

[2] The quantity $\hbar\mathbf{k}$ thus assumes the role of a generalized momentum. For this reason it is frequently called the "crystal momentum" (Shockley, *op. cit.*, p. 143). For a free electron the quantum-mechanical mean value $\mathbf{p}$ of the momentum, for which we have derived the formula $\mathbf{p} = (m/\hbar)\, \mathrm{grad}_\mathbf{k}\, E(\mathbf{k})$, is, in fact, identical with the quantity $\hbar\mathbf{k}$. See Eq. (VII.6.31).

the limit

Angular frequency → 0

An unbridgeable contradiction appears to separate the two statements "continuous acceleration within a band and no transitions into higher bands" and "no transitions within the same band, but only transitions to higher bands with conservation of the wave vector."[1]

We must comment on this point that for the transition to the limit $\omega \to 0$ not only an electrostatic but also a magnetostatic field of equal magnitude is left. We shall see in the study of the calculations reported below that a further reason for the difficulties encountered in the passage to the limit $\omega \to 0$ may rest in the fact that the perturbation loses its periodicity in space in this limiting case. This makes it impossible to work with a finite fundamental domain of the crystal and with energy states of the unperturbed problem which are at least in principle discrete. However, the size of the fundamental domain should have no physical significance, and we do not readily see how, from this point of view, we can arrive at a decision, below which frequency ω transitions within the same band dominate and transitions into the next higher band are insignificant.[2] Apart from this we have the impression that the prohibition of optical transitions within the same band is statistical in nature. In the following calculations only matter, namely, the electron in the crystal, is subjected to statistical quantum laws, whereas the electromagnetic alternating field is treated classically. We hope that the question may eventually be solved whether, under these circumstances, working with an infinitely large fundamental domain, with a continuous distribution of allowed energy values within the allowed bands, and with a consequently necessary wave-packet formulation for the electron, leads to a finite probability

---

[1] The situation is not simplified by the fact that the calculation for an electromagnetic alternating field given below permits the transition to the limit "angular frequency → 0" at least formally and that here transitions to neighboring states of the same band remain forbidden. In carrying through the calculation, we shall expressly indicate for what initial assumptions such a formal passage to the limit "angular frequency → 0" becomes inadmissible.

However, the contradiction is tempered to a certain extent by the fact that even a field which is constant in time effects transitions into higher bands; it is true that this has been noted so far only for strong external fields (Zener effect, §7). More recently it has been found, however, that these transitions into higher bands play a role in certain problems even for weak constant fields. [See D. Pfirsch and E. Spenke, *Z. Physik*, **137**: 309 (1954).]

[2] Here a comparison of the angular frequency ω of the alternating field with the angular frequency $E_{CV}/\hbar$ pertaining to the transition "conduction band → valence band" may be more appropriate.

for transitions within the same band even for an alternating field in satisfactory manner, so that in the limit $\omega \to 0$ this probability for transitions within the same band dominates and the probability of transitions into the next higher band becomes of minor importance.

After these preliminary remarks, we reproduce the description of the action of an electromagnetic alternating field on an electron in a crystal which is now customary.[1] The electromagnetic field strengths **E** and **H** are derived from a vector potential[2]

$$
\left.
\begin{aligned}
\mathbf{A} &= \{A_x, 0, 0\} \\
A_x &= -\frac{cF}{\omega e}\sin\frac{\omega}{c}(y - ct)
\end{aligned}
\right\} \qquad \text{(VII.8.02)}
$$

with the aid of the equations

$$
\mathbf{E} = -\frac{1}{c}\frac{\partial \mathbf{A}}{\partial t} \qquad \text{(VII.8.03)}
$$

$$
\mathbf{H} = \operatorname{curl}\mathbf{A} \qquad \text{(VII.8.04)}
$$

The quantity F has here the meaning of a force amplitude, since **E** and **H** take the form

$$
\mathbf{E} = \{E_x, 0, 0\}
$$

with
$$
E_x = -\frac{1}{e}F\cos\frac{\omega}{c}(y - ct) \qquad \text{(VII.8.05)}
$$

and
$$
\mathbf{H} = \{0, 0, H_z\}
$$

with
$$
H_z = +\frac{1}{e}F\cos\frac{\omega}{c}(y - ct) \qquad \text{(VII.8.06)}
$$

In the presence of a vector potential **A**, the Schrödinger equation becomes[3]

$$
-\frac{\hbar^2}{2m}\Delta\psi - eU(\mathbf{r})\cdot\psi - j\frac{e\hbar}{mc}\mathbf{A}\cdot\operatorname{grad}\psi = +j\hbar\frac{\partial}{\partial t}\psi \qquad \text{(VII.8.07)}
$$

---

[1] See, e.g., Fröhlich, op. cit., pp. 354 and 355.

[2] For simplicity, we have here assumed a crystal with $\varepsilon = 1$ and $\mu = 1$. Otherwise, a refractive index $n = \sqrt{\varepsilon\mu}$ would have to be introduced in (VII.8.02)

$$
A_x = -\frac{cF}{\omega e}\sin\omega\cdot\frac{n}{c}\left(y - \frac{c}{n}t\right)
$$

and (VII.8.04) would have to take the form $\mu\mathbf{H} = \operatorname{curl}\mathbf{A}$. Incidentally, $c = $ velocity of light $= 3\cdot 10^{10}$ cm-sec^{-1}.

[3] See, e.g., Weizel, op. cit., vol. II, p. 881, Eq. (24).

or specifically for (VII.8.02)

$$-\frac{\hbar^2}{2m}\Delta\psi - eU(\mathbf{r})\psi + \frac{F\cdot\hbar}{2m\omega}[e^{+j\frac{\omega}{c}(y-ct)} - e^{-j\frac{\omega}{c}(y-ct)}]\frac{\partial}{\partial x}\psi = +j\hbar\frac{\partial}{\partial t}\psi$$

(VII.8.08)

To obtain a solution we write

$$\psi(\mathbf{r},\,t) = \sum_l c_l(t)\psi_l(\mathbf{r},\,t)$$

(VII.8.09)

where the $\psi_l(\mathbf{r},\,t) = \psi_l(\mathbf{r})\,e^{-jE_lt/\hbar}$ are all the solutions (for all bands) of the unperturbed equation, i.e., of (VII.8.08) for $F = 0$. These solutions are periodic in space, with the fundamental domain of the crystal as period. The formula (VII.8.09) can hence represent a solution of the perturbed problem (VII.8.08) with $F \neq 0$ only if this solution is also periodic in the fundamental domain. However, for $\omega \to 0$ the perturbation term takes the form

$$+j\frac{F\hbar}{mc}(y - ct)\frac{\partial}{\partial x}\psi$$

and ceases to be periodic. Under these circumstances the solution $\psi(\mathbf{r},\,t)$ also cannot be periodic in space with a period constant in time, i.e., in a fixed fundamental domain. Hence the formula (VII.8.09), which is periodic in space, can no longer represent $\psi(\mathbf{r},\,t)$.[1] Thus, with the formulation (VII.8.09) we renounce even now the possibility of a meaningful transition to the limit $\omega \to 0$.

Substitution of (VII.8.09) in (VII.8.08) and utilization of the fact that the $\psi_l(\mathbf{r},\,t)$ satisfy the unperturbed equation [i.e., (VII.8.08) with $F = 0$] lead to

$$+\frac{F\hbar}{2m\omega}\sum_l c_l(t)[e^{+j\frac{\omega}{c}(y-ct)} - e^{-j\frac{\omega}{c}(y-ct)}]\frac{\partial}{\partial x}\psi_l = j\hbar\sum_l \dot{c}_l(t)\psi_l$$ (VII.8.10)

To determine the infinite number of unknown coefficients $c_l(t)$, we multiply from the left with $\psi_n^*(\mathbf{r},\,t)$ and integrate over the fundamental domain. In view of the orthogonality of the $\psi_n(\mathbf{r})$, $\psi_l(\mathbf{r})$ we then

[1] The case of the free electron acted upon by an external field F, which is treated at the beginning of §6, is apparently an example to the contrary. Here also the Schrödinger equation (VII.6.06) contains an aperiodic term. Nevertheless, the verified solution (VII.6.07) is periodic at every instant of time t. However, this opposing example is not valid since the period is time dependent, whereas, as emphasized above, (VII.8.09) has the fundamental domain as a fixed, invariable period at all times.

obtain

$$\int_{V_{\text{fund}}} \psi_n^* \psi_l \, dV = \delta_{nl} = \begin{cases} 1 & \text{for } n = l \\ 0 & \text{for } n \neq l \end{cases} \quad \text{(VII.8.11)}$$

$$+ \frac{1}{j} \frac{F}{2m\omega} \sum_l c_l(t) \cdot \int_{V_{\text{fund}}} \psi_n^*(\mathbf{r}, t) \, [e^{+j\frac{\omega}{c}(y-ct)} - e^{-j\frac{\omega}{c}(y-ct)}] \frac{\partial}{\partial x} \psi_l(\mathbf{r}, t) \, dV$$

$$= \sum_l \dot{c}_l(t) \, \delta_{nl} \quad \text{(VII.8.12)}$$

On the right side of (VII.8.12), we utilize (VII.8.11). On the left side we place the time factors, which are constant in space, ahead of the integral and obtain

$$+ \frac{F}{2m\hbar\omega} \sum_l c_l(t) \cdot [e^{-\frac{j}{\hbar}(E_l - E_n + \hbar\omega)t} \cdot \int_{V_{\text{fund}}} \psi_n^*(\mathbf{r}) \, e^{+j\frac{\omega}{c}y} \cdot \frac{\hbar}{j} \frac{\partial}{\partial x} \psi_l(\mathbf{r}) \, dV$$

$$- e^{-\frac{j}{\hbar}(E_l - E_n - \hbar\omega)t} \cdot \int_{V_{\text{fund}}} \psi_n^*(\mathbf{r}) \, e^{-j\frac{\omega}{c}y} \cdot \frac{\hbar}{j} \frac{\partial}{\partial x} \psi_l(\mathbf{r}) \, dV] = \dot{c}_n(t) \quad \text{(VII.8.13)}$$

If we proceed from an initial state in which only one particular state $l = s$ is occupied, we must set for $t = 0$

$$c_l(0) = \begin{cases} 1 & \text{for } l = s \\ 0 & \text{for } l \neq s \end{cases}$$

As long as $c_s \approx 1$ and $c_{l \neq s}(t) \ll 1$, we can then write by way of approximation[1]

$$+ \frac{F}{2m\hbar\omega} \cdot [\pi_{ns}^{(+)} \cdot e^{-\frac{j}{\hbar}(E_s - E_n + \hbar\omega)t} - \pi_{ns}^{(-)} \cdot e^{-\frac{j}{\hbar}(E_s - E_n - \hbar\omega)t}] = \dot{c}_n(t)$$

$$\text{(VII.8.14)}$$

where we have used the abbreviations

$$\left. \begin{aligned} \pi_{ns}^{(+)} &= \int_{V_{\text{fund}}} \psi_n^*(\mathbf{r}) \, e^{+j\frac{\omega}{c}y} \frac{\hbar}{j} \frac{\partial}{\partial x} \psi_s(\mathbf{r}) \, dV \\ \pi_{ns}^{(-)} &= \int_{V_{\text{fund}}} \psi_n^*(\mathbf{r}) \, e^{-j\frac{\omega}{c}y} \frac{\hbar}{j} \frac{\partial}{\partial x} \psi_s(\mathbf{r}) \, dV \end{aligned} \right\} \quad \text{(VII.8.15)}$$

---

[1] These assumptions are certainly fulfilled for a while at the beginning of the process. The "smallness of the perturbation" remains valid longer in proportion as the force amplitude F is smaller.

Carrying out the integration with respect to the time then yields

$$
c_n(t) = \frac{F}{2m\hbar\omega}\left[\pi_{ns}^{(+)}\frac{e^{-\frac{j}{\hbar}(E_s-E_n+\hbar\omega)t}-1}{-\frac{j}{\hbar}(E_s-E_n+\hbar\omega)}\right.
$$

$$
\left.-\pi_{ns}^{(-)}\frac{e^{-\frac{j}{\hbar}(E_s-E_n-\hbar\omega)t}-1}{-\frac{j}{\hbar}(E_s-E_n-\hbar\omega)}\right]
$$

$$
=\frac{F}{2m\hbar\omega}\left[\pi_{ns}^{(+)}\cdot\frac{e^{-j\frac{1}{2}\left(\frac{E_s-E_n}{\hbar}+\omega\right)t}-e^{+j\frac{1}{2}\left(\frac{E_s-E_n}{\hbar}+\omega\right)t}}{-2j\frac{1}{2}\left(\frac{E_s-E_n}{\hbar}+\omega\right)}\cdot e^{-j\frac{1}{2}\left(\frac{E_s-E_n}{\hbar}+\omega\right)t}\right.
$$

$$
\left.-\pi_{ns}^{(-)}\cdot\frac{e^{-j\frac{1}{2}\left(\frac{E_s-E_n}{\hbar}-\omega\right)t}-e^{+j\frac{1}{2}\left(\frac{E_s-E_n}{\hbar}-\omega\right)t}}{-2j\frac{1}{2}\left(\frac{E_s-E_n}{\hbar}-\omega\right)}\cdot e^{-j\frac{1}{2}\left(\frac{E_s-E_n}{\hbar}-\omega\right)t}\right]
$$

$$
=\frac{F}{2m\hbar\omega}\left[\pi_{ns}^{(+)}\cdot\frac{\sin\frac{1}{2}\left(\frac{E_s-E_n}{\hbar}+\omega\right)t}{\frac{1}{2}\left(\frac{E_s-E_n}{\hbar}+\omega\right)}\cdot e^{-j\frac{1}{2}\left(\frac{E_s-E_n}{\hbar}+\omega\right)t}\right.
$$

$$
\left.-\pi_{ns}^{(-)}\cdot\frac{\sin\frac{1}{2}\left(\frac{E_s-E_n}{\hbar}-\omega\right)t}{\frac{1}{2}\left(\frac{E_s-E_n}{\hbar}-\omega\right)}\cdot e^{-j\frac{1}{2}\left(\frac{E_s-E_n}{\hbar}-\omega\right)t}\right]
$$

$$
c_n(t)=\frac{F}{2m\hbar\omega}\left[\pi_{ns}^{(+)}\frac{\sin\frac{1}{2}\left(\omega-\frac{E_n-E_s}{\hbar}\right)t}{\frac{1}{2}\left(\omega-\frac{E_n-E_s}{\hbar}\right)}\cdot e^{-j\frac{1}{2}\left(\omega-\frac{E_n-E_s}{\hbar}\right)t}\right.
$$

$$
\left.-\pi_{ns}^{(-)}\cdot\frac{\sin\frac{1}{2}\left(\omega+\frac{E_n-E_s}{\hbar}\right)t}{\frac{1}{2}\left(\omega+\frac{E_n-E_s}{\hbar}\right)}\cdot e^{+j\frac{1}{2}\left(\omega+\frac{E_n-E_s}{\hbar}\right)t}\right] \qquad \text{(VII.8.16)}
$$

We shall now compare the absolute value of the two terms in the brackets. The exponentials in the two terms are immaterial in this respect since their exponent is imaginary, so that they are simply phase factors with absolute value 1. We consider below an absorption process in which the energy E_n of the electron after the process is greater than that before the process (E_s)

$$
E_n > E_s \qquad\qquad \text{(VII.8.17)}
$$

and write

$$\omega = \frac{E_n - E_s}{\hbar} + \delta\omega = \omega_{ns} + \delta\omega \qquad (VII.8.18)$$

Then the time factor of the first term in brackets is

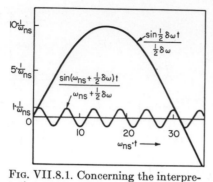

$$\frac{\sin \tfrac{1}{2}\delta\omega \cdot t}{\tfrac{1}{2}\delta\omega}$$

and that of the second term in brackets is

$$\frac{\sin (\omega_{ns} + \tfrac{1}{2}\delta\omega)t}{\omega_{ns} + \tfrac{1}{2}\delta\omega}$$

FIG. VII.8.1. Concerning the interpretation of Eq. (VII.8.16).

Figure VII.8.1 shows the time variation of the two factors for $\delta\omega = \omega_{ns}/5$. Both factors increase initially in proportion to t. After a short time the second factor bends over, whereas the first factor rises to much higher values. Hence we can neglect the second term in (VII.8.16) and obtain for the probability of occupation of the state n after a time t

$$|c_n(t)|^2 = \left(\frac{F}{2m\hbar\omega}\right)^2 (\pi_{ns}^{(+)})^2 \left[\frac{\sin \tfrac{1}{2}(\omega - \omega_{ns})t}{\tfrac{1}{2}(\omega - \omega_{ns})}\right]^2 \qquad (VII.8.19)$$

Furthermore, we see from Fig. VII.8.1 that the time factor in (VII.8.19) attains increasingly high values as ω approaches

$$\omega_{ns} = \frac{E_n - E_s}{\hbar}$$

i.e., as the law of conservation of energy

$$E_n = E_s + \hbar\omega \qquad (VII.8.20)$$

Final energy of the electron = initial energy of the electron
$$+ \text{ energy of the light quantum}$$

is more nearly satisfied. Apart from the fulfillment of the law of conservation of energy, we also demand a relation concerning the momentum. This follows from the factor $(\pi_{ns}^{(+)})^2$ in (VII.8.19). From (VII.8.15), we have

$$\pi_{ns}^{(+)} = \int_{V_{\text{fund}}} \psi_n^*(\mathbf{r}) \, e^{+j\frac{\omega}{c}y} \frac{\hbar}{j} \frac{\partial}{\partial x} \psi_s(\mathbf{r}) \, dV \qquad (VII.8.15)$$

If we substitute the form $u(\mathbf{r}; \mathbf{k})\, e^{j\mathbf{k}\cdot\mathbf{r}}$ for the eigenfunction $\psi(\mathbf{r})$ of the electron in the crystal, we obtain

$$\pi_{ns}^{(+)} = \hbar \int_{V_{\text{fund}}} u^*(\mathbf{r}; \mathbf{k}_n) \left(k_{sx} u(\mathbf{r}; \mathbf{k}_s) - j\frac{\partial}{\partial x} u(\mathbf{r}; \mathbf{k}_s) \right) e^{j(\mathbf{k}_{\text{field}} + \mathbf{k}_s - \mathbf{k}_n)\cdot\mathbf{r}}\, dV$$

(VII.8.21)

Here
$$\mathbf{k}_{\text{field}} = \left\{0, \frac{\omega}{c}, 0\right\}$$
(VII.8.22)

is the wave vector of the electromagnetic wave propagated in the y direction, so that $\mathbf{k}_{\text{field}} \cdot \mathbf{r} = (\omega/c)y$.

Since the modulation factors $u(\mathbf{r}; \mathbf{k})$ have lattice periodicity, this is true also of their derivatives. Hence the entire factor in the integrand ahead of the exponential also has lattice periodicity. If now the fundamental domain is so chosen that its edges are integer multiples of the wavelength of the electromagnetic wave, which is possible in view of the arbitrary choice of the fundamental domain, the exponential factor in the integrand is periodic in the fundamental domain and the theorem of Appendix I may be applied. Hence the integral $\pi_{ns}^{(+)}$ and, with it, the transition probability from state s to state n vanish completely unless the exponent

$$\mathbf{k}_{\text{field}} + \mathbf{k}_s - \mathbf{k}_n = 0$$
(VII.8.23)

This means that the crystal momentum $\hbar\mathbf{k}$ of the electron after the absorption process is equal to the sum of the momentum of the light quantum $\hbar\mathbf{k}_{\text{field}}$ and of the crystal momentum of the electron before the absorption process:

$$\hbar\mathbf{k}_n = \hbar\mathbf{k}_{\text{field}} + \hbar\mathbf{k}_s$$
(VII.8.24)

Thus the law of conservation of momentum (VII.8.23) or (VII.8.24) must be satisfied in addition to the law of conservation of energy (VII.8.20).

For an emission process we have $E_n < E_s$. Then the second term in the brackets of (VII.8.16) is the critical term. The law of conservation of energy takes the form

$$E_n = E_s - \hbar\omega$$

Final energy of electron = initial energy of electron
$$- \text{energy of emitted light quantum}$$

An examination of the coefficient $\pi_{ns}^{(-)}$ yields the law of conservation of momentum

$$\hbar \mathbf{k}_n = \hbar \mathbf{k}_s - \hbar \mathbf{k}_{\text{field}}$$

Final value of crystal momentum
$$= \text{initial value of crystal momentum}$$
$$- \text{momentum of emitted light quantum}$$

If the electromagnetic wave is a light wave, the wave number $\mathbf{k}_{\text{field}}$ is of the order of 10^5 cm^{-1} since the wavelength is of the order of 10^{-5} cm. Compared with the range $2\pi/a \approx 2 \cdot 10^8$ cm^{-1} of the wave number $\mathbf{k}$ of the electron in the crystal, the change in the electron wave vector $\mathbf{k}$ by the light wave vector $\mathbf{k}_{\text{field}}$ is thus very slight.[1] If the transition of the electron would take place between two states of the same band, this would be a transition between closely adjoining states, and the laws of conservation of energy and momentum, (VII.8.20) and (VII.8.24), respectively, could be written in the form

$$\Delta E \qquad\qquad = \hbar\omega$$

$$\hbar |\Delta \mathbf{k}| = \hbar \cdot |\mathbf{k}_{\text{field}}| = \hbar \frac{\omega}{c}$$

Division of the first equation by the second

$$\frac{1}{\hbar} |\text{grad}_{\mathbf{k}} E| = c$$

and application of Eq. (VII.5.10) lead to the value of the electron velocity $\mathbf{v}$

$$|\mathbf{v}| = c$$

Thus the velocity of the electron in the two closely adjoining states, between which a transition would be effected by collision with a light quantum, would have to be equal to the velocity of light c. In fact, the electrons are much slower than this,[2] both in metals and in semiconductors [see Eqs. (VIII.4.09) and (VIII.4.27)]. For these slow electrons a collision with a light quantum cannot possibly lead to a transition to a neighboring state in the same band; instead, in an optical absorption process, the electron must pass over into another band effectively with conservation of its wave vector.

This theorem is of great importance in the theory of crystalline phosphors. Here we are concerned with an understanding of the experimentally established fact that an electron raised by the absorption of a light quantum from the valence band into the conduction

---

[1] This does not apply for the absorption of X-rays in view of their short wavelength.

[2] Apart from this the, simple Schrödinger equation employed in the discussion up to now would not be adequate for electron velocities of the order of that of light. All relations which have been derived would have to be modified relativistically.

band cannot simply return to the valence band with the emission of light.

This impossibility is made plausible by the fact that the requirement of conservation of the wave vector **k** permits only a single state of the valence band to serve as final state for the transition. It is extremely improbable that just this state is unoccupied. The combination of the two requirements for an emission process, namely, (1) final state unoccupied and (2) conservation of the **k** vector, makes an emission process in the ideal crystal practically impossible. The theory of crystal phosphors concludes from these considerations that optical emission processes in these solids are tied to the presence of defects in the ideal lattice. However, we cannot enter into details on this point.[1]

§9. The Influence of Atomic Imperfections and of Thermal Lattice Vibrations on the Motion of an Electron in a Crystal

a. Four Different Types of Deviations from Ideal Lattice Periodicity

In our past discussions, exact lattice periodicity was assumed for the potential energy of an electron in a crystal. This assumption applies only for an ideal occupancy of the lattice sites in the crystal under consideration. In real crystals, such an ideal occupation of lattice sites is out of question. We must expect vacancies at lattice sites and occupation of interstitial sites as well as the substitution of foreign atoms for lattice atoms. We have discussed such atomic imperfections[2] or lattice defects in greater detail in Chap. II.

Apart from these atomic imperfections, we find in a real crystal so-called structural defects, such as mosaic structures and dislocations. Furthermore, a material may frequently be available only in poly-crystalline form. Then the complete crystal is traversed by an infinite number of crystallite boundaries.

We must also note that, apart from these perturbations of ideal lattice periodicity which are constant in time, the atoms, ions, or molecules composing the crystal vibrate about their positions of rest

---

[1] See, e.g., N. Riehl and M. Schön, *Z. Physik*, **114**: 682 (1939), in particular p. 687; or N. Riehl, "Physik und technische Anwendung der Lumineszenz," pp. 103ff, Springer-Verlag OHG, Berlin, 1940.

[2] With regard to the concepts of dislocations and lattice defects see, e.g., H. G. F. Winkler, "Struktur und Eigenschaften der Krystalle," Springer-Verlag OHG, Berlin, 1950.

with an amplitude depending on the temperature of the crystal. These thermal lattice vibrations also have a strong influence on the motion of the electron in the crystal.

Of the deviations from ideal lattice periodicity which have been named, the first and the last have been investigated more closely with respect to their effects on the motion of an electron in a crystal. However, we shall not report here on the results obtained, much less give their derivation. These matters are too complicated for that, at least for this introductory treatment. We are rather concerned with clarifying the concepts which are commonly employed in this connection, such as the collision mean free time τ, the mean free path l, and the electron mobility μ.

These concepts originated in the classical electron theory of Riecke, Drude, and H. A. Lorentz at the beginning of this century and were carried over into the modern electron theory, which was developed on a wave-mechanical basis around 1930. In this process, the concepts in question lost much of their original graphic meaning. Hence an outline of the original classical reasoning seems necessary just for an understanding of the terminology used. After this, we shall indicate the concrete meaning of the collision time τ, the mean free path l, and the electron mobility μ from the presently accepted quantum-mechanical point of view.

b. Collision Time τ, Mean Free Path l, Electron Mobility μ, and Conductivity σ in Classical Electron Theory

The classical electron theory of metals proceeds from the hypothesis that, in a metal, many electrons—of the order of 1 per atom—are so freely mobile that they behave like a classical Maxwell-Boltzmann gas. Thus, a particular electron moves with uniform velocity $\mathbf{v}_1$ through the lattice until it suffers, after a time τ_{tr_1}, a collision and hence changes its velocity abruptly into $\mathbf{v}_2$.[1]

The electron retains this new velocity for a time interval τ_{tr_2}, up to the next collision, at which the velocity is changed to $\mathbf{v}_3$, etc. We now make the crude simplifying assumption

$$\tau_{tr_1} = \tau_{tr_2} = \tau_{tr_3} = \cdots = \tau_{tr} = \text{collision time}[2] \quad (VII.9.01)$$

---

[1] The lattice atoms and the remaining electrons were naturally regarded as collision partners. We shall see later, on p. 250, what difficulties arose herefrom.

[2] This unfortunately widely accepted designation is not very apt. After all, we are concerned with the time which elapses between two collisions and not with the duration of a collision itself. A designation such as "free time of flight" or "mean free time" appears more appropriate in view of its parallelism with "mean free path."

Furthermore, only the direction, but not the magnitude, of the velocity will be assumed to be changed in a collision:

$$|\mathbf{v}_1| = |\mathbf{v}_2| = |\mathbf{v}_3| = \cdots = v_{\text{th}} \qquad (\text{VII.9.02})$$

Then, between two successive collisions, the electron always travels the distance

$$\tau_{\text{tr}} \cdot v_{th} = l = \text{mean free path} \qquad (\text{VII.9.03})$$

Figure VII.9.1 shows the path of an electron under these circumstances.

So far, we have assumed the absence of external forces. We now imagine a voltage applied to the crystal, so that an electrostatic field $\mathbf{E}$ exists within the crystal. This exerts a force $\mathbf{F} = -e\mathbf{E}$ on the electron.

Every one of the originally straight paths between two collisions is now distorted into a parabola (see Fig. VII.9.2) since the external force effects an acceleration

FIG. VII.9.1.

$$\dot{\mathbf{v}} = \frac{1}{m}\,\mathbf{F} = -\frac{e}{m}\,\mathbf{E} \qquad (\text{VII.9.04})$$

and hence a velocity increment

Direction of external force ⟶

FIG. VII.9.2

Path of an electron with and without external force for the simplifying assumption of constant free path length.

$$\mathbf{v}_{\text{incr}} = -\frac{e}{m}\,\mathbf{E}t \qquad (\text{VII.9.05})$$

As long as

$$|\mathbf{v}_{\text{incr}}| \ll v \qquad (\text{VII.9.06})$$

during the entire time between two collisions, there is practically no change in the collision time τ_{tr} and the velocity increment (VII.9.05) increases in a single free flight from 0 to $(e/m)\mathbf{E}\tau_{\text{tr}}$. Its mean value is hence

$$\mathbf{v}_{\text{incr}} = -\frac{1}{2}\frac{e}{m}\,\mathbf{E}\tau_{\text{tr}} = -\mu\mathbf{E} \qquad (\text{VII.9.07})$$

The proportionality factor

$$\left.\begin{array}{l} \mu = \dfrac{e}{m}\,\tau \qquad \text{with}[1]\ \tau = \tfrac{1}{2}\tau_{\text{tr}} \\[2ex] \text{or} \qquad \left(\dfrac{\mu}{\text{cm}^2/\text{volt-sec}}\right) = 1.76 \cdot 10^{15}\left(\dfrac{\tau}{\text{sec}}\right) \end{array}\right\} \qquad (\text{VII.9.08})$$

[1] The "mean" collision time τ would thus be equal to half the arithmetic mean value of the individual collision times $\tau_{\text{tr}_1}, \tau_{\text{tr}_2}, \tau_{\text{tr}_3}, \ldots \tau_{\text{tr}_n}$. The factor $\frac{1}{2}$ obtained in this crude consideration must not be taken too seriously, however. In actuality, much more complex averaging processes lead finally to a mean col-

is called the electron mobility. The reason for this will become plainer presently, on page 248. Its dimension cm²/(volt-sec) follows from the ratio of velocity cm-sec⁻¹ and field strength volt-cm⁻¹.

We might be satisfied with this digression into classical electron theory. However, for much that follows it will be advantageous to proceed on this classical basis to the conductivity formula.

To this end we shall make our notions somewhat more concrete (see Fig. VII.9.3). Let the crystal volume under consideration be a block with a cross section Q and a length L. A voltage U is applied by a battery and an external metallic circuit to the end surfaces of the block by means of large surface electrodes. This produces within the crystal a field strength

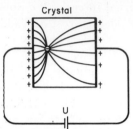

Crystal

$$\mathbf{E} = \frac{U}{L} \qquad (\text{VII.9.09})$$

FIG. VII.9.3. An electron and the charges induced by it on the electrodes of the crystal. These induced charges change with a displacement of the electron and a corresponding current occurs in the external circuit.

The lines of force originating from an arbitrary selected electron produce induced charges on the electrodes at the end surfaces. If the electron is displaced by a distance $\mathbf{v} \cdot dt$, these induced charges are changed. The charge required for this is supplied or withdrawn by the metallic circuit. Thus, for every motion $\mathbf{v}$ of a single selected electron there exists a current I_{single} in the external circuit. Its magnitude follows simply from the law of conservation of energy. The field $\mathbf{E}$ within the crystal does an amount of work

$$\mathbf{v} \cdot \mathbf{F} \cdot dt = -e\mathbf{v} \cdot \mathbf{E} \cdot dt \qquad (\text{VII.9.10})$$

on the electron in question and thus increases, e.g., the kinetic energy of the electron. This energy must ultimately be supplied by the battery, from which the energy $U \cdot I_{\text{single}} \cdot dt$ is withdrawn for a current I_{single} in a time dt. Hence we must have

$$-e\mathbf{v} \cdot \mathbf{E} \cdot dt = U \cdot I_{\text{single}} \cdot dt \qquad (\text{VII.9.11})$$

and hence

$$I_{\text{single}} = -e \cdot \mathbf{v} \cdot \frac{\mathbf{E}}{U} \qquad (\text{VII.9.12})$$

---

lision time τ, and this involves many modifications in numerical factors. For the sketchy considerations which follow, it is sufficient to identify τ simply with the arithmetic mean value τ_{tr}.

For the simple geometry assumed we have, according to (VII.9.09),

$$I_{\text{single}} = -ev_x \cdot \frac{1}{L}$$

if the x direction corresponds to the longitudinal dimension of the crystal. The mean current density referred to the cross section Q of the crystal is

$$i_{\text{single}} = -ev_x \frac{1}{L} \frac{1}{Q} = -\frac{e}{V} v_x \qquad \text{(VII.9.13)}$$

Herewith Eq. (VII.5.13) found on page 208 has been derived on a corpuscular basis.

From here it is but a short step to the basic formula for the conductivity. Since all the conduction electrons contribute to the conduction of a body, we shall—at least for this digression into classical electron theory—pass briefly beyond the bounds established by the "behavior of the single electron" even for this §9 and deal with the totality of the conduction electrons. The electron gas represents a cloud of particles which, in the absence of an external field, pass each other along the rectilinear zigzag paths of Fig. VII.9.1. Here equally large positive and negative x components of the velocity are, on the average, equally frequent so that the current contributions (VII.9.13) of the individual electrons cancel each other on the average. Hence there is no current. However, if an external field is applied, the zigzag paths are made up of parabolic arcs as in Fig. VII.9.2. According to Eq. (VII.9.07) every particle receives on the average a velocity increment $-\mu\mathbf{F}$, and since this average velocity increment is the same for all particles of the cloud, the cloud as a whole drifts slowly with the common drift velocity

$$\mathbf{v}_{\text{drift}} = -\mu\mathbf{E} \qquad \text{(VII.9.07)}$$

The contributions (VII.9.13) of the individual electrons no longer cancel, but add to lead to a total current density

$$\mathbf{i} = N \cdot \left(-\frac{e}{V}\right) \cdot \mathbf{v}_{\text{drift}} = \left(-e\frac{N}{V}\right) \cdot (-\mu\mathbf{E})$$

Introducing the concentration of the electrons

$$n = \frac{N}{V}$$

we obtain
$$\mathbf{i} = e\mu n\mathbf{E} \qquad \text{(VII.9.14)}$$

Comparison with Ohm's law

$$\mathbf{i} = \sigma \cdot \mathbf{E}$$

leads to an expression for the conductivity σ

$$\sigma = e\mu n$$

or $\left(\dfrac{\sigma}{\text{ohm}^{-1}\ \text{cm}^{-1}} \right) = 1.6 \cdot 10^{-19} \left(\dfrac{\mu}{\text{cm}^2/\text{volt-sec}} \right) \cdot \left(\dfrac{n}{\text{cm}^{-3}} \right)$ (VII.9.15)

The meaning of the designation "mobility" for the proportionality factor μ becomes here particularly plain, since (VII.9.15) shows that the conductivity σ of the crystal increases with the "mobility" of the n conduction electrons of the crystal. For the concentration n of the conduction electrons in metals we may in general substitute the number of valence electrons, i.e., approximately $4 \cdot 10^{22}$ cm^{-3}, which corresponds to 1 per atom. For a metallic conductivity of about $4 \cdot 10^5$ ohm^{-1} cm^{-1}, we then obtain a mobility[1] $\mu \approx 60$ cm^2 volt^{-1} sec^{-1}. For this mobility Eq. (VII.9.08) yields a collision time $\tau = 3.6 \cdot 10^{-14}$ sec and (VII.9.03) a mean free path $\tau_{\text{tr}} v_{\text{th}} = 2\tau v_{\text{th}} = 7 \cdot 10^{-6}$ cm if we write for the thermal velocity in metals $v_{\text{th}} = 10^8$ cm sec^{-1}.[2] For a lattice constant $3 \cdot 10^{-8}$ cm, this mean free path is equal to 200 lattice constants! We shall discuss presently, on page 250, the difficulties which arose for the classical theory out of these large values of the mean free path.

The past discussions permit us to check from what field strengths on Ohm's law (VII.9.14) must fail (apart from the deviations which may result at lower field strength from experimental imperfections, such as boundary resistances between individual crystallites). As soon as the drift velocity (VII.9.07) becomes comparable with the thermal velocity v_{th}, the condition (VII.9.06) is violated and the time of free flight of an electron is no longer determined primarily by its initial velocity after its last collision. The simple proportionality (VII.9.04) between mean velocity increment and field strength is then lost, and Ohm's law is no longer valid.

The critical field strength is thus obtained from[3]

$$|\mathbf{v}|_{\text{drift}} = \mu \cdot |\mathbf{E}| \approx v_{\text{th}}$$

$$|\mathbf{E}_{\text{crit}}| \approx \frac{v_{\text{th}}}{\mu}$$ (VII.9.16)

[1] The metallic mobilities lie in fact in the range from 10 to 100 cm^2 volt^{-1} sec^{-1}. See, e.g., F. Seitz, "The Modern Theory of Solids," p. 183, McGraw-Hill Book Company, Inc., New York, 1940.

[2] For this value, see Eq. (VIII.4.09).

[3] The condition $\mu E \ll v_{\text{th}}$ may be multiplied with the concentration n and states then that the particle current density $\mu n E$ in the field must be very small compared with the unidirectional thermal particle current density $v_{\text{th}} \cdot n/\sqrt{6\pi}$. (With regard to the unidirectional thermal current, see p. 82, footnote 1. The factor

We shall make plausible on pages 301 and 307 that we may write for the order of magnitude of the thermal velocity in metals 10^8 cm sec^{-1} (independently of temperature!) and in semiconductors 10^7 cm sec^{-1} $\sqrt{T/300°\mathrm{K}}$ (see also page 256).

For the metallic mobilities[1] between 10 and 100 cm^2 volt^{-1} sec^{-1} estimated on page 248, we thus obtain for metals critical field strengths between 10^6 and 10^7 volt cm^{-1}. These are values whose experimental realization is out of question.

For semiconductors and insulators, the range of mobilities is much larger. Thus, for germanium with $\mu = 3.6 \cdot 10^3$ cm^2 volt^{-1} sec^{-1}, the critical field strength at room temperature would be about $3 \cdot 10^3$ volt cm^{-1}. In fact, we observe true deviations from Ohm's law for germanium even at $6 \cdot 10^2$ volt cm^{-1}.[2] Only a much more careful study of the collision processes makes possible an understanding of these phenomena.[3]

Even within the scope of classical theory the past considerations have merely created a formal basis on which a theory might be constructed. In particular, the collision processes must be investigated, and this demands a statement regarding the collision partners. As already mentioned in footnote 1, page 244, from a classical point of view the lattice atoms and the remaining electrons come here primarily into consideration.

In the absence of more precise views regarding the structure of atoms at the time in question (1900–1910), studies of the collisions of electrons with hard, immobile spheres were carried out. For this model the magnitude of the electron velocity after the collision is exactly equal to that before the collision, and for the direction of the electron after the collision every direction is equally probable, regardless of the direction of the electron before the collision.

Thus, in this model, the electron has no "memory of its past before the collision" with respect to its direction. We shall see presently what basic objections can be raised against this collision model. Before this, we shall sketch briefly a consequence of this model, which will be of importance for what follows.

In the calculation of the electrical conductivity to be discussed in §10, we shall have to answer the question how many electrons of a group of uniform velocity and direction are eliminated by collision

---

$1/\sqrt{6\pi}$ can be added on the right since we are at any rate dealing only with order-of-magnitude considerations.)

[1] See Seitz, *op. cit.*, p. 183.

[2] E. J. Ryder and W. Shockley, *Phys. Rev.*, **81**: 139 and 140 (1951).

[3] W. Shockley, *Bell System Tech. J.*, **30**: 990 (1951).

processes in a time interval dt. If, on the average, a time τ elapses between two collisions of an electron, dt/τ terminal points of such times fall on the average into the time interval dt. Thus an electron suffers in the interval dt on the average dt/τ collisions, and N electrons suffer $N\,dt/\tau$ collisions. Thus collisions eliminate in an interval dt on the average

$$dN = N \cdot \frac{dt}{\tau} \qquad\qquad (\text{VII.9.17})$$

electrons from a group with uniform velocity and direction. The number N of the electrons of this group with uniform velocity hence decreases exponentially with time:

$$N = N(0)\, e^{-\frac{t}{\tau}} \qquad\qquad (\text{VII.9.18})$$

The mean collision time τ, which was first thought of as the arithmetic mean of a series of times of free flight $\tau_{tr_1}, \tau_{tr_2}, \ldots \tau_{tr_n}$, thus attains the meaning of a relaxation time which controls the decay in time of an electron group of uniform velocity. At a later point (page 252) it will prove very important that the mean collision time τ enters the calculation of the conductivity not as an arithmetic mean of successive free times of flight, but as a relaxation time.

We now turn to the already mentioned basic difficulties which arise for the classical electron theory from the fact that the observed values of the metallic conductivities lead to mean free paths of the order of 10^2 lattice constants,[1] as we have seen on page 248.

Since the classical electron theory had to regard the lattice atoms themselves (as well as the remaining electrons) as collision partners, it became incomprehensible how an electron could fly freely through some hundred closely packed collision partners without suffering a change in direction.[2]

Nothing was changed in this respect when first W. Pauli[3] and then A. Sommerfeld,[4] in 1927, applied Fermi statistics in place of Maxwell-Boltzmann statistics to the gas of the free conduction electrons and were thus able to overcome other basic difficulties of the classical elec-

---

[1] For germanium, even up to 500 lattice constants.

[2] An effort to evade the difficulty by assuming that the range of interaction of the atoms with their neighbors, which determines lattice binding, is much greater than the effective cross section for high-speed conduction electrons is simply another formulation of a situation which is incomprehensible from a classical standpoint.

[3] W. Pauli, *Z. Physik*, **41**: 81 (1927).

[4] A. Sommerfeld, *Naturwiss.*, **15**: 825 (1927); **16**: 374 (1928).

tron theory.[1] It is true that Sommerfeld demanded even at the end of his first paper: "To perfect the theory it would be necessary to introduce the mean free path in a more physical manner, e.g., in the sense of wave mechanics, by studying the scattering of the de Broglie waves at the lattice of the metal atoms, taking at the same time due account of the thermal agitation of this lattice."

This was accomplished by F. Bloch.[2] It then became clear that an ideal lattice constituted no obstacle whatsoever for electrons of suitable wave number so that the observed mean free paths of hundreds of lattice constants were in no sense incomprehensible. Bloch showed, furthermore, that deviations from exact lattice periodicity constituted the real obstacles to electron motion and considered in this connection thermal lattice vibrations in particular. At a much later date, Conwell and Weisskopf[3] investigated the effect of another type of deviations from lattice periodicity, namely, the scattering of electrons by charged atomic impurities. We shall defer the consideration of the lattice vibrations and consider first impurity scattering. With these spatially defined collision partners, it is of course more nearly possible to establish a relationship with classical notions than for the infinitely extended thermal lattice vibrations.

c. Scattering of an Electron in a Crystal by a Charged Imperfection

It is after all our objective to translate the concepts of collision time τ and mean free path l which have been elucidated on a classical corpuscular basis into present-day wave-mechanical terms. Hence we shall consider impurity scattering first from a classical corpuscular standpoint. The problem is here the same as that of the familiar Rutherford scattering of particles by heavy atomic nuclei. The negative electron, e.g., moves about the positively charged impurity on a hyperbolic path (Fig. VII.9.4) or turns away from a negatively charged impurity along a hyperbolic path (Fig. VII.9.5).

From a mathematical treatment of these circumstances, we obtain the so-called transition probabilities, i.e., the probabilities that an

---

[1] Pauli explained the temperature independence and weakness of the paramagnetism of the alkali metals, Sommerfeld the absence of a contribution to the specific heat of a solid from the conduction electrons (apart from other results).

[2] F. Bloch, *Z. Physik*, **52**: 555 (1928); **57**: 545 (1929). Shortly before then, Sommerfeld's student W. V. Houston had treated the scattering of electron waves in analogy with Debye scattering of X-rays at thermal density variations in the crystal, see *Z. Physik*, **48**: 449 (1928).

[3] E. Conwell and V. F. Weisskopf, *Phys. Rev.*, **69**: 258 (1946); **77**: 388 (1950).

electron have a velocity $\mathbf{v}'$ after "collision" with the charged impurity, if it had the velocity $\mathbf{v}$ before the collision. Once again, we shall not enter into details, but indicate merely that the results for Rutherford scattering are quite different from those for the collision of electrons with hard spheres, where all directions of motion were equally probable after the collision. For Rutherford scattering the electron does not lose its memory of its original direction, but continues to show a definite preference for it. Deviations by small angles are more probable than deviations by large angles. This has an important consequence in the transition from the arithmetic mean value of successive free times of flight to a relaxation time.

If we now define a relaxation time by the decay of a current carried initially by a group of N electrons with uniform velocity and direction, the decay of this current is identical with the decay of the number N

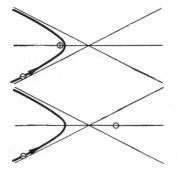

Fig. VII.9.4. The negative electron flies around a positive lattice defect.

Fig. VII.9.5. The negative electron is deflected away from a negative lattice defect.

of the electrons, provided that the collisions blot out memory. In this case, the velocities of the electrons which have been removed from the group by collisions are equally distributed over all directions and do not contribute to the current. However, as soon as the original direction is preferred (or discriminated against) after the collisions, the electrons which have been removed from the group continue to contribute to the current and the current decays more slowly (or more rapidly) than the number N of the electrons which have remained in the group.

We must, therefore, distinguish between the relaxation time of the number N of the electrons of uniform velocity and direction, on the one hand, and the relaxation time of the current carried by them, on the other. The relaxation time of the number N continues to be identical with the arithmetic mean τ of the successive times of free flight. This is not true, however, of the relaxation time of the current contribution when the collisions do not blot out memory, as, e.g., for impurity scattering.

This current relaxation time is of primary importance for the calculation of the conductivity.   Even so, it is commonly designated as mean collision time.   We see how the simple graphic meaning as an arithmetic mean value of successive free times of flight has gradually evaporated.   We see furthermore that, for the calculation of the mean collision time as relaxation time of a current contribution, we are concerned only with the knowledge of certain transition probabilities between a state before the "collision" and the states after the "collision."   This is important because the wave-mechanical treatment of scattering processes does not readily lead to the picture of the thermal zigzag path in Fig. VII.9.2.

The scattering of an electron at a charged impurity has also been treated with the aid of the Schrödinger equation for a point charge.[1] This exact treatment on a wave-mechanical basis has given the same values for the transition probabilities as the previously described classical corpuscular treatment with the hyperbolic paths of an electron particle.   This is not too surprising since we know from general quantum mechanics that, by the formation of wave packets, we can demonstrate the corpuscular traits of particle behavior in so far as this is consistent with the uncertainty relations.   We shall make increasing use of the possibility of representing wave-mechanical results in particle language.

d. Scattering of an Electron in a Crystal by Thermal Lattice Vibrations

Apart from impurity scattering, the thermal vibrations of the lattice components about their positions of rest have claimed the special attention of the modern theory of solids as further obstacles to the motion of an electron in a crystal.   The vibrations of the individual lattice components are coupled by the strong forces which lead to the formation of the lattice.   Low frequencies among these vibrations can occur only when neighboring lattice components move approximately in phase.   We are then dealing with elastic or acoustic vibrations.   At high frequencies, neighboring lattice components will vibrate in phase opposition.   If the neighbors have opposite electric charge (heteropolar ionic lattices, such as NaCl), such a vibration leads to a high-frequency electric dipole moment and an electromagnetic wave is emitted.   We speak, then, of optical vibrations.

The distinction between acoustical and optical vibrations becomes mandatory when a lattice is made up of components of different

[1] W Gordon, *Z. Physik*, **48**: 180 (1928).   N. F. Mott, *Proc. Roy. Soc. (London)*, **A118**: 542 (1928).   S. Temple, *Proc. Roy. Soc. (London)*, **A121**: 673 (1928).

masses. Then the total spectrum of the characteristic oscillations of the crystal splits into several branches. Of these, the acoustical branch embraces the frequencies 0 up to a limiting frequency for which the heavy components alone are in oscillation, whereas the light components are at rest (Fig. VII.9.6). Finally, at the lowest optical frequency the heavy components are at rest and the light ones alone in oscillation.[1] The highest optical frequency is that at which the two sublattices oscillate in opposition without deformation (Fig. VII.9.6).

At a finite temperature, all these oscillations are excited to some degree. The exact lattice periodicity is perturbed. The perturbation potential which is superposed on the lattice potential $U(\mathbf{r})$ is also periodic, with the wavelength of the lattice wave in question as period. The potential energy of the electron depends on its position relative to the wave. Thus the coordinates of the lattice components and the coordinates of the electron enter into the perturbation potential. The perturbation potential couples the lattice wave and the electron wave.

In the treatment of this perturbation problem we find, as for the perturbation of an electron in a crystal by an electromagnetic wave (§8), that an electron with wave vector $\mathbf{k}$ is excited to transitions into another state $\mathbf{k}'$. Just as there, such a transition must satisfy the law of conservation of energy

$$E(\mathbf{k}') = E(\mathbf{k}) \pm \hbar\omega_{\text{lattice}} \qquad (\text{VII.9.19})$$

and the "law of conservation of momentum"

$$\mathbf{k}' = \mathbf{k} \pm \mathbf{k}_{\text{lattice}} \qquad (\text{VII.9.20})$$

Equations (VII.9.19) and (VII.9.20) show that the scattering process of an electron by a lattice wave can also be described in corpuscular terms by stating that an electron collides with a "phonon"[2] and absorbs or emits the energy and momentum of a phonon. It is plausible that, again, a mean collision time may be calculated as relaxation time with the aid of computed transition probabilities.

Figure VII.9.6 shows incidentally that the thermal lattice vibrations have wavelengths down to two lattice constants. Hence the wave

---

[1] In comparing the highest acoustical and the lowest optical oscillations, the distinction between acoustical and optical oscillations, which is still apparent in a comparison of low or median acoustical oscillations with optical oscillations, is thus effaced. For further detail regarding these types of oscillations see, e.g., Weizel, *op. cit.*, vol. II, p. 1385.

[2] See pp. 13 to 14 and Fig. I.2.9.

numbers $2\pi/a$ of these vibrations traverse the same interval $(-\pi/a,$ $+\pi/a)$ as the k numbers of the electron waves [see Eq. (VII.2.08)]. This contrasts sharply with the wave numbers $2\pi/\lambda$ of light waves which, because of the relatively long waves of visible light, are small

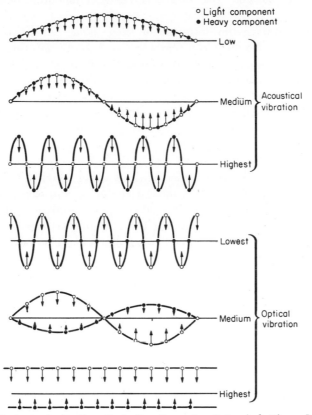

FIG. VII.9.6. Acoustical and optical vibrations of a diatomic lattice.   Mass ratio $m_\bullet : m_\circ = 2:1$.

In principle, the heavy masses vibrate with larger amplitude than the light masses for all acoustical vibrations (i.e., also for the low and medium vibrations at the very top). This effect vanishes only for $\lambda = \infty$. For the wavelengths $\lambda = 24\,a$ and $\lambda = 48\,a$ assumed above it can no longer be demonstrated in a drawing, however. Similarly, for the medium optical vibration the amplitude ratio is practically already $-\frac{1}{2}$, though this value is attained exactly only for $\lambda = \infty$. a = equilibrium distance between $\circ$ and $\bullet$ = half the lattice constant.

compared to π/a. Thus the argument of page 242, which led to the conclusion that collisions with photons could result only in electron transitions into the next higher band with approximate conservation of the k numbers, does not apply for thermal lattice vibrations. In collisions with phonons, transitions between quantum states of the same band are entirely possible. Transitions into the next higher band, on the other hand, do not occur in general for phonon collisions. The energy of the thermal lattice vibrations does not suffice for this—except in the special case of the intrinsic semiconductor (see pages 16 to 18).

The quantitative development of these ideas constitutes unquestionably one of the most complex phases of solid-state theory. Thus extensive discussions have dealt with the question of whether the electrons participate in the distribution of the internal thermal energy of the crystal over the several degrees of freedom.[1] Furthermore, Bardeen and Shockley[2] have introduced the so-called deformation potentials E_{1n} and E_{1p} in an effort to relate the electron mobility to other properties of the crystal.

However, we cannot discuss any of these matters in greater detail.

Here we are merely concerned with showing roughly how the concepts of mean collision time τ, mean free path l, and electron mobility μ, with definitions originally derived from corpuscular models, can be carried over into wave-mechanical theory and, furthermore, that the results of exact wave-mechanical calculations can also be expressed in corpuscular terms.

The results can then always be expressed in the classical form:

Mean free path:
$$l = v_{\text{th}} \cdot \tau \qquad (\text{VII.9.21})$$

Mean thermal electron velocity for semi-conductors:[3]
$$v_{\text{th}} = \sqrt{\frac{3kT}{m_{\text{eff}}}}$$
$$\frac{v_{\text{th}}}{\text{cm sec}^{-1}} = 1.168 \cdot 10^7 \cdot \sqrt{\frac{m}{m_{\text{eff}}}} \cdot \sqrt{\frac{T}{300°\text{K}}} \qquad (\text{VII.9.22})$$

Thermal electron velocity for metals[4] (velocity at Fermi level):
$$v_{\text{th}} = \left(\frac{3}{8\pi}\right)^{\frac{1}{3}} \frac{h}{m_{\text{eff}}} n^{\frac{1}{3}} \quad \begin{array}{l}\text{(independent of} \\ \text{temperature)}\end{array}$$
$$\left(\frac{v_{\text{th}}}{\text{cm sec}^{-1}}\right) = 7.71 \cdot 10^7 \left(\frac{m}{m_{\text{eff}}}\right) \cdot \left(\frac{n}{10^{22}\ \text{cm}^{-3}}\right)^{\frac{1}{3}}$$

$$(\text{VII.9.23})$$

[1] The so-called Peierls reversal processes play here an important role. See H. A. Bethe in Geiger and Scheel, op. cit., vol. XXIV, part 2, p. 536.

[2] W. Shockley and J. Bardeen, Phys. Rev., 77: 407 (1950); Shockley, op. cit., pp. 264ff.

[3] For derivation, see Eq. (VIII.4.27).

[4] For derivation, see Eq. (VIII.4.09).

Drift velocity: $\qquad\qquad \mathbf{v}_{\text{drift}} = -\mu\mathbf{E}$ (VII.9.24)

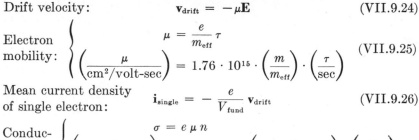

Electron mobility:
$$\mu = \frac{e}{m_{\text{eff}}}\tau$$
$$\left(\frac{\mu}{\text{cm}^2/\text{volt-sec}}\right) = 1.76 \cdot 10^{15} \cdot \left(\frac{m}{m_{\text{eff}}}\right) \cdot \left(\frac{\tau}{\text{sec}}\right)$$
(VII.9.25)

Mean current density of single electron:
$$\mathbf{i}_{\text{single}} = -\frac{e}{V_{\text{fund}}}\mathbf{v}_{\text{drift}}$$
(VII.9.26)

Conductivity:
$$\sigma = e\,\mu\,n$$
$$\left(\frac{\sigma}{\text{ohm}^{-1}\,\text{cm}^{-1}}\right) = 1.60 \cdot 10^{-19} \left(\frac{\mu}{\text{cm}^2/\text{volt-sec}}\right) \cdot \left(\frac{n}{\text{cm}^{-3}}\right)$$
(VII.9.27)

Carrying the ideas indicated here to their logical conclusion will then give information concerning the relationship of the quantities l, τ, v_{th}, n, and μ with the temperature and the crystal parameters (such as the elastic constants of the crystal, the deformation potentials E_{1n} and E_{1p}, etc.) for any particular model, as for instance, a metal or a semiconductor with a given impurity concentration.

e. Zener's Oscillation and the Mean Free Path

We shall end with a note on the oscillation of the electrons in an energy band under the influence of a constant external force, as described in §7. According to (VII.9.26), such an oscillation would be accompanied by an alternating current. We would obtain the strange result that a field $\mathbf{E}$, constant in time, would produce an alternating current. The oscillation of an electron in its energy band was a consequence of the validity, unrestricted in time, of the acceleration law $\dot{\mathbf{k}} = \mathbf{F}/\hbar$. If, according to classical ideas, the acceleration process is permitted to last indefinitely, a constant field will also fail to produce a constant current, but instead a current which increases without limit. In fact, this is prevented by collisions, and similarly, collisions prevent the full development of the Zener oscillations. We have seen in §7, page 230, that the oscillation is not limited to the energy band, but that the electron would also oscillate back and forth in space over a distance $(E_{\text{top}} - E_{\text{bottom}})/(e|\mathbf{E}|)$. For a width of the energy band

$$E_{\text{top}} - E_{\text{bottom}} \approx 1 \text{ ev}$$

and at a field strength of 1 volt cm^{-1} this distance would be 1 cm. Since the mean free paths are of the order of 10^{-5} to 10^{-6} cm, the electron is deflected by collisions long before it can traverse a full cycle of oscillation. Only for field strengths of 10^5 to 10^6 volt cm^{-1} would the oscillation amplitude become smaller than the mean free path so that the oscillation may take precedence over the disordered thermal motion. However, at these field strengths there is a rapid increase in the probability that the electron leaves its band and passes over into the next band (see §7). Thus, even if such field strengths could be realized experimentally, a constant field would not produce alternating current. Thus we are still left with the form of motion of an electron under the simultaneous influence of a field and of collisions with phonons and impurities which was represented in corpuscular terms in Fig. VII.9.2.

§10. The Transition to the Many-electron Problem and the Calculation of the Conductivity

a. Introduction

Even in the introductory paragraph (page 166) we have pointed out that the transition from the one-electron problem treated in preceding paragraphs to the many-electron problem existing in reality need not involve the construction of suitable many-electron eigenfunctions. For many purposes it suffices to specify how the electrons of the solid body are distributed over the energy states of the one-electron problem, i.e., the quantum states of the band model.

This question is in part answered by the Pauli principle, which states that a quantum state can be occupied by only two electrons, which must have opposite spins. From this it follows that the state of lowest energy, i.e., the normal state, is realized when the electrons of the crystal occupy the system of levels of the band spectrum from the bottom up with just two[1] electrons per state. It is true that this normal state is realized only at absolute zero temperature. At finite temperatures, that macroscopic state will be observed for which the number of microscopic states realizing it is a maximum. The determination of the number of microscopic possibilities of realization and the finding of the macrostate with the maximum number of these possibilities is a problem of statistics. Because of the Pauli principle, an electron ensemble is governed by Fermi statistics. Fermi statistics teach that at finite temperatures there occurs, as compared with the normal state in which the quantum states are occupied from the bottom up with two electrons apiece, a loosening up which is described by the function

$$f(E) = \frac{1}{e^{\frac{E - E_F}{kT}} + 1} \tag{VII.10.01}$$

[1] Two because of the spin!

The function $f(E)$ indicates the probability that a quantum state with energy E is occupied. Figure VII.10.1 shows[1] that practically all states with energies below the "Fermi level" E_F are occupied and practically all states above the Fermi level E_F are unoccupied. The transition takes place within a few multiples of kT (k = Boltzmann constant) and hence becomes discontinuous for $T \to 0$. Quantum states whose

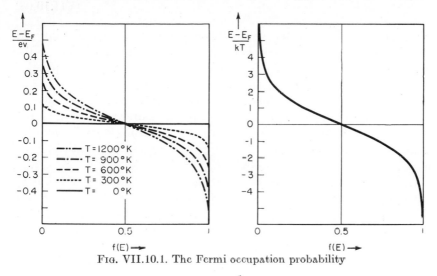

Fig. VII.10.1. The Fermi occupation probability

$$f(E) = \frac{1}{e^{\frac{E - E_F}{kT}} + 1}$$

energy coincides with the Fermi level E_F are just half occupied and half unoccupied, since

$$f(E_F) = \frac{1}{e^0 + 1} = \frac{1}{1 + 1} = \frac{1}{2} \qquad \text{(VII.10.02)}$$

The position and the temperature dependence[2] of the Fermi level E_F depend on the distribution of the quantum states along the energy

[1] In graphic representations of the function $f(E)$, the energy E is commonly plotted as abscissa and $f(E)$ as ordinate. Since, however, in a later application of $f(E)$ in an energy-level diagram the energy is always plotted on the vertical axis, the same was done in the present representation of $f(E)$. We thus arrive directly at the horizontal Fermi level E_F, which will later become of great importance.

[2] The difference $E - E_F$ has been plotted instead of the energy E on the ordinate scale of the left graph of Fig. VII.10.1. This representation should not mislead us into thinking that the Fermi level is independent of temperature. It is true that this is approximately, but not strictly, so for metals. For semiconductors the Fermi level normally depends strongly on temperature.

scale, since E_F is determined by the requirement that the total number of electrons to be accommodated is fixed, e.g., equal to N:

$$2 \int_{E=-\infty}^{E=\infty} D(E) \cdot f(E) \cdot dE = 2 \int_{E=-\infty}^{E=\infty} D(E) \frac{1}{e^{\frac{E-E_F}{kT}} + 1} dE = N$$

$$\text{(VII.10.03)}$$

Here $D(E)$ is the density of quantum states in an energy interval $(E, E + dE)$ which can be occupied with two electrons apiece. The functional dependence $D(E)$ depends entirely on the crystal in question or the model under consideration.

We shall defer the quantitative treatment of specific models to Chap. VIII and derive here only a few fundamental results which rest on the fact that only the energy E of the quantum state in question appears in (VII.10.01) and no other parameters of the state such as, in particular, the wave vector **k**.

On the basis of this fact, we shall show first of all that there is no current at thermal equilibrium. This result is, of course, merely a test of the ideas and models developed so far. For a true thermodynamic equilibrium, the principle of detailed balancing tells us that every microprocess is as frequent as its opposite and the current contribution from any one electron is balanced by an electron moving in the opposite direction. Hence, if the models and ideas developed so far would lead to a current even at thermal equilibrium, this would prove only the incorrectness of these models and ideas.

We then proceed to a brief consideration of fluctuations about the state of equilibrium and obtain thus a first proof that a crystal with only fully occupied bands must be an insulator.

We obtain two further proofs for this statement as we leave, subsequently, the study of the state of thermal equilibrium and consider the totality of the electrons under the influence of an external field. In this instance there may be a net current; it may be calculated in two ways.

First, the current contributions of the individual electrons may be summed. Second, the distribution of the electrons over the quantum states of the crystal in **k** space may be considered. For thermal equilibrium, this is centrally symmetric. An external force distorts it asymmetrically. This distortion results, in general, in a current.

Both methods yield the current zero for a fully occupied band and thus provide the two proofs mentioned regarding the dropping out of a fully occupied band with respect to the conductivity. We apply the first method also to a partly occupied band. It yields then the relation for the conductivity which was already obtained in Eq. (VII.9.27) on the basis of classical electron theory:

$$\sigma = e\mu n$$

b. Thermal Equilibrium

Here the electrons are distributed over the several quantum states in accord with the Fermi probability of occupation (VII.10.01). The latter contains only the energy E of the quantum state in question, not its wave vector $\mathbf{k}$. It may now be shown that for every crystal the relation

$$E(\mathbf{k}) = E(-\mathbf{k}) \qquad \text{(VII.10.04)}$$

must be satisfied.

Thus the function $E(\mathbf{k})$ must always be centrally symmetric in $\mathbf{k}$ space. Hence, in the one-dimensional example, it cannot vary as

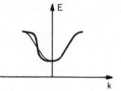

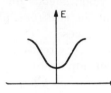

FIG. VII.10.2. Asymmetric $E(k)$-varia-tion. Both $+k$ and $-k$ belong to specific eigenvalues E. However, this is not generally true.

FIG. VII.10.3. Symmetrical $E(k)$-varia-tion. Both $+k$ and $-k$ belong to every arbitrary eigenvalue E.

shown in Fig. VII.10.2, but must vary instead as shown in Fig. VII.10.3. Thus for every eigenvalue there must be apart from $\psi(x; k)$ with the wave factor e^{+ikx} a second eigenfunction with the wave factor e^{-ikx}. This follows quite generally from the fact that the Hamiltonian oper-ator $-(\hbar^2/(2m))\Delta - eU(\mathbf{r})$ is real. For, if we pass from the normal Schrödinger equation

$$(H_{op} - E)\psi(\mathbf{r}; \mathbf{k}) = 0$$

to its complex conjugate

$$(H_{op} - E)\psi^*(\mathbf{r}; \mathbf{k}) = 0$$

we see that for the same eigenvalue E there is both an eigenfunction [i.e., $\psi(\mathbf{r}; \mathbf{k})$] with the wave factor $e^{i\mathbf{k}\cdot\mathbf{r}}$ and one [i.e., $\psi^*(\mathbf{r}; \mathbf{k})$] with the wave factor $e^{-i\mathbf{k}\cdot\mathbf{r}} = e^{+i(-\mathbf{k})\cdot\mathbf{r}}$, which was to be proved.

Thus it follows from Eqs. (VII.10.01) and (VII.10.04) that a state $+\mathbf{k}$ and a state $-\mathbf{k}$ are occupied with equal probability at thermal equilibrium. However, as a further consequence of central symmetry

(VII.10.04), their contributions to the current density

$$- \frac{e}{V_{\text{fund}}} \frac{1}{\hbar} \operatorname{grad}_k E(\mathbf{k})$$

[see Eq. (VII 5.13) on page 208] are equal and opposite. Thus, at thermal equilibrium, current contributions of opposite sign always occur with equal probability. Hence there is no current. In corpuscular terms we may say simply: At thermal equilibrium, electrons with equal, but oppositely directed, velocity occur with equal frequency and hence compensate each other with respect to the current.

c. Thermal Noise

The preceding statement, that at thermal equilibrium the probability of occupation of a quantum state by an electron depends only on its energy E and not on its wave vector $\mathbf{k}$, applies only for a time average. Spontaneous fluctuations take place about this mean distribution of the electrons, giving rise to the so-called thermal noise of ohmic resistances.

Here we must already make a distinction between two cases which will play an important role in what follows.

As we discuss, in Chap. VIII, the distribution of the electrons over the quantum states of the one-electron problem in greater detail, we shall encounter, as one possible case, the situation that all places in the uppermost energy band containing any electrons whatsoever are fully occupied. The next allowed band is empty. In another case, the uppermost allowed energy band containing electrons is partly occupied.

Since electrons can leave the band in which they find themselves only by the action of very strong fields (§7) or that of photon collisions (§8) and since we have excluded such external forces for the present, thermal fluctuations can lead only to transitions to other states in the same band. In a fully occupied band, these states are, however, occupied. Now it is immaterial whether we say that in a fully occupied band thermal fluctuations consist of an exchange of places between electrons or whether we say that in a fully occupied band thermal fluctuations are not possible. From the standpoint of quantum theory, electrons are indistinguishable. It matters only whether a state is occupied by any electron, not by which electron.[1] Hence there can be

---

[1] If two electrons exchange places, the eigenfunction of the many-electron problem (in zero approximation, the so-called Slater determinant) merely changes sign. This does not signify a change in the "physical situation" of the state of the many-electron problem.

The wave-mechanical equivalent of the "corpuscular" statement of the indis-

no thermal fluctuations in a fully occupied band. If a crystal has only fully occupied bands and no partly occupied band, it can exhibit no thermal noise. Otherwise, the mean-square fluctuation current $\overline{I^2}$ within a frequency band df for a short-circuited conductor at temperature T is related to the ohmic resistance R of the conductor according to the well-known theorem of Nyquist[1] by the relation

$$\overline{I^2} = \frac{4kT}{R} \cdot df \qquad\qquad (\text{VII}.10.05)$$

By this equation, thermal noise vanishes only for $R = \infty$, i.e., for an insulator. We have here a first indication that a crystal with only fully occupied bands is an insulator. This will be confirmed when, next, we consider the totality of the electrons in a crystal under the influence of an external force.

d. Calculation of the Conductivity by Summing the Contributions of the Individual Electrons

The electric field **E** exerts on every electron the force

$$\mathbf{F} = -e\mathbf{E} \qquad\qquad (\text{VII}.10.06)$$

We have seen on page 213, Eq. (VII.6.12), that the electrons change their state **k** in accord with the law

$$\hbar\dot{\mathbf{k}} = \mathbf{F} \qquad\qquad (\text{VII}.6.12)$$

In §9 we followed the fate of an individual electron under the simultaneous influence of an external force **F** and of collisions with phonons and impurities and determined its contribution to the current density. If we now sum over all the electrons, we must obtain the total current density.

In carrying out the summation, we shall limit ourselves to the "one-dimensional" case so as to avoid unnecessary mathematical

---

tinguishability of the electrons is the axiom that among all the solutions of the Schrödinger equation of a many-particle problem only the symmetrical or the antisymmetric solutions have physical reality and, hence, need be considered. From this standpoint, the counting prescriptions of Bose and Fermi statistics represent simply the counting of the symmetrical and antisymmetric eigenfunctions, respectively, of a many-electron problem; see, e.g., L. Nordheim in Müller-Pouillet, "Lehrbuch der Physik," vol. IV, part 4, p. 251.

[1] H. Nyquist, *Phys. Rev.*, **32**: 110 (1928). We prefer to introduce the mean-square current fluctuation $\overline{I^2}$ of a short-circuited conductor rather than the mean-square voltage $\overline{u^2}$ at the ends of a conductor in open circuit because in the latter case a spontaneous primary fluctuation produces a field within the conductor. We then no longer have the force-free case here under consideration.

complications.   Thus the motion of the electrons has only one degree of freedom, namely, the x axis.   Similarly, the field strength points in the x direction and the lattice potential $U = U(x)$ depends only on x.   In order to be able to separate clearly the concepts of current and current density, we consider, in spite of the restriction of the direction of the force and the electron motion to the x axis, a crystal which has a cross section Q perpendicular to the x axis and has a length of G lattice constants a along the x axis, so that its volume is $Q \cdot Ga$. Then we obtain from (VII.9.26), (VII.9.24), and (VII.9.25)

$$\mathbf{i}_{\text{single}} = \frac{1}{Q \cdot Ga} \frac{e^2 \tau}{m_{\text{eff}}(k)} \mathbf{E}$$

The summation of the individual contributions follows, for the assumption that the quantum states are filled up to a k number k_{bound}:

$$\mathbf{i} = \int \mathbf{i}_{\text{single}} \, dN = \int\limits_{k = -k\,\text{bound}}^{k = +k\,\text{bound}} \frac{1}{V_{\text{fund}}} \frac{e^2 \tau}{m_{\text{eff}}(k)} \mathbf{E} \frac{dN}{dk} \cdot dk \quad \text{(VII.10.07)}$$

The number dN of electrons which can be accommodated in the k interval $(k, k + dk)$ is equal to twice[1] the number of the quantum states in this interval.   According to page 170, a quantum state claims an interval $2\pi/aG$ on the k axis.   Thus there are $Ga \cdot dk/2\pi$ quantum states in the interval $(k, k + dk)$, and

$$dN = 2 \cdot \frac{Ga}{2\pi} \, dk \quad\quad\quad \text{(VII.10.08)}$$

electrons can be accommodated.   If we use Eq. (VII.6.28) for the effective mass in (VII.10.07), we obtain

$$\mathbf{i} = e^2 \mathbf{E} \tau \int\limits_{k = -k\,\text{bound}}^{k = +k\,\text{bound}} \frac{1}{\hbar^2} E''(k) \cdot \frac{1}{Q \cdot Ga} 2 \frac{Ga}{2\pi} \, dk$$

$$= \frac{e^2 \mathbf{E} \tau}{Q} \cdot \frac{1}{\pi} \frac{1}{\hbar^2} [E'(+k_{\text{bound}}) - E'(-k_{\text{bound}})]$$

In view of the general central symmetry (VII.10.04) of $E(k)$, we can conclude, furthermore, that

$$\mathbf{i} = \frac{e^2 \mathbf{E} \tau}{Q} \cdot \frac{1}{\pi} \frac{1}{\hbar^2} \cdot 2E'(+k_{\text{bound}}) \quad\quad \text{(VII.10.09)}$$

Let us consider first the case of the fully occupied band.   Since at a band edge the $E(k)$ curve is horizontal (see Figs. VII.3.10c to VII.3.12),

---

[1] Because of the electron spin, a quantum state can be occupied by two electrons.

we have in this case $E'(k_{\text{bound}}) = 0$.   We thus have the result that the fully occupied band supplies no current, in the presence of an electric field **E** as well as at thermal equilibrium.   A fully occupied band does not contribute to the conductivity.

As our next example we consider a very slightly occupied band. Then only the states close to the bottom edge of the band are occupied. Here the approximation

$$E = E_C + \frac{\hbar^2}{2m_{\text{eff}}}\, k^2 \qquad\qquad \text{(VII.10.10)}$$

is valid.   Hence

$$E'(k_{\text{bound}}) = \frac{\hbar^2}{m_{\text{eff}}} \cdot k_{\text{bound}} \qquad\qquad \text{(VII.10.11)}$$

On the other hand, k_{bound} may be expressed with the aid of (VII.10.08) in terms of the total number N of electrons in the volume $V = Q \cdot Ga$ of the crystal:

$$N = \frac{1}{\pi} Ga\, [(+k_{\text{bound}}) - (-k_{\text{bound}})] = \frac{2}{\pi} Gak_{\text{bound}} \quad \text{(VII.10.12)}$$

or

$$k_{\text{bound}} = \frac{\pi}{2} \frac{N}{Ga}$$

With (VII.10.11) and (VII.10.12), (VII.10.09) becomes

$$\mathbf{i} = \frac{e^2 \mathbf{E}\tau}{Q} \cdot \frac{1}{\pi} \cdot \frac{1}{\hbar^2} \cdot 2\, \frac{\hbar^2}{m_{\text{eff}}} \cdot \frac{\pi}{2} \cdot \frac{N}{Ga}$$

or, introducing the concentration $n = N/(Q \cdot Ga)$ of the electrons,

$$\mathbf{i} = e \cdot n \cdot \frac{e}{m_{\text{eff}}}\, \tau \cdot \mathbf{E} \qquad\qquad \text{(VII.10.13)}$$

For a slightly occupied band the conductivity, defined by

$$\mathbf{i} = \sigma \cdot \mathbf{E} \qquad\qquad \text{(VII.10.14)}$$

thus becomes

$$\sigma = e \cdot n \cdot \mu \qquad\qquad \text{(VII.10.15)}$$

Here we have introduced the electron mobility

$$\mu = \frac{e}{m_{\text{eff}}} \cdot \tau \qquad\qquad \text{(VII.9.25)}$$

which occurred in Eq. (VII.9.07) or (VII. 9.24) as a proportionality factor between the mean velocity increment of an electron and the field strength **E**.   This leads to a purely corpuscular standpoint. It was shown on pages 246 to 248 how the conductivity formula (VII.10.15) is obtained from it.

e. The Distortion of the Equilibrium Distribution of the Electrons and the Calculation of the Conductivity

At the beginning of §10 we noted that we could obtain important results from general traits of the electron distribution over the several quantum states, without concerning ourselves with details. As one such trait we have utilized the fact that at thermal equilibrium the electrons occupy symmetrically the centrally symmetric pattern

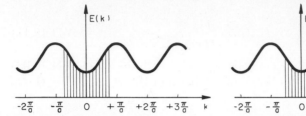

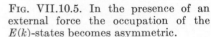

FIG. VII.10.4. In the absence of an external force the occupation of the $E(k)$-states is symmetrical.

FIG. VII.10.5. In the presence of an external force the occupation of the $E(k)$-states becomes asymmetric.

$E(\mathbf{k})$ (see Fig. VII.10.4). Now, an external field perturbs the equilibrium distribution. All electrons uniformly seek, in accord with Eq. (VII.6.12),

$$\dot{\mathbf{k}} = \frac{1}{\hbar}\,\mathbf{F} \qquad\qquad \text{(VII.6.12)}$$

to occupy other $\mathbf{k}$ vectors, which point more nearly in the direction of $\mathbf{F}$. Since (VII.6.12) does not contain the quantum state $\mathbf{k}$ itself, we find that the equilibrium distribution of the electrons in $\mathbf{k}$ space tends to drift with uniform velocity without change in shape[1] or density.

At the same time, we have seen in connection with the treatment of the "oscillation" within a band of a single electron, on pages 257 to 258, that collisions with phonons and impurities prevent an actual development of this oscillation. In considering the totality of the electrons, we must similarly take account of the fact that, in fact, thermal equilibrium is attained through collisions of the electrons with phonons and impurities and that in case of a deviation from thermal equilibrium these collisions provide a retarding impulse which tends to reconvert the perturbed distribution into the equilibrium distribution.

Thus we see that the application of an external field $\mathbf{E}$ to the crystal results in a slightly perturbed distribution of the electrons over the

---

[1] For the one-dimensional example of Fig. VII.10.4, the "shape" of the $\mathbf{k}$ distribution is simply the width of the occupied k interval.

quantum states, of such nature that the equilibrium distribution is shifted slightly from its symmetrical position in the direction of larger k numbers (Fig. VII.10.5). The resulting current and hence the conductivity are derived from the magnitude of the shift.

We shall not carry this idea further at this point. Instead, we shall be satisfied with pointing out that, from this standpoint, the dropping out of a fully occupied band for the conductivity is easily recognized. In Fig. VII.10.6 we have shown the occupation of a full band with and without external field. Since the states in the k interval $+\pi/a < k < +3\pi/a$ are fully equivalent to the states in the interval $-\pi/a < k < +\pi/a$, the states which are missing in the interval $-\pi/a < k < +\pi/a$ after application of the field are exactly compensated by those which have been added in the interval $+\pi/a < k < +3\pi/a$.

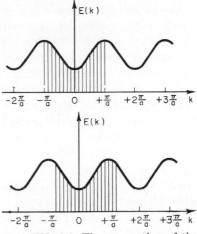

Fig. VII.10.6. The occupation of the $E(k)$ states for a fully occupied band. Upper figure: without external force. Lower figure: with external force.

Thus the application of the field has actually made no change in the distribution of the electrons. Just as in the absence of a field, there is no current.

f. Concluding and Summarizing Remarks

It must be emphasized repeatedly that the argument of §9 and §10 represents only a superficial outline of theories which are very complex in substance. Thus we have treated the collision time τ as independent of the quantum state **k**, which is not generally correct. The statistical scattering of the free times of flight and, particularly, the coupling of the velocities before and after collision render very difficult the precise realization of the method first described, in which the current is calculated from the contributions of the individual electrons. Even in classical electron theory, this led H. A. Lorentz to abandon this method, which had been used by Riecke and Drude, and to replace it by considerations of the deviation from the equilibrium distribution. The second method is also tied less closely to the corpuscular picture and makes it possible to work directly with transition probabilities at a collision. Hence all authors have used it in effect for more precise wave-mechanical treatment of the ideas outlined here in §9 and §10.

§11. Conclusions from the Band Model Regarding the Conduction of a Particular Crystal Lattice

In the solution of practical problems we frequently seek electronic solids with quite definite conduction properties. [Examples: (1) Resistivity $= 10^1$ to 10^2 ohm-cm, temperature coefficient of resistance as small as possible; or (2) resistivity as small as possible, temperature coefficient as large as possible; or (3) resistivity as large as possible and, at the same time, electron mobility μ as large as possible.] No proof is needed to show that a theory of conductivity which might predict whether a certain element or compound is a conductor or insulator would be of value in meeting such requirements. The person who is less familiar with the field may be surprised, however, that such "predictions" of theory are of great value even in the study of the conduction properties of a chemical compound which is already available, at least in the laboratory. We might think that in such a case a measurement would attain the objective more quickly, and, in particular, with greater certainty than an application of theory.

However, a purely experimental procedure can lead to crude errors. In conductivity measurements, difficulties frequently arise simply from the fact that the contacts commonly introduce barrier layers. The measurement of voltages with zero-current probes proves helpful, but demands relatively large specimens. The main difficulty, however, arises from the fact that the conductivity of most semiconductors and insulators is extremely sensitive to minimal impurities or defects in structure and texture. Hence it is often extremely doubtful whether the measured specimens have those conduction properties of the material in question which are characteristic of it in a highly perfect state.

A historical example may show that this assertion is by no means contrived. For a long time it was undecided whether the elements silicon and germanium, in their purest form, were metals or insulators, and in 1930 reputable experimenters decided emphatically in favor of their metallic character. However, when these two elements, approximately ten years later, attained importance as materials for detectors, specimens of increasing perfection became available for measurements, and just the reverse was found to be correct. Today silicon and germanium are even regarded as prototypes of electronic semiconductors.

What potentialities does the theory have for determining the conduction properties of a solid? The nearest starting point is here, of course, the assertion of the band model that a fully occupied band does not contribute to the conductivity (see pages 263, 264, and 267) and that a solid body can be a conductor only if its band model includes incompletely occupied bands. A very simple procedure, which, however, may frequently lead to erroneous conclusions, suggests itself for the application of this statement. We can observe the occupation of the individual electron levels of the atoms forming the lattice and conclude from the complete or incomplete occupation of these atomic levels regarding the complete or incomplete occupation of the "corresponding" bands of the crystal lattice.

From this point of view it is to be expected that the lattices of the condensed noble gases (Ne, Ar, Kr, X) with closed shells of eight in the individual atoms are insulators. This is so in fact. Also for the alkali metals Li, Na, K, Rb, and Cs this primitive argument applies. From the fact that there is here a single s electron outside a closed shell of eight, we deduce half-occupancy of a corresponding s band and hence metallic conductivity. It scarcely requires mention that for an ionic lattice (e.g., NaCl) the complete or incomplete occupation of shells in the ions Na^+ and Cl^- and not in the neutral atoms Na and Cl must be considered. In any case, in view of the shells of eight of Na^+ and Cl^-, we must regard the insulating character of the NaCl lattice as another confirmation of the elementary standpoint.

The alkaline earths Be, Mg, Ca, Sr, and Ba have two s electrons in their outermost shell. From the foregoing elementary point of view, their crystals should have a fully occupied s band and hence be insulators. The contrary is known to be true. The explanation may be sought in the fact that for these atoms an empty p term lies above the fully occupied s term. When the atoms are brought together in a crystal, these terms split up into bands and overlap apparently, so that the insulating gap between the s and p bands is closed.

A further failure of the primitive point of view occurs for the lattice of solid hydrogen. Like the alkali atoms, the hydrogen atom has a single s electron. Nevertheless, solid hydrogen is an insulator, in contrast with Li, Na, K, Rb, and Cs. We shall see that the explanation rests in the fact that hydrogen does not form an atomic lattice, but a molecular lattice,[1] i.e., a hexagonal close-packed lattice[2] in which the individual lattice points have a separation of 3.75 A and are occupied by H_2 molecules rather than by H atoms. Within the molecules, the two H atoms are known to have a separation of 0.74 A.[3]

In a molecular lattice (see, e.g., Fig. VII.11.1) we are no longer

[1] See, e.g., J. D'Ans and E. Lax, "Taschenbuch für Chemiker und Physiker," pp. 164 and 178, Springer-Verlag OHG, Berlin, 1943.

[2] See, e.g., P. P. Ewald, "Kristalle und Röntgenstrahlen," p. 150, Springer-Verlag OHG, Berlin, 1923.

[3] See D'Ans and Lax, *op. cit.*, p. 118.

dealing with a "simple translation lattice" (commonly designated as Bravais lattice), but with a "translation lattice with basis." For

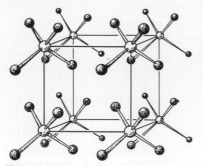

these lattices we no longer obtain all[1] lattice points by giving the components l_1, l_2, l_3 of the number trio $\mathbf{l} = (l_1, l_2, l_3)$ in the equation for the radius vector $\mathbf{R}_l$ of a lattice point

$$\mathbf{R}_l = l_1\mathbf{a}_1 + l_2\mathbf{a}_2 + l_3\mathbf{a}_3 \quad (\text{VII.11.01})$$

all positive and negative integer values; in this manner we obtain only the corners of the individual unit cell, and we must extend the "basis" of the unit cell, namely, the m vectors $\mathbf{r}_1 \ldots \mathbf{r}_m$ which lead from the corner of the unit cell to the m atoms in the cell, from these corners. A lattice can be described in infinitely many ways.[2] Thus the face-centered cubic and the body-centered cubic lattices (see Figs. VII.11.2 and

FIG. VII.11.1. Carbon tetraiodide as example of a molecular lattice. C atoms: white. I atoms: black.

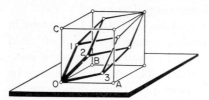

FIG. VII.11.2. Face-centered cubic lattice.

First representation: translation lattice with basis; orthogonal axes of translation: OA, OB, OC. Four atoms of basis: 0, 1, 2, 3.

Second representation: simple translation lattice; oblique axes of translation: 01, 02, 03.

From P. P. Ewald in Geiger and Scheel, vol. XXIII, part 2, p. 239, Fig. 46.

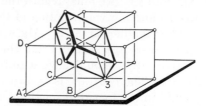

FIG. VII.11.3. Body-centered cubic lattice.

First representation: translation lattice with basis; orthogonal axes of translation: AB, AC, AD. Two atoms of basis: A, 0.

Second representation: simple translation lattice; oblique axes of translation: 01, 02, 03.

From P. P. Ewald in Geiger and Scheel, vol. XXIII, part 2, p. 239, Fig. 47.

VII.11.3) cease to be simple translation lattices if orthogonal axes of translation $\mathbf{a}_1$, $\mathbf{a}_2$, $\mathbf{a}_3$ are employed, but become instead lattices with a basis of four and two atoms, respectively. With oblique axes of translation $\mathbf{a}_1$, $\mathbf{a}_2$, $\mathbf{a}_3$, they can be represented as simple translation lattices.

[1] More precisely, all and only all lattice points. In this connection, see the discussion on p. 271 on the diamond lattice and Fig. VII.11.4 corresponding to it.

[2] See Ewald, *op. cit.*, p. 272.

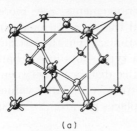

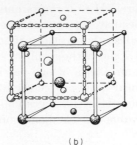

(a)   (b)

Every C atom has four neighbors placed at the corners of a tetrahedron.

Formation of the diamond lattice by two interlaced face-centered cubic lattices.

FIG. VII.11.4. Diamond lattice: all atoms C

Zinc blende lattice: black atoms Zn,
white atoms S.

In a molecular lattice this cannot be done in any way; the geometrical relationships themselves prevent representation as a simple translation lattice (see Fig. VII.11.1). This is not true exclusively for a molecular lattice. The diamond lattice (see Fig. VII.11.4) also cannot be regarded as a simple translation lattice; it consists of two face-centered cubic lattices which are displaced by a quarter of a body diagonal. It is true that translation axes $\mathbf{a}_1$, $\mathbf{a}_2$, $\mathbf{a}_3$ can readily be indicated for which every C atom has a radius vector $l_1\mathbf{a}_1 + l_2\mathbf{a}_2 + l_3\mathbf{a}_3$ with integer l_1, l_2, l_3. However, if we assign all positive and negative integer values to the l_1, l_2, l_3, we meet many points which are not occupied by C atoms. This cannot happen in a simple translation lattice, in whose definition on page 270 we should speak more precisely of "all and only all" lattice points rather than simply of "all" lattice points (see also footnote 1, page 270). Whereas for the molecular lattice and the diamond lattice purely geometrical circumstances prevent representation as a Bravais translation lattice, we find that for compounds such as NaCl the occupation of the

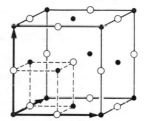

FIG. VII.11.5. The NaCl lattice might be regarded as a simple translation lattice with three orthogonal axes $a/2$ if the alternating occupation of the lattice points by Na and Cl atoms did not demand a different representation, e.g., as lattice with three orthogonal axes a and a basis of four Na and four Cl atoms.

lattice points by different kinds of atoms or ions forces us to regard them as translation lattices with basis (see Fig. VII.11.5), even when geometry alone would lead us to describe them as simple translation lattices.

Figure VII.11.6 shows one-dimensional analogues of an atomic and a molecular lattice. These linear arrangements are more easily handled mathematically than the actual three-dimensional ones; Fig. VII.11.7 shows the result of such calculations.[1] On the left half of the figure, an s term of one particular atom type splits into a band when in a linear atom lattice the identical lattice distance a between adjoining potential wells is gradually reduced from very large values to the small value b. The band contains two places per atom (see page 179).

—•—•—•—•—•—•—   ˈ—ᴔ—ᴔ—ᴔ—ᴔ—ᴔ—ᴔˈ

Atomic lattice   Molecular lattice

Fɪɢ. VII.11.6. Linear chains.

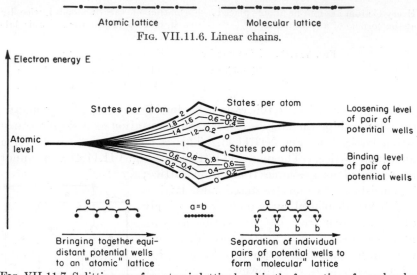

Fɪɢ. VII.11.7. Splitting up of an atomic lattice band in the formation of a molecular lattice. Qualitative representation. The thin lines within the band indicate the total number of states in the band lying below them. To the lower "molecular" level belongs a "binding" eigenfunction $\psi_+(\mathbf{r}) = \psi_{At}(r_a) + \psi_{At}(r_b)$. To the upper "molecular" level belongs a "loosening" eigenfunction $\psi_-(\mathbf{r}) = \psi_{At}(r_a) - \psi_{At}(r_b)$. See Eqs. (VI.2.01 and 2.02) and footnote on p. 155.

In the right half of the figure, the atoms are again separated. However, in this process the atoms retain the separation b in pairs and only the separation between adjoining pair centers is continuously increased. Thus, in the same right half of the figure, a linear molecular lattice is dilated until the molecules are practically separate. We see that the

---

[1] Since, as in the band model, we are here dealing with the one-electron problem (in a periodic potential field), the solution for the limiting case of separated molecules can also be compared only with the eigenfunctions of the molecular ion, from which the procedure of Hund and Mulliken can then construct the many-electron eigenfunctions of the molecule by linear combinations. See also the legend of Fig. VII.11.7.

continuous energy band of the atom lattice splits in the middle and that we obtain two separate bands with one place per atom. Thus, if the lattice points in such a linear molecular lattice are occupied by hydrogen atoms, electrons just fill completely all places of the lower band. The upper band remains empty. Thus we obtain an insulator. The transfer of these considerations to the three-dimensional H_2 lattice is certainly permissible.

In the example just described of a diatomic molecular lattice, there are two atoms in a unit cell. Each of the bands, therefore, has again two places per cell. Hence if we replace the phrase "two places per atom" with the phrase "two places per elementary unit cell of translation," we would seem to cover correctly both atomic and molecular lattices and might hope to arrive at a generally valid rule—eventually after introduction of a statistical weight ω for an atomic level with $(\omega - 1)$-fold degeneracy. However, this also is an illusion. A calculation for the case described—e.g., with the aid of Bloch's approximation—shows that the splitting between the two molecular bands vanishes when the distances of an atom from its two neighbors become just equal (we now traverse Fig. VII.11.7 from the right to the left). The fact that the rule "two places per elementary cell" applies also for the atomic lattice arises from the fact that at the instant at which the separations of an atom from its two nearest neighbors become equal the elementary cell becomes half as large as before in the molecular lattice. Thus the number of elementary cells is doubled, and hence the doubling of places in the one band which resulted from the closing of the gap between the molecular bands is just compensated.

Now the equalizing of the distances to the neighbors need not always be accompanied by the appearance of a smaller unit cell. Even so, two molecular bands can merge into a single atomic band. Thus if two face-centered cubic lattices are so placed that they are displaced relative to each other by a small fraction of a body diagonal, we have a molecular lattice. If the lattice points are occupied by atoms with an s electron, we have once more two molecular bands with two places in an energy band for each elementary unit cell (constructed with the surface diagonals! See Fig. VII.11.2). If, now, the lattices are displaced further, we reach the diamond lattice for a displacement by one-fourth of the body diagonal. The separations of an atom from its four neighbors become equal. The molecular bands merge into a single s band. However, no smaller unit cell is obtained, so that we have a band with four places per elementary unit cell in such a lattice.

The instructive example of the actual diamond lattice (atom with two $2s$ and two $2p$ electrons), which we shall discuss next, shows in addition that the atomic states, which are split up in bringing the atoms together, can group themselves quite differently from the atom, so that the setting up of a more or less automatic rule for counting the places in the bands becomes entirely impossible. In the isolated C atom, the $2p$ level is occupied by only two electrons, although, by the Pauli principle, there is place for six electrons. Hence the primitive

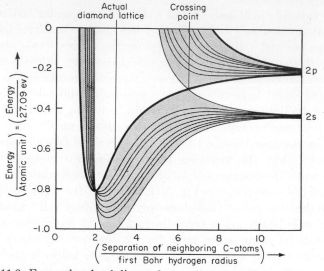

Fig. VII.11.8. Energy bands of diamond according to F. Hund and B. Mrowka. For large atomic separations the $2s$ band contains two states per atom. The $2p$ band contains 6 states per atom, of which, in the present approximation, only the central third splits up; the lower and the upper thirds of the $2p$ states are represented by the heavily drawn boundaries of the $2p$ band. See the text with respect to the behavior for smaller atomic separations.

standpoint might lead us to expect metallic conductivity for diamond. Such a consideration is valid, however, only for very widely separated C atoms; a calculation for diamond yields the system of levels shown in Fig. VII.11.8.[1] We have a $2s$ band with two places per atom and a $2p$ band with six places per atom only for very large values of the

[1] F. Hund and B. Mrowka, *Ber. Verhandl. sächs Akad. Wiss. Leipzig, Math-phys. Kl.*, **87**: 185 and 325 (1935), in particular p. 192. Since in the isolated C atom there are not only two $2s$ electrons but also two $2p$ electrons, it seems reasonable to suggest that the Bloch approximation should be carried out with p functions. Hund and Mrowka have, however, carried out the Bloch approximation with s functions only and have utilized p functions only in the cellular method of Wigner and Seitz. Thus Eq. (VII.11.02) indicates only the band splitting of the atomic $2s$ level and says nothing regarding the band splitting of the atomic $2p$ level above it.

lattice constant. As the lattice constant is reduced continuously, retaining the tetrahedral arrangement of the individual C atoms—i.e., for geometrically similar reduction of the lattice dimensions—the lower edge of the $2p$ band and the upper edge of the $2s$ band cross. The decisive point is that, at the crossing, a fractional band of two places per atom leaves the upper band and merges with the $2s$ band below it, so that to the left of the crossing point the lower band has four places per atom and the band lying above it has also only four places per atom. Thus, to the left of the crossing the four electrons of the L shell of the C atom fill completely the lower band, which is followed by an insulating gap, and the band with four more places per atom lying above it remains empty.

Another surprising phenomenon occurring in the band theory of the diamond lattice may be related to this peculiar behavior of the $2p$ states. The Brillouin approximation, starting from free electrons, leads to a theorem regarding polyhedra in $\mathbf{k}$ space, the Brillouin zones (see page 189). In the Bloch approximation, starting from bound electrons, we also meet a polyhedron in $\mathbf{k}$ space, the periodicity polyhedron, outside of which the energy values repeat themselves periodically (see page 181). For the cubic, face-centered cubic, and body-centered cubic lattices treated in most textbooks, the Bloch periodicity polyhedron and the first Brillouin zone are identical. This is no longer true for the diamond lattice. According to Hund and Mrowka,[1] the Bloch approximation with atomic s functions yields for the diamond lattice

$$E = E° + 4C$$
$$\pm 2R \sqrt{1 + \cos\frac{a}{2}k_x \cdot \cos\frac{a}{2}k_y + \cos\frac{a}{2}k_y \cdot \cos\frac{a}{2}k_z + \cos\frac{a}{2}k_z \cdot \cos\frac{a}{2}k_x}$$

$$(\text{VII.11.02})$$

whereas for a simple face-centered cubic lattice we have[2]

$$E = E° + C$$
$$+ 4A \left(\cos\frac{a}{2}k_x \cdot \cos\frac{a}{2}k_y + \cos\frac{a}{2}k_y \cdot \cos\frac{a}{2}k_z + \cos\frac{a}{2}k_z \cdot \cos\frac{a}{2}k_x \right)$$

$$(\text{VII.11.03})$$

The dependence on the components k_x, k_y, k_z of the wave vector $\mathbf{k}$ thus occurs for both lattices through the same expression $\cos ak_x/2 \cdot$

[1] *Ibid.*

[2] See, e.g., A. Sommerfeld and H. A. Bethe in Geiger and Scheel, *op. cit.*, vol. XXIV, part 2, p. 387, Eq. (12.15).

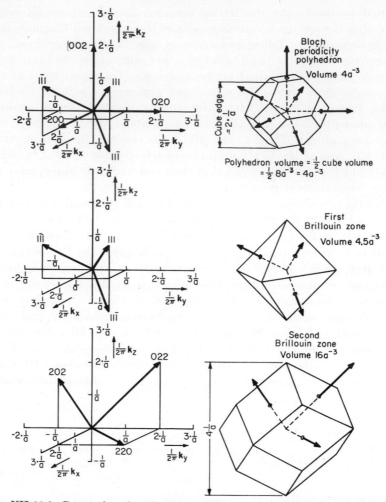

FIG. VII.11.9. Concerning the Bloch and Brillouin approximations for diamond.

$\cos ak_y/2 + \cos ak_y/2 \cdot \cos ak_z/2 + \cos ak_z/2 \cdot \cos ak_x/2$. Thus both lattices have the same Bloch periodicity polyhedron, i.e., the octahedron with the points cut off shown in Fig VII.11.9.

Concerning the first Brillouin zone of the diamond lattice, we know that it must be at least as large as that of the face-centered cubic lattice, since no additional Bragg reflections are produced by inserting into each other the two face-centered cubic lattices of which the diamond lattice consists (see Fig. VII.11.4).[1] On the other hand, certain

---

[1] Ewald, *op. cit.*, p. 91.

reflections can drop out, since the beams reflected by the two sublattices can cancel each other because of suitable phase differences.[1] In fact, for diamond the (200) planes, cutting off the points of the octahedron, drop out, so that the first Brillouin zone of diamond is the complete (111) octahedron. For the second Brillouin zone, a rhombic dodecahedron, formed by the (220) planes, is obtained (see Fig. VII.11.9).[2]

In the Bloch approximation, nothing is changed as compared with a face-centered cubic lattice in so far as we still obtain an s band with two places per atom. We recognize this as follows: According to Fig. VII.11.9, the Bloch periodicity polyhedron has, by elementary geometry, a volume $4a^{-3}$. According to §2, page 182, a k state requires a volume $(2\pi)^3/V_{fund}$ in k space and a volume $1/V_{fund}$ in the $k/2\pi$ space used in Fig. VII.11.9 because the vector $k/2\pi$ is also plotted in the construction of the Brillouin zones (see Figs. VII.3.5 and VII.3.6). We can hence accommodate $4V_{fund}a^{-3}$ different k states in the periodicity polyhedron with the volume $4a^{-3}$. On the other hand, the fundamental domain contains V_{fund}/a^3 elementary cubes with edge a. For the face-centered cubic lattice, every elementary cube contains four atoms. Thus there are $4V_{fund}a^{-3}$ atoms in the fundamental domain. Thus, for the face-centered cubic lattice the periodicity polyhedron provides space for $4V_{fund}a^{-3}$ different k states for $4V_{fund}a^{-3}$ atoms, or one k state per atom. Since by (VII.11.03) one energy value in the s band belongs to every k state, we obtain for the face-centered cubic lattice an s band with one energy value per atom or, because of the spin, two places per atom.

In the diamond lattice there are instead eight atoms in the elementary cube a^3. It would seem, hence, that we would obtain an s band with only one place per atom. However, according to (VII.11.02), the s band of the diamond lattice consists of two sub-bands, because of the two signs of the root; these merge, however, since the term under the radical vanishes, e.g., for $ak_x/2 = \pi, ak_y/2 = 0, ak_z/2 = \pi/2$.

---

[1] The condition for this is that the "structure factor"

$$S_h = \sum_{t=1}^{t=m} e^{-2\pi j(h \cdot r_t)}$$

for the reflections at a family of planes h vanishes. The summation index $t = 1$, 2, . . . , m indicates the several sublattices in this expression; the m vectors r_t construct the basis within a unit cell. See, e.g., Ewald, *op. cit.*, p. 279.

[2] See N. F. Mott and H. Jones, "Properties of Metals and Alloys," p. 159, Clarendon Press, Oxford, 1936.

The complete s band formed by the two sub-bands thus contains twice as many places as for the face-centered cubic lattice. Hence the doubling of the number of atoms in an elementary cube is compensated, and we obtain once more an s band with two places per atom. This evidently corresponds to the conditions for a diamond lattice with very large lattice constant, i.e., the level system to the right of the crossing point in Fig. VII.11.8.

We can draw the following conclusion from the Brillouin approxima-tion: Since the cubes with edge a contain four atoms in the face-centered cubic lattice and eight atoms in the diamond lattice, the number of places per atom in diamond is half as large as for the face-centered cubic lattice. Thus we would obtain one place per atom in the diamond lattice. Since, however, the points of the octahedron are not cut off for the diamond lattice, an exact calculation yields 1.125 places per atom, provided that we restrict ourselves to the first Brillouin zone. Only the next Brillouin zone, namely, the rhombic (220) dodecahedron, contains together with the first zone again a whole number of places per atom, namely, four. If we assume that there is band overlap between the first and second zone, but not between the second and the third zone, we obtain an energy band which is completely filled by the four valence electrons in the L shell of the C atom. This evi-dently corresponds to the circumstances for a diamond lattice with small lattice constant, i.e., the system of levels in Fig. VII.11.8 to the left of the crossing point. Thus, here the behavior of the valence electrons is to some extent covered by the Brillouin approximation, whereas the two strongly bound $1s$ electrons must be added to the nucleus.

Thus we see that the insulating character of diamond is by no means obvious from the standpoint of the band model and can be understood only with the aid of a more careful study of the splitting of the atomic states, in particular the $2p$ states. Whereas in this instance the "more careful study" has been carried out by Hund and Mrowka[1] on the one hand and by Kimball[1] on the other,[2] the same does not apply to cobalt monoxide, CoO. Yet here also the high resistance ($\rho \approx 10^8$ ohm-cm) found experimentally is rather difficult to understand. CoO crystal-lizes in a rock-salt lattice, whose lattice points are occupied by Co^{++}

[1] F. Hund and B. Mrowka, *Ber. Verhandl. sächs. Akad. Wiss. Leipzig, Math.-phys. Kl.*, **87**: 185 and 325 (1935); G. E. Kimball, *J. Chem. Phys.*, **3**: 560 (1935).

[2] Large-scale investigations of the band structure of the diamond lattice have been undertaken in the last few years by Herman (Radio Corporation of America). See F. Herman, *Phys. Rev.*, **88**: 1210 (1952); and **93**: 1214 (1954); F. Herman and J. Callaway, *Phys. Rev.*, **89**: 518 (1953); and F. Herman, J. Callaway, and F. S. Acton, *Phys. Rev.*, **95**: 371 (1954).

and O^{--} ions.[1] Whereas the O^{--} ions have a closed shell of 8 electrons, the $3d$ level of the Co^{++} ions is occupied by only 5 electrons, whereas it could accommodate 10 electrons. We, therefore, expect a half-occupied $3d$ band in the crystal and, hence, metallic conductivity, in contradiction with experiment. Hund[2] suggests as a way out that the $3d$ band is so narrow and consequently the effective mass of the electrons so large that, in spite of a normal mean free path of the conduction electrons, very small mobilities and, hence, very small conductivity are obtained. In this way we might "just about understand the insulating nature of these crystals."[3]

MnO represents a similar case. In fact, these compounds with incompletely filled $3d$ shells of the cations quite generally lead to difficulties. The existence of these "open-band semiconductors" has at times been regarded as a failure of the band model, and the conduction mechanism in these compounds has been treated on the basis of atomistic models.[4]

Finally, we note that simple conclusions from the occupation of the shells in isolated atoms or ions regarding the occupation of the bands in the crystal and, hence, the insulator or metal character of the lattice in question are quite unreliable in view of the phenomena which have been discussed—namely, band overlap, splitting of bands with the formation of molecules, branching off of a sub-band at a crossing point of band boundaries, and the possibility of very narrow bands with large effective masses and hence small mobility of the conduction electrons. This unreliability can be reduced only if, in the particular case in question, the level splitting is calculated by the methods of Wigner and Seitz[5] or of Slater.[6,7]

[1] See D'Ans and Lax, *op. cit.*, p. 180.

[2] F. Hund, *Physik. Z.*, **36**: 725 (1935), in particular, p. 728. Also reprinted in *Z. tech. Phys.*, **16**: 331 (1935), in particular p. 334.

[3] *Ibid.*

[4] J. H. de Boer and E. J. W. Verwey, *Proc. Phys. Soc. (London)*, **49**: 59 (1935); W. Schottky, *Z. Elektrochem.*, **45**: 33 (1939), in particular, p. 57; H. Dressnandt, *Z. Physik*, **115**, 369 (1940); C. Wagner and E. Koch, *Z. physik. Chem.*, **B32**: 439 (1936); R. Peierls, *Proc. Phys. Soc. (London)*, **49**: 72 (1937).

In the evaluation of past experimental results for these compounds, we should never forget that the preparation of satisfactory specimens is made very difficult by deviations from stoichiometric composition, by inhomogeneous structure of the specimens, and by polycrystallinity. We have already seen from the previously mentioned erroneous conclusions regarding the nature of conduction in Si and Ge what basic errors can result from measurements on imperfect specimens.

[5] E. Wigner and F. Seitz, *Phys. Rev.*, **43**: 804 (1933).

[6] J. C. Slater, *Phys. Rev.*, **45**: 794 (1934).

[7] The reader will find a compilation of more recent work in this field in G. V. Raynor, *Repts. Progr. Phys.*, **15**: 173 (1952).

Even when such generally extensive studies are carried out, there always remains an uncertainty regarding the justification of the band model itself. We must not forget that, as a one-electron approximation for a many-electron problem, the band model can at best take summary account of the interaction of the electrons through the potential curve employed in the approximation of Wigner, Seitz, and Slater. No final answer has as yet been given to the valid question as to whether this is always admissible or whether, in some cases, the failure of the remaining electrons to get out of the way of the reference electron may undercut the basis of the band model, namely, the periodicity of the potential field.

Thus the band model can only give some pointers regarding the likelihood that a particular crystal may be a conductor or an insulator or an intrinsic semiconductor. It will be advantageous here to employ methods which are largely empirical, such as comparisons with crystals of the same structure but different composition, utilization of regularities in the periodic system of elements, etc. This opens up the broad field of crystal chemistry, for which we shall merely indicate the reference texts.[1]

§12. Problems

Problems on One-dimensional Periodic Potentials

1. Many of the essential features of the band picture can be shown even by very simple one-dimensional models. Consider, for example, a one-dimensional lattice, consisting of (positive) delta functions, with a lattice constant l:

$$U(x) = +S \sum_{n=-\infty}^{+\infty} \delta(nl) \qquad \text{(VII.12.01)}$$

Between the δ functions the ψ functions are plane waves:

$$\psi(x) = A\,e^{i\varkappa x} + B\,e^{-i\varkappa x} \qquad \varkappa = \sqrt{\frac{2mE}{\hbar^2}} \qquad \text{(VII.12.02)}$$

At the potential wells these waves have to be matched properly, as shown in Prob. 1 of Chap. VI, §5. This provides two equations for the relationship between the coefficients A and B in adjoining cells. Two additional equations follow from the

---

[1] U. Dehlinger, "Chemische Physik der Metalle und Legierungen," Akademische Verlagsgesellschaft, Leipzig, 1939; A. Eucken, "Lehrbuch der chemischen Physik," vol. II, part 2, 3d ed., Leipzig, 1949; F. Halla, "Kristallchemie und Kristallphysik metallischer Werkstoffe," J. A. Barth, Leipzig; W. Hume-Rothery, "The Structure of Metals and Alloys," Monograph and Report Series of the Institute of Metals, No. 1, London, 1950; L. Pauling, "The Nature of the Chemical Bond," 2d ed., New York/London, 1945; A. F. Wells, "Structural Inorganic Chemistry," Clarendon Press, Oxford, 1945; H. G. F. Winckler, "Struktur und Eigenschaften der Krystalle," Springer-Verlag OHG, Berlin, 1950.

requirement that ψ multiplies itself simply with e^{jkl} in advancing by exactly one lattice spacing l. These, then, are four homogeneous linear equations for the four coefficients A and B in two adjoining cells. In order that these four equations be compatible, their determinant must vanish. This provides an equation for k as a function of x and, therefore, as a function of the energy as well.

Set up the four equations mentioned, and show that their determinant vanishes if

$$\cos kl = \cos xl + \frac{mS}{\hbar^2 x} \sin xl \qquad (VII.12.03)$$

2. Plot the right side of Eq. (VII.12.03) as a function of xl (qualitatively!) and show that it follows from Eq. (VII.12.03) that allowed and forbidden bands alternate up to the highest energies. Show that the forbidden bands correspond to a Bragg reflection. At what energy inside the forbidden band is the Bragg condition fulfilled exactly?

3. Give an approximation formula for the widths of the forbidden bands as a function of the band number and of the quantities S and l.

4.* Calculate the effective masses of the electrons near the upper and lower edges of the allowed bands. How do they depend upon the band number and upon S and l?

5. Assume that S in Eq. (VII.12.01) is negative. Show, then, that for $E > 0$, Eq. (VII.12.03) still holds, and give the corresponding equation for $E < 0$. Show that for $E < 0$ always one and only one allowed band exists.

6.* Show that each allowed band splits into two bands if the delta functions are no longer equidistant and equally strong, but when instead

a. Either their distance alternates between $l + \Delta l$ and $l - \Delta l$, or,

b. Their strength alternates between $S + \Delta S$ and $S - \Delta S$.

Explain this splitting in terms of Bragg reflections and of the structure of the Brillouin zone.[1]

7. In Prob. 1, replace the delta functions by regular square potential barriers of the width b and the height V_0. Show that Eq. (VII.12.03) is then replaced for $0 < E < V_0$ by

$$\cos kl = \cosh \lambda b \cos xa + \frac{\lambda^2 - x^2}{2\lambda x} \sinh \lambda b \sin xa \qquad (VII.12.04)$$

where x has the same meaning as previously and

$$\lambda = \sqrt{\frac{2m}{\hbar^2}(V_0 - E)} \qquad (VII.12.05)$$

$$a = l - b \qquad (VII.12.06)$$

Answer the questions of Prob. 2 for this new case.

8.* It has been shown that the forbidden bands correspond to Bragg reflections of the electrons inside the crystal. This is most clearly demonstrated by the delta potential where the contribution of each atom to the reflected wave comes from a single point. When the atoms have a finite extension, the different parts of the individual atom all contribute separately to the reflected wave. For certain energies and directions, the contributions from the different parts of the same atom can destroy themselves mutually so that no reflection could occur even if the

---

[1] For a more general treatment, see Saxon and Hutner, *Philips Research Repts.*, **4:** 81 (1949).

Bragg reflection condition were satisfied. For certain values of the lattice constant, the Bragg condition and the condition for zero amplitude of the scattered waves actually do coincide. The forbidden band will, then, have zero width.

Analyze this situation for the potential of Prob. 7. Show that the different forbidden bands vanish for certain lattice constants, and show that this happens when the waves reflected from the front of the square barriers interfere with those reflected from the back in such a way as to destroy each other.

Problems on Deviations from Ohm's Law

9. In Eq. (VII.9.06) it was assumed that the kinetic energy gained by an electron between two collisions is small compared to its thermal kinetic energy. This resulted in a proportionality between the drift velocity v and the electric field, that is, in a constant mobility. It was also shown in §9 that in high electric fields the initial assumption may no longer hold. While a rigorous treatment of this subject would be beyond the scope of this book, one can obtain a qualitative understanding from the following simplified model. Calculate the current-voltage relationship for fields E such that

$$e\mathbf{E}l \gg \tfrac{3}{2}kT$$

making the following assumptions: (a) the mean free path l is independent of both the field and the particle velocity, and (b) the electron loses all its kinetic energy during every collision.

Calculate the differential conductivity $di/d\mathbf{E}$ at an electric field of $\mathbf{E} = 10^4$ volt-cm^{-1} for n-type germanium of 1 ohm-cm low-field resistivity. Assume $\mu_n = 3{,}600$ cm^2 volt^{-1} sec^{-1} and $m_{\text{eff}} = \tfrac{1}{4}m$.

10. How is the result of the preceding problem modified if the mean free path is constant only for velocities below a certain velocity $v_{\max}$, and if the electrons lose all their kinetic energy as soon as they have been accelerated up to $v_{\max}$? This is the kind of assumption one would have to make if there existed a scattering mechanism that is inactive below a certain kinetic energy but has a very high scattering efficiency above. Shockley[1] has pointed out that the scattering of electrons by the so-called optical phonons would be such a process.

11. In the two preceding problems it was tacitly assumed that the electron is not accelerated to such high energies that the effective mass changes. Small mass changes would, of course, have no great influence upon the current-voltage relationship. But if the electron is actually driven into a region of negative mass, it will be decelerated and the Zener oscillations described in §7 and §9 will set in. As mentioned in §9e, for mean free path lengths l of about 10^{-5} cm, the fields necessary for this to happen lie above the breakdown fields. But at higher values of l, the oscillations could actually set in before breakdown.

It was also previously assumed that at every collision the electron loses all its energy. This again may not hold at very high fields since the maximum energy an electron can transfer to the lattice in a collision is equal to $h\nu_{\max}$, where $\nu_{\max}$ is the highest vibrational frequency of the lattice. One may, therefore, expect that in very high fields the average energy loss per collision will approach a limiting value.

What would be the current-field relationship for fields so high that Zener oscillations do occur (but not breakdown), assuming that both the collision frequency and the amount of energy lost per collision are independent of the field?

[1] W. Shockley, *Bell System Tech. J.*, **30**: 990 (1951).

CHAPTER VIII

Fermi Statistics of the Electrons in a Crystal

In this chapter, as mentioned on page 260, the connection between the position of the Fermi level E_F and the electron concentration n will be computed for a number of models. In §2 it will be shown that within a solid or within a system of solids in thermal equilibrium the Fermi level E_F has everywhere the same value. This statement is often formulated in the concise, though perhaps not rigorously correct, rule: "In thermal equilibrium, the Fermi level is horizontal." To begin with, the Fermi distribution and the Fermi level E_F are defined only for states of thermal equilibrium. However, if the relationship between concentration n and Fermi level E_F is established for non-equilibrium states, a Fermi level E_F is defined whose slope depends on the total current. This subject will be discussed in §3, together with the related subject of the identity of Fermi level E_F and electro-chemical potential. In §4 we shall deal with the Fermi Statistics of electrons in metals and insulators. The simplest case of an impurity semiconductor will be examined in §5. Among the main results of these last two paragraphs will be the law of mass action (I.3.03) between electrons and holes and the law of mass action (II.6.04) between donors and conduction electrons.

§1. The Electron Gas in a Potential Well

On page 260 a method was indicated whereby the relationship between E_F and n is obtained. The first model to which we apply this method is an electron gas with concentration n, which is confined in a well because a high positive potential exists within the well so that the potential energy E_{pot} of the electrons is strongly negative while it is assumed to be zero outside the well (Fig. VIII.1.1). In this case the total energy E of an electron is

$$E = E_{\text{pot}} + \frac{1}{2m}\, p^2 \qquad\qquad \text{(VIII.1.01)}$$

In order to establish the density of states $D(E)$, we could determine the eigenfunctions and the energy eigenvalues E of an electron in the potential well under consideration. However, this treatment would be beyond the scope of this book, and it would also preclude a direct application of the results to the next model to be discussed, i.e., a crystal with metallic properties. We shall therefore use a treatment

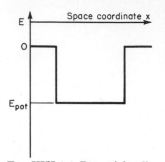

which can be applied directly to crystals, though it may seem very artificial in connection with the model of the electron gas in the potential well.

According to this treatment, we regard the constant potential within the well as a special case of a periodic lattice potential (i.e., the special case where the "amplitude" of the potential equals zero), and we introduce "unit cells" of arbitrary magnitude a.

Fig. VIII.1.1. Potential well.   Further, we combine an arbitrary number G of unit cells in each axial direction to a "fundamental domain" of volume $V_{\text{fund}} = (Ga)^3$. We can then apply the result obtained on page 182: "A quantum state requires a volume $(2\pi)^3/V_{\text{fund}}$ in $\mathbf{k}$ space."[1]

The question now arises as to what volume in $\mathbf{k}$ space belongs to the energies between E and $E + dE$. To answer this we use (VII.6.04) and replace (VIII.1.01) by

$$E = E_{\text{pot}} + \frac{\hbar^2}{2m} |\mathbf{k}|^2$$

where $\mathbf{k}$ is the wave vector of the electron, or

$$|\mathbf{k}| = k = \frac{\sqrt{2m}}{\hbar} (E - E_{\text{pot}})^{\frac{1}{2}} \qquad \text{(VIII.1.02)}$$

Hence in the space of the wave vectors $\mathbf{k}$, $E = \text{const}$ represents spherical surfaces about the origin, and the condition

$$E < \text{energy of the states to be counted} < E + dE$$

defines a spherical shell of volume $4\pi k^2 \cdot dk$.

Now, according to page 182, a single quantum state requires a volume $(2\pi)^3/V$ in $\mathbf{k}$ space; hence the number $D(E)\, dE$ of the quantum

[1] The number N of the electrons which have to be accommodated in the arbitrary fundamental domain is nV; hence the arbitrary volume V of the fundamental domain will drop out on p. 285 and a result will be obtained which is free from these arbitrary assumptions (VIII.1.07).

states in the energy range $[E, E + dE]$ is given by the equation

$$D(E) \, dE = \frac{4\pi k^2 \, dk}{(2\pi)^3/V}$$

or

$$D(E) = V \cdot \frac{1}{2\pi^2} k^2 \frac{dk}{dE}$$

Finally, using (VIII.1.02), one obtains

$$D(E) = V \cdot \frac{1}{2\pi^2} \frac{2m}{\hbar^2} (E - E_{pot}) \cdot \frac{\sqrt{2m}}{\hbar} \frac{1}{2} (E - E_{pot})^{-\frac{1}{2}}$$

With $\hbar = h/2\pi$, the number of electrons that can be accommodated (equal to *twice* the number of the quantum states) is

$$2D(E) \, dE = V \cdot 4\pi \left(\frac{2m}{h^2}\right)^{\frac{3}{2}} (E - E_{pot})^{\frac{1}{2}} \, dE$$

$$2D(E) \, dE = V \cdot 2 \left(\frac{2\pi mkT}{h^2}\right)^{\frac{3}{2}} \frac{2}{\sqrt{\pi}} \left(\frac{E - E_{pot}}{kT}\right)^{\frac{1}{2}} d\left(\frac{E}{kT}\right) \quad \text{(VIII.1.03)}$$

We now introduce an "effective density of states N" in the potential well:[1]

$$N = 2 \cdot \left(\frac{2\pi mkT}{h^2}\right)^{\frac{3}{2}} = 2.5 \cdot 10^{19} \left(\frac{T}{300°K}\right)^{\frac{3}{2}} \text{cm}^{-3} \quad \text{(VIII.1.04)}$$

and for the number $2D(E) \, dE$ of the electrons that can be accommodated in the energy range between E and $E + dE$ (equal to twice the number of the quantum states in this range), we finally obtain

$$2D(E) \, dE = V \cdot N \cdot \frac{2}{\sqrt{\pi}} \left(\frac{E - E_{pot}}{kT}\right)^{\frac{1}{2}} d\left(\frac{E}{kT}\right) \quad \text{(VIII.1.05)}$$

Hence the requirement (VII.10.03) established on page 260, in the case of the present model of the electron gas in the potential well, takes the form

$$V \cdot N \cdot \frac{2}{\sqrt{\pi}} \int_{E = E_{pot}}^{E = \infty} \frac{1}{e^{\frac{E - E_F}{kT}} + 1} \left(\frac{E - E_{pot}}{kT}\right)^{\frac{1}{2}} d\left(\frac{E}{kT}\right) = N$$

Introduction of the integration variable

$$\eta = \frac{E - E_{pot}}{kT}$$

---

[1] Here it must be mentioned that N is not a density of states in the same sense as the term $D(E)$. $D(E)$ represents a number of states per unit of the energy scale and hence has the dimension (energy)$^{-1}$ = $\text{cm}^{-2}\text{g}^{-1}\text{-sec}^2$. On the other hand, N has the dimension cm^{-3} and can therefore be regarded as a number of states per unit volume of the potential well (or, later, of the crystal). See footnote 1, p. 318.

and of the concentration of the electron gas

$$n = \frac{N}{V} \qquad \text{(VIII.1.06)}$$

leads finally to the determining equation for E_F:

$$\frac{2}{\sqrt{\pi}} \int\limits_{\eta=0}^{\eta=\infty} \frac{1}{e^{\eta - \frac{E_F - E_{\text{pot}}}{kT}} + 1} \sqrt{\eta}\, d\eta = \frac{n}{N} \qquad \text{(VIII.1.07)}$$

A comparison of (VIII.1.07) with the defining equation (A.II.1) of the function $\zeta(n/N)$, which is treated in Appendix II, shows that in

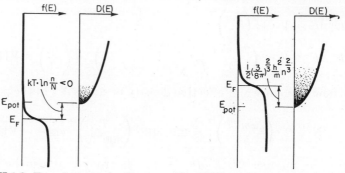

FIG. VIII.1.2. Few electrons in the potential well. $n \ll N$: no degeneracy. Maxwell-gas.

FIG. VIII.1.3. Many electrons in the potential well. $n \gg N$: strong degeneracy. Fermi-gas.

order to satisfy (VII.10.03) and (VIII.1.07) the Fermi level E_F must be formulated as follows:

$$E_F = E_{\text{pot}} + \zeta\left(\frac{n}{N}\right) \qquad \text{(VIII.1.08)}$$

We now consider the two limiting cases of small and large concentration: According to Eq. (A.II.2), one obtains for $n \ll N$

$$E_F = E_{\text{pot}} + kT \cdot \ln \frac{n}{N} \qquad \text{(VIII.1.09)}$$

In this case the Fermi level lies *below* the lowest available energy level E_{pot} because $\ln n/N < 0$ since $n \ll N$ (see Fig. VIII.1.2). In the energy distribution of the electrons

$$N(E)\, dE = 2D(E)f(E)\, dE$$

$$= VN \frac{2}{\sqrt{\pi}} \left(\frac{E - E_{\text{pot}}}{kT}\right)^{1/2} \frac{1}{e^{\frac{E - E_F}{kT}} + 1}\, d\left(\frac{E}{kT}\right) \qquad \text{(VIII.1.10)}$$

we have
$$e^{\frac{E-E_F}{kT}} = e^{\frac{E-E_{pot}}{kT}} \cdot e^{\frac{E_{pot}-E_F}{kT}} > e^{\frac{E_{pot}-E_F}{kT}} \gg 1$$

because $E - E_{pot}$ is positive in any case and $E_{pot} - E_F$ is strongly positive in the present case. Hence the general formula (VIII.1.10) applicable for the model under consideration can, in the limiting case of small concentration $n \ll N$, be simplified to

$$N(E)\, dE = VN \frac{2}{\sqrt{\pi}} \left(\frac{E-E_{pot}}{kT}\right)^{\frac{1}{2}} e^{-\frac{E-E_F}{kT}} d\left(\frac{E}{kT}\right)$$

$$N(E)\, dE = VN\, e^{\frac{E_F-E_{pot}}{kT}} \cdot \frac{2}{\sqrt{\pi}} \left(\frac{E-E_{pot}}{kT}\right)^{\frac{1}{2}} e^{-\frac{E-E_{pot}}{kT}} d\left(\frac{E}{kT}\right)$$

$$\text{(VIII.1.11)}$$

Using (VIII.1.09) and (VIII.1.06), we finally obtain

$$N(E)\, dE = N \cdot \frac{2}{\sqrt{\pi}} \left(\frac{E-E_{pot}}{kT}\right)^{\frac{1}{2}} e^{-\frac{E-E_{pot}}{kT}} d\left(\frac{E-E_{pot}}{kT}\right) \quad \text{(VIII.1.12)}$$

We see that the effective density of states N, in whose definition (VIII.1.04) the Planck constant appeared, has dropped out completely. The electron gas shows the classical Maxwell distribution. *If the electron gas is sufficiently diluted, it behaves like a Maxwell gas in a space with the potential energy E_{pot}.*

In the opposite limiting case of $n \gg N$, one obtains from equation (A.11.3)

$$E_F = E_{pot} + kT \left(\frac{3}{4}\right)^{\frac{2}{3}} \pi^{\frac{1}{3}} \left(\frac{n}{N}\right)^{\frac{2}{3}} \quad \text{(VIII.1.13)}$$

or, using (VIII.1.04),

$$E_F = E_{pot} + \frac{1}{2} \left(\frac{3}{8\pi}\right)^{\frac{2}{3}} \frac{h^2}{m} n^{\frac{2}{3}}$$

In other words, the Fermi level lies now *above* the lowest available level E_{pot} (see Fig. VIII.1.3). No general simplifications can be applied in the energy distribution of the electrons (VIII.1.10). The gas shows nonclassical behavior, and we talk of a *degenerate* or *Fermi gas*. We call the concentration above which degeneracy occurs the degeneracy concentration. It is approximately equal to the effective density of states N.

However, at high electron energies $E \gg E_F$, the exponential term in the denominator of the distribution function $f(E)$ predominates again and the equation (VIII.1.10) is simplified for the distribution of the high-energy electrons to

$$N(E)\, dE = VN \frac{2}{\sqrt{\pi}} \left(\frac{E-E_{pot}}{kT}\right)^{\frac{1}{2}} e^{-\frac{E-E_F}{kT}} d\left(\frac{E}{kT}\right) \quad \text{(VIII.1.14)}$$

Comparison with (VIII.1.12) shows that this tail of the electron distribution in the direction of high energies $E \gg E_F > E_{pot}$ corresponds almost to a Maxwell gas of potential energy E_F and concentration N ("Maxwell tail"). The analogy would be complete if instead of the factor $[(E - E_{pot})/kT]^{1/2}$ we would have the factor $[(E - E_F)/kT]^{1/2}$. However, this difference is immaterial at the high energies which we are considering.

For the problem of surmounting potential barriers, for instance, for the question of how many electrons can leave the potential well, only the high-energy electrons are of importance. Hence in problems of this type a Fermi gas can be treated like a Maxwell gas with the concentration N and the potential energy[1] E_F.

§2. The General Condition for Thermal Equilibrium: $E_F = \text{const}$

The last remark makes the solution of the following problem relatively simple. Let two potential wells I and II be separated by a high potential barrier (see Fig. VIII.2.1). After a certain period of time, the electron concentrations in these will adjust themselves in such a way that as many electrons will surmount or tunnel through the potential barrier in unit time from left to right as from right to left. Thereafter, the concentrations n_I and n_{II} will not change any more, i.e., thermal equilibrium is established. It may now be asked what is the ratio of the concentrations n_I and n_{II} in this stationary final state?

We have just learned that the electron current emerging from potential well I can be computed as though the potential well contained a Maxwell gas of concentration N with the potential energy E_{F_I}. Correspondingly, the number of electrons emerging per unit time from well II is equal to the emission current which would be produced by a Maxwell gas of the same concentration N with the potential energy $E_{F_{II}}$. Hence the emission currents can be equal only if

$$E_{F_I} = E_{F_{II}} \qquad \text{(VIII.2.01)}$$

[1] This makes it plausible that the emission law for a Fermi gas is derived from the Richardson emission law for a Maxwell gas by inserting into the equation applicable for the Maxwell gas the value of N defined by (VIII.1.04) for the concentration of the gas and the difference between the potential energy outside the well and the Fermi level E_F for the depth of the potential well. Regarding the emission law for a Fermi gas see, e.g., A. Sommerfeld in H. Geiger and K. Scheel, "Handbuch der Physik," vol. XXIV, part 2, p. 350, Eq. (4.13), Springer-Verlag OHG, Berlin, 1933. In this equation one has to use $G = 2$ (*ibid.*, p. 337). Regarding the Richardson emission law for a Maxwell gas see *ibid.*, p. 351, Eq. (4.15).

If the electron concentration in both wells is so low that degeneracy has not yet set in and that therefore the thermal equilibrium between two Maxwell gases of different potential energy has to be determined, the Fermi levels E_{F_I} and $E_{F_{II}}$ are computed from (VIII.1.09) and (VIII.2.01) changes into

$$E_{pot_I} + kT \ln \frac{n_I}{N} = E_{pot_{II}} + kT \ln \frac{n_{II}}{N}$$

$$n_I = n_{II} \, e^{\frac{E_{pot_{II}} - E_{pot_I}}{kT}} \qquad \text{(VIII.2.02)}$$

This, however, is the well-known "Boltzmann equilibrium" between two Maxwell gases.[1]

If the electron concentrations are high enough for degeneracy, the equilibrium condition (VIII.2.01) is still valid, but it has now to be used with (VIII.1.13) instead of (VIII.1.09). However, we do not want to discuss this in detail but rather look once more at condition (VIII.2.01).

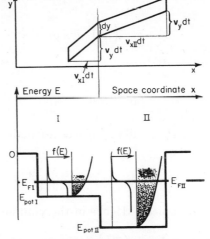

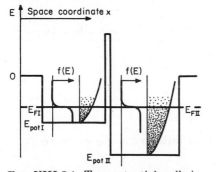

FIG. VIII.2.1. Two potential wells in thermal equilibrium: $E_{F_I} = E_{F_{II}}$.

FIG. VIII.2.2. Thermal equilibrium of two spaces I and II with different potential energy E_{pot_I} and $E_{pot_{II}}$.

The validity of this condition $E_F = \text{const}$ extends far beyond the particular example under consideration. In order to prove this, we start by dropping the high potential barrier between the two potential wells (see Fig. VIII.2.2). Furthermore, we think of the principle of detailed balancing, according to which every microprocess is as frequent as the reverse process if a real thermal equilibrium exists.

[1] See the very instructive discussion of the barometric altitude formula in R. Becker, "Vorstufe zur theoretischen Physik," p. 137, Springer-Verlag OHG, Berlin, 1950.

Therefore the condition of equality for the electron currents in the two directions has to be defined more rigorously by saying that this condition applies not only for the *total* currents through an imaginary separating plane between the two spaces I and II, but also for any arbitrary velocity group of a given magnitude and direction.

For a quantitative derivation we start from the fact that a group of electrons with velocities between $\{v_{xI}, v_y, v_z\}$ and $\{v_{xI} + dv_{xI}, v_y + dv_y, v_z + dv_z\}$ occupy the volume dv_{xI}, dv_y, dv_z in velocity space. The wave numbers k_x, k_y, k_z are connected with the velocities, according to (VII.6.31) and (VII.5.09), by

$$k_x = \frac{1}{\hbar} p_x = \frac{m}{\hbar} v_x \qquad k_y = \frac{m}{\hbar} v_y \qquad k_z = \frac{m}{\hbar} v_z \quad \text{(VIII.2.03)}$$

Hence the group of electrons under consideration occupies the volume $(m/\hbar)^3 \, dv_{xI} \, dv_y \, dv_z$ in **k** space which[1] contains

$$\frac{\left(\dfrac{m}{\hbar}\right)^3 dv_{xI} \, dv_y \, dv_z}{\dfrac{(2\pi)^3}{V}} = V \cdot \left(\frac{m}{h}\right)^3 dv_{xI} \, dv_y \, dv_z \quad \text{(VIII.2.04)}$$

quantum states and, because of the spin, can accommodate twice as many electrons.

Of the available places a fraction

$$\frac{1}{e^{\frac{1}{kT}[E - E_{F_I}]} + 1}$$

is occupied. Hence in the volume V of ordinary space we have

$$2 \cdot \left(\frac{m}{h}\right)^3 \cdot \frac{dv_{xI} \, dv_y \, dv_z}{e^{\frac{1}{kT}\left[E_{\text{pot}_I} + \frac{m}{2}(v_{xI}^2 + v_y^2 + v_z^2) - E_{F_I} \right]} + 1} \cdot V \quad \text{(VIII.2.05)}$$

electrons of the velocity group under consideration.

During the time dt all those electrons of the velocity group under consideration which are within the parallelepiped of Fig. VIII.2.2 pass through a unit area $dy \cdot dz$ of an imaginary separating plane between the two spaces I and II. As the parallelepiped volume is $dy \, dz \, v_{xI} \, dt$, one obtains for the number of electrons, with the use of (VIII.2.05),

[1] According to p. 182, one quantum state requires the volume $(2\pi)^3/V$ in **k** space.

$$2 \cdot \left(\frac{m}{h}\right)^3 \cdot \frac{v_{x\mathrm{I}} \cdot dv_{x\mathrm{I}} \cdot dv_y \cdot dv_z}{e^{+\frac{1}{kT}\left[E_{\mathrm{pot}_{\mathrm{I}}} + \frac{m}{2}(v_{x\mathrm{I}}{}^2 + v_y{}^2 + v_z{}^2) - E_{F_{\mathrm{I}}}\right]} + 1} \; dy \, dz \, dt \quad \text{(VIII.2.06)}$$

After entering space II, these electrons have the velocity $v_{x\mathrm{II}}$, v_y, v_z, because the tangential component does not change. The law of conservation of energy states that

$$E_{\mathrm{pot}_{\mathrm{I}}} + \frac{m}{2}\,(v_{x\mathrm{I}}^2 + v_y^2 + v_z^2) = E_{\mathrm{pot}_{\mathrm{II}}} + \frac{m}{2}\,(v_{x\mathrm{II}}^2 + v_y^2 + v_z^2) \quad \text{(VIII.2.07)}$$

Differentiation yields

$$v_{x\mathrm{I}} \, dv_{x\mathrm{I}} = v_{x\mathrm{II}} \, dv_{x\mathrm{II}} \quad\quad\quad\quad \text{(VIII.2.08)}$$

The microscopic reverse process to an electron of group $\{v_{x\mathrm{I}}, v_y, v_z\}$ traversing the element of area $dy \cdot dz$ consists of an electron of group $\{-v_{x\mathrm{II}}, -v_y, -v_z\}$ traversing the same element of area $dy \cdot dz$. In analogy to (VIII.2.06), the frequency of this reverse process during the time dt is

$$2 \cdot \left(\frac{m}{h}\right)^3 \cdot \frac{v_{x\mathrm{II}} \, dv_{x\mathrm{II}} \, dv_y \, dv_z}{e^{+\frac{1}{kT}\left[E_{\mathrm{pot}_{\mathrm{II}}} + \frac{m}{2}(v_{x\mathrm{II}}{}^2 + v_y{}^2 + v_z{}^2) - E_{F_{\mathrm{II}}}\right]} + 1} \; dy \, dz \, dt \quad \text{(VIII.2.09)}$$

The detailed balance at thermal equilibrium requires the equality of (VIII.2.06) and (VIII.2.09). If we now bear in mind (VIII.2.08) and (VIII.2.07), we obtain

$$E_{F_{\mathrm{I}}} = E_{F_{\mathrm{II}}} \quad\quad\quad\quad \text{(VIII.2.10)}$$

This proves that the condition $E_F = \text{const}$ also applies to the case of two neighboring potential wells *without* a high separating barrier and, furthermore, that it ensures detailed balancing at thermal equilibrium. It is obvious that this result can be generalized by approximating continuous $E_{\mathrm{pot}}(x)$ curves[1] with stepped variations.

---

[1] Here we think in the first place of the space variation of the electrostatic macropotential which we have encountered in Chaps. IV and V in the barrier layers of rectifiers and p-n junctions.

Apart from this, Thomas and Fermi have regarded the electron shell of a heavy atom, by way of a model, as a highly degenerate electron gas which is contained in a potential well. The atomic nucleus as well as the electron shell contribute to the potential variation in space in accordance with the Poisson equation:

$$\Delta V = -4\pi\rho = +4\pi e n$$

Thomas and Fermi obtain a relation between local potential $V(x)$ and electron concentration $n(x)$ from the condition that the Fermi level $E_F = -eV + \zeta$ must be constant in space. For ζ they use the value applicable for the limiting case of

An electron gas filling a space in which the potential energy E_{pot} of an electron varies from place to place will in thermal equilibrium distribute itself in this space in such a way that the Fermi level E_F becomes independent of the position:

$$E_F = \text{const} \tag{VIII.2.11}$$

As the Fermi level E_F can be computed from the potential energy $E_{pot}(x)$ and the density $n(x)$ by (VIII.1.08), the condition (VIII.2.11) relates the change of concentration $n(x)$ and the spatial distribution $E_{pot}(x)$ of the potential energy of an electron by

$$E_F = E_{pot}(x) + \zeta\left(\frac{n(x)}{N}\right) = \text{const} \tag{VIII.2.12}$$

In the case of sufficient dilution

$$n(x) \ll N$$

the general equilibrium condition (VIII.2.12) changes with the aid of equation (A.II.2) into the well-known Boltzmann principle

$$n(x) \sim e^{-\frac{1}{kT}E_{pot}(x)} \tag{VIII.2.13}$$

of the Maxwell gas.

§3. The Significance of the Fermi Level

$$E_F = E_{pot}(x) + \zeta\left(\frac{n(x)}{N}\right) \text{ for Nonequilibrium States}$$

We have seen in the last paragraph that the concentration $n(x)$ of an electron gas[1] adjusts itself at thermal equilibrium in a region with

---

a highly degenerate gas (VIII.4.07)

$$\zeta = \frac{1}{2}\left(\frac{3}{8\pi}\right)^{2/3}\frac{h^2}{m}\, n^{2/3}$$

They obtain thus

$$-eV(x) + \frac{1}{2}\left(\frac{3}{8\pi}\right)^{2/3}\frac{h^2}{m}\, n^{2/3} = \text{const}$$

At a great distance from the atom, the electron concentration $n = 0$. If we set here also the potential $V = 0$, the constant becomes zero and we obtain

$$n(x) = \frac{\pi}{3}\frac{8}{h^3}\,(2meV(x))^{3/2} \tag{VIII.2.131}$$

By using this expression for n in the Poisson equation, we obtain the Thomas-Fermi differential equation. [See A. Sommerfeld, "Atombau und Spektrallinien," vol. II, p. 693, Eq. (14), Vieweg-Verlag, Brunswick, Germany, 1944.] Equation (VIII.2.131) is the exact counterpart to the Boltzmann principle (VIII.2.13).

[1] With some changes in sign, the following discussion can also be applied to holes. See pp. 375 and 377.

potential energy $E_{\text{pot}}(x)$ varying in space, so as to fulfill the condition

$$E_{\text{pot}}(x) + \zeta\left(\frac{n(x)}{N}\right) = E_F = \text{const} \qquad \text{(VIII.2.12)}$$

We now assume that the potential energy E_{pot} is produced by an electrostatic potential $V(x)$ with field strength $\mathbf{E}(x) = -V'(x)$:

$$\frac{d}{dx} E_{\text{pot}}(x) = -eV'(x) = +e\mathbf{E}(x) \qquad \text{(VIII.3.01)}$$

If we differentiate (VIII.2.12) with respect to x, utilize (VIII.3.01), and finally multiply by the electron mobility μ_n and the concentration $n(x)$, we obtain

$$+ e\mu_n n(x) \cdot \mathbf{E}(x) + \mu_n \cdot n(x) \cdot \frac{d\zeta}{dn} \cdot n'(x) = 0 \quad \text{(VIII.3.02)}$$

The thermal equilibrium therefore results from the mutual compensation of the field current $e\mu_n n(x)\mathbf{E}(x)$ and of a current component $+\mu_n n(x)(d\zeta/dn)n'(x)$, which is caused by a concentration gradient $n'(x)$ and which must consequently be regarded as a generalized diffusion current. Since the quantity ζ is a function of the concentration n only (see Fig. A.II.1 in Appendix II) the expression $\mu_n n(x)(d\zeta/dn)n'(x)$ does not contain the field strength $\mathbf{E}(x)$ at all and hence represents the diffusion current even in those cases where the electric field does not have exactly the value required for the compensation of the diffusion current. Therefore, even in nonequilibrium cases, one has to use for the diffusion current i_{diff} the equation derived from the equilibrium condition (VIII.3.02)

$$i_{\text{diff}} = +\mu_n n(x) \cdot \frac{d\zeta}{dn} \cdot n'(x) = +\mu_n \cdot \frac{d\zeta}{d \ln n} \cdot n'(x) \quad \text{(VIII.3.03)}$$

or

$$i_{\text{diff}} = +\mu_n \cdot n(x) \cdot \frac{d}{dx} \zeta \qquad \text{(VIII.3.04)}$$

If one adds to this generalized diffusion current the field current $+e\mu_n n(x) \cdot (-dV/dx)$, one obtains for the total current under nonequilibrium conditions

$$i_{\text{tot}} = \mu_n n(x) \frac{d}{dx}[-eV(x) + \zeta(x)] = \mu_n \cdot n(x) \cdot \frac{d}{dx}[E_{\text{pot}}(x) + \zeta(x)]$$

or
$$i_{\text{tot}} = +\mu_n \cdot n(x) \cdot \frac{d}{dx} E_F(x) \qquad \text{(VIII.3.05)}$$

If we compare (VIII.3.04) and (VIII.3.05) with

$$i_{\text{field}} = e\mu_n n(x)\mathbf{E}(x) = \mu_n n(x) \cdot (-e) \cdot V'(x)$$

i.e., with

$$i_{\text{field}} = +\mu_n \cdot n(x) \cdot \frac{d}{dx} E_{\text{pot}}(x) \qquad \text{(VIII.3.06)}$$

we arrive at the following conclusion.

The Fermi level $E_F(x)$ and the function $\zeta(x)$ play the same role for the total current i_{tot} and the diffusion current i_{diff}, respectively, as does the potential energy $E_{\text{pot}} = -eV(x)$ for the field current i_{field}. Hence the function $\zeta(x)$ is called the chemical potential and E_F the electrochemical potential of the electron gas.[1]

If we compare Eq. (VIII.3.03) for the diffusion current with the form in which it is usually written

$$i_{\text{diff}} = (-e) \cdot (-D \cdot n'(x)) \qquad \text{(VIII.3.07)}$$

we obtain the following equation for the diffusion coefficient

$$D = \frac{\mu_n}{e} \frac{d\zeta(n)}{d \ln n} \qquad \text{(VIII.3.08)}$$

This means that the diffusion coefficient is, as a rule, a function of the concentration; for instance, in the Fermi limiting case $n \gg N$ of page 301, Eq. (VIII.4.07)

$$\zeta = \frac{1}{2} \left(\frac{3}{8\pi}\right)^{2/3} \frac{h^2}{m_{\text{eff}}} n^{2/3} \qquad \text{(VIII.4.07)}$$

will result for the chemical potential. This leads to the following expression for the diffusion coefficient:

$$D = \frac{1}{3} \frac{\mu_n}{e} \left(\frac{3}{8\pi}\right)^{2/3} \frac{h^2}{m_{\text{eff}}} n^{2/3} = \frac{2}{3} \frac{\mu_n}{e} \zeta(n) \qquad \text{(VIII.3.09)}$$

On the other hand, in the Maxwell limiting case $n \ll N$,

$$\zeta = kT \ln \frac{n}{N}$$

[see Eq. (A.II.2)] causes the diffusion coefficient to become *in*dependent of the concentration:

---

[1] In the use of these terms, one generally does not differentiate between "potential" and "potential energy." However, this is not done in mechanics either, so that the procedure in electrostatics constitutes an exception. Besides, the terms chemical and electrochemical potential are derived from thermodynamics where the equilibrium condition "electrochemical potential = const" is deduced from the second law. See W. Schottky and H. Rothe, Physik der Glühelektroden, in Wien and Harms, "Handbuch der Experimentalphysik," vol. 13, part 2, p. 18, Eq. (5), Akademische Verlagsgesellschaft, Leipzig, 1928.

$$D = \mu_n \frac{kT}{e} \qquad (VIII.3.10)$$

This is the well-known Nernst-Townsend-Einstein equation.[1]

The use of the electron mobility μ_n in the preceding discussion and the interpretation of the expression $e\mu_n n(x)\mathbf{E}(x)$ as field current indicate that only a negligible deviation from thermal equilibrium has been assumed. Ohm's equation

Field current density = conductivity $\times$ field strength

and the diffusion equation

Diffusion current density
$$= \text{diffusion coefficient} \times \text{concentration gradient}$$

are justified only if the condition is fulfilled that the field and diffusion currents are small in relation to the thermal current in one direction (see page 248, footnote 1). This assumption is, in fact, contained in the word electron "gas." The typical example of the reverse case is represented by the electrons in a vacuum tube; here the thermal velocities are negligibly small compared with the common rush of the electrons from cathode to anode, and one therefore does not usually talk of an electron gas but rather of an "electron avalanche" or a similar term. Hence, if the concept of the electrochemical potential is to be used in nonequilibrium applications, one has to make sure that the resulting current is small compared with the unidirectional thermal current, i.e., that the deviation from thermal equilibrium is slight.

---

[1] W. Nernst, *Z. Phys. Chem.*, **2**: 613 (1888), particularly, p. 615. J. S. Townsend, *Trans. Roy. Soc. (London)*, **A193**: 129 (1900), particularly, p. 153. A. Einstein, *Ann. Physik*, **17**: 549 (1905), particularly pp. 554 and 555.

C. Wagner in *Z. physik. Chem.*, **B11**: 139 (1931), and, particularly, in *Z. physik. Chem.*, **B21**: 25 (1933), generalizes the ideas expressed in the above papers by leaving open the functional dependence of the chemical potential ζ on the concentration. For this reason, he obtains the relationship between current density (or migration velocity) and the gradient of the electrochemical potential in a *general* form [see *Z. physik. Chem.*, **B21**: 29 (1933), Eq. (6)]. W. Schottky, in *Wiss. Veröffentl. Siemens-Werken*, **14**: No. 2, 1 (1935), particularly p. 4, Eqs. (1), (1′), (2), (2′) and p. 12, Eq. (15), has also found in a general form the proportionality between current density and the gradient of the electrochemical potential. The same applies to C. Herring and M. H. Nichols in *Revs. Mod. Phys.*, **21**: 185 (1949), particularly p. 196, Eq. (I.6.2).

In *Bell System Tech. J.*, **28**: 435 (1949), W. Shockley discusses the case of the Maxwell gas and introduces the electrochemical potentials of the electrons and holes under the name of "quasi Fermi levels" or "imrefs" whereby he can prove the proportionality of the total current of the particle type concerned with the gradient of a generalized potential, i.e., the electrochemical potential [*ibid.*, p. 451, Eq. (3.5)].

§4. Fermi Statistics in Metals and Insulators

In the preceding paragraphs we have discussed the electron gas in the potential well as a first model and inserted, subsequently, considerations concerning equilibrium and nonequilibrium states in regions with space-varying potential.   We shall now turn from the single-electron

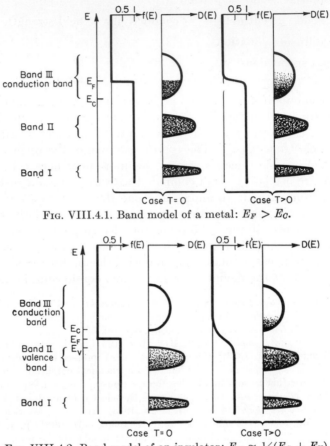

FIG. VIII.4.1. Band model of a metal: $E_F > E_C$.

FIG. VIII.4.2. Band model of an insulator: $E_F \approx \frac{1}{2}(E_C + E_V)$.

problem to the many-electron problem, i.e., we shall carry out the distribution of the electrons among the quantum states of the single-electron problem in the case of a *crystal*, from the point of view of Fermi statistics.   We have seen in Chap. VII, §2 to §4, that here the quantum states are arranged in bands so that we have to distinguish between two cases, namely, that in which the Fermi level at the temperature $T = 0$ falls into an allowed band and that in which it falls into a forbidden band (see Figs. VIII.4.1 and VIII.4.2).

a. The Band Models of a Metal and of an Insulator at Temperature $T = 0$

We have seen on pages 263 and 267 that a fully occupied band cannot produce a current and therefore drops out for the conduction process. The case of Fig. VIII.4.1 with the Fermi level within an allowed band leads to a band that is only partially occupied; in other words, on applying an external field, a current is produced and we have the case of a metal. The partially occupied band is called the "conduction band." On the other hand, in the case of Fig. VIII.4.2 with the Fermi level E_F *between* two allowed bands, the bands below the Fermi level E_F are completely occupied and therefore drop out for the conduction process. The band above the Fermi level, however, in which conduction processes could take place if any electrons were present and which is therefore called the conduction band, is empty. Such a crystal does not carry any current when an external field is applied (at least at $T = 0$); we have the case of an insulator or of an "intrinsic semiconductor" (see pages 16 to 20).

During the last few years the lattices of Group IV of the periodic system which are insulators at $T = 0$, namely, carbon in the form of diamond, silicon, germanium, and gray tin, have gained particular importance. The four outer valence electrons of these elements just fill the last band below the Fermi level E_F completely at $T = 0$. Therefore this band is often called the valence band. A more general term is "bound electron band."[1]

If one is interested, beyond these general statements, in the exact position of the Fermi level E_F in a metal or in an insulator which is,

---

[1] If one explains the elimination of the "valence band" for conduction processes, not with the considerations of pages 263 to 267, but by the fact that the electrons occupying this band are tightly bound to the four neighboring atoms by homopolar pair formation, one leaves the whole concept of the band model (the Hund-Mulliken approximation) and passes over to the atomistic model (Heitler-London approximation). The same consideration applies, if, for instance, one explains the insulating nature of an NaCl crystal by the strong binding of the electrons in the M shell of the Cl ion (the L shell of the Na^+ which is also fully occupied lies at a lower level; hence the *highest* fully occupied band is not associated with it). See, for instance, F. Hund, *Z. tech. Phys.*, **16**: 333 (1935), Fig. 3.

One need not worry about this oscillation between the band model and the atomistic concept. On the contrary, one can have greater confidence in the result obtained from one concept if it is also derived from the other concept, as is the case here with the elimination of a fully occupied band from the conduction processes.

for instance, important for work-function problems as was mentioned above on page 287, information about the density of states $D(E)$ is essential. In discussing these problems, we shall consider temperatures $T > 0$ right from the start.

b. The Band Model of a Metal at Temperatures $T > 0$

In the case drawn in Fig. (VIII.4.1), bands I and II are practically completely occupied, not only at temperature $T = 0$, but also at higher temperatures. (Concerning the case of extremely high temperatures see page 300.) Hence, for the calculation of the position of the Fermi level E_F in accordance with condition (VII.10.03), one can use either all the electrons and all three bands I, II, and III or only the "conduction electrons" of the "conduction band III." In the second procedure, one reduces the number of available electron places and the number of electrons to be accommodated by the same number, i.e., the number of electron places in I and II. If we decide to make the computation only with the conduction electrons and only with the places available in band III, this is done mainly for reasons of simplicity. In this case, we require information only about the nature of the density of states $D(E)$ within the conduction band.[1] Furthermore, in view of the discussion in Chap. VI, the description of the behavior of the strongly bound electrons in the lower energy levels with the aid of the band model, i.e., with the Hund-Mulliken approximation, is of doubtful validity. Therefore, it is desirable for fundamental reasons, too, that the inner electron shells of each atom be added to the atom cores causing the periodic potential and that the band model be applied only to the electrons of the outermost shell.

In the determining equation (VII.10.03) for E_F, we now must use the energy E_C of the lower edge of the conduction band as the lower integration limit:

$$2 \int_{E=E_c}^{E=\infty} D(E) \frac{1}{e^{\frac{E-E_F}{kT}} + 1} \, dE = N \qquad \text{(VIII.4.01)}$$

where N is now the number of conduction electrons in the conduction band. Naturally, a more or less explicit evaluation of (VIII.4.01) can be attempted only if more accurate information about the distribution of the density of states $D(E)$ in the conduction band is available. Here one starts frequently from the approximation (VII.4.04) or (VII.6.19) which, with the aid of Eq. (VII.6.23), $m_{\text{eff}} = \hbar^2/E''(|\mathbf{k}_C|)$, and with

---

[1] Concerning the shape of $D(E)$ which is shown only diagrammatically in Fig. VIII.4.1, see p. 299, footnote 1, and p. 303, footnote 3.

$E_{\text{bound}} = E_C$, takes the form

$$E = E_C + \frac{\hbar^2}{2m_{\text{eff}}} |\mathbf{k} - \mathbf{k}_C|^2 \qquad \text{(VIII.4.02)}$$

However, the warning of pages 180 and 200 must be repeated, i.e., that (VII.2.23), (VII.4.04), and (VIII.4.02) are simplifying assumptions which, to take an example, are not fulfilled in the case of the cubic face-centered lattice at one band edge (the upper for negative exchange integral, the lower for positive exchange integral). Even if at the band edge $\mathbf{k} = \mathbf{k}_C$ Eq. (VIII.4.02) is fulfilled, it is not strictly correct to use the same m_{eff} higher up in the band.

If we compare the equation derived from (VIII.4.02)

$$|\mathbf{k} - \mathbf{k}_C| = \frac{\sqrt{2m_{\text{eff}}}}{\hbar} (E - E_C)^{\frac{1}{2}}$$

with (VII.1.02) and if we substitute $E_{\text{pot}} \to E_C$, $m \to m_{\text{eff}}$, and $\mathbf{k} \to \mathbf{k} - \mathbf{k}_C$, we can repeat exactly the computation of the density of states $D(E)$ carried out for the model of the potential well, and in analogy to (VIII.1.05) we obtain

$$2D(E) \, dE = V \cdot N_C \cdot \frac{2}{\sqrt{\pi}} \left(\frac{E - E_C}{kT} \right)^{\frac{1}{2}} d\left(\frac{E}{kT} \right) \qquad \text{(VIII.4.03)}$$

where the effective density of states N in the potential well is replaced by the effective density of states N_C in the conduction band.[1] Correspondingly, the definition of N_C is derived from that of N [Eq. (VIII.1.04)] by the substitution $m \to m_{\text{eff}}$:

$$N_C = 2 \cdot \left(\frac{2\pi m_{\text{eff}} kT}{h^2} \right)^{\frac{3}{2}} = 2.5 \cdot 10^{19} \left(\frac{m_{\text{eff}}}{m} \right)^{\frac{3}{2}} \cdot \left(\frac{T}{300°\text{K}} \right)^{\frac{3}{2}} \text{cm}^{-3}$$
$$\text{(VIII.4.04)}$$

Using (VIII.4.03) in (VIII.4.01) and introducing the integration variable $\eta = (E - E_C)/kT$ as well as the concentration $n = N/V$, one obtains as the determining equation for E_F:

$$\frac{2}{\sqrt{\pi}} \int_{\eta=0}^{\eta=\infty} \frac{1}{e^{\eta - \frac{E_F - E_C}{kT}} + 1} \sqrt{\eta} \, d\eta = \frac{n}{N_C} \qquad \text{(VIII.4.05)}$$

Finally, by comparing (VIII.4.05) with the defining equation (A.II.1)

---

[1] It is apparent from (VIII.4.03) that the hypothesis (VIII.4.02) leads to zero state density $D(E)$ at the band edge $E = E_C$. Only in the linear case this does not apply, see Fig. VII.2.7.

of the function ζ discussed in Appendix II on page 384, one gets

$$E_F = E_C + \zeta\left(\frac{n}{N_C}\right) \qquad \text{(VIII.4.06)}$$

Hence, on the basis of the assumption (VIII.4.02) the conduction electrons behave like a free electron gas with a potential energy which equals the total energy E_C of the electrons at the lower edge of the conduction band. For the mass of the electrons, one has to use the effective mass

$$m_{\text{eff}} = \frac{\hbar^2}{E''(k_C)} \qquad \text{(VII.6.23)}$$

The foregoing treatment in which the fully occupied band below the conduction band is ignored and where the concentration n of the conduction electrons is considered temperature independent is permissible[1] only as long as

$$n \gg N_C$$

The number of conduction electrons in metals is about one per atom; hence $n \approx 10^{22}$ cm^{-3}. For N_C to reach this order of magnitude, one has to have

$$N_C = 2.5 \cdot 10^{19} \left(\frac{T}{300°\text{K}}\right)^{3/2} \text{cm}^{-3} \approx 10^{22} \text{ cm}^{-3}$$

$$\text{or} \quad T \approx 300°\text{K} \cdot \left(\frac{10^{22}}{2.5 \cdot 10^{19}}\right)^{2/3} \approx 300°\text{K} \cdot (4 \cdot 10^2)^{2/3} = 300°\text{K} \cdot 55$$

$$= 16{,}500°\text{K}$$

At such temperatures the metal is molten and therefore the case $n \leq N_C$ is of no interest. This means: *The electron gas in metals is always strongly degenerate.*

In many problems, therefore, the limiting value given by Eq. (A.II.3) can be used for ζ in (VIII.4.06)

$$\zeta = kT \cdot \left(\frac{3}{4}\right)^{2/3} \pi^{1/3} \left(\frac{n}{N_C}\right)^{2/3} \qquad \text{(A.II.3)}$$

From this, together with (VIII.4.04), one obtains for ζ the tempera-

---

[1] In this case, ζ is positive and the Fermi level $E_F = E_C + \zeta$ will lie within the conduction band in the temperature range in which we are interested. The band below the conduction band lies so far below the Fermi level E_F that it will remain fully occupied with great accuracy even when the slope of the Fermi distribution flattens with increasing temperature and the electrons move from states below E_F to states above E_F. The band below the conduction band lies, in the case $n \gg N_C$, too far below E_F to be noticeably affected by this process.

ture-independent[1] value

$$\zeta = \frac{1}{2}\left(\frac{3}{8\pi}\right)^{2/3}\frac{h^2}{m_{\text{eff}}}n^{2/3} \qquad \text{(VIII.4.07)}$$

Using the equation $\qquad E_F - E_C = \zeta = \frac{m_{\text{eff}}}{2}v_{\text{th}}^2 \qquad$ (VIII.4.08)

one obtains for the velocity v_{th} of those electrons which are, energetically, at the Fermi level E_F

$$v_{\text{th}} = \left(\frac{3}{8\pi}\right)^{1/3}\frac{h}{m_{\text{eff}}}n^{1/3} = 7.71 \cdot 10^7 \text{ cm-sec}^{-1} \cdot \left(\frac{m}{m_{\text{eff}}}\right)\cdot\left(\frac{n}{10^{22}\text{ cm}^{-3}}\right)^{1/3}$$

$$\text{(VIII.4.09)}$$

in other words, *the order of magnitude of v_{th} is 10^8 cm-sec^{-1}.* Here the thermal velocity v_{th} has been computed as the velocity of the electrons at the Fermi level. This seems reasonable if one bears in mind that in a Fermi gas an increment of energy—be it from an external field or in the form of heat—changes only the energetic distribution of the electrons near the Fermi level while the electrons in the lower energy levels are not affected.

There are two other methods for estimating the velocity of the electrons at the Fermi level ($\approx$ center of the band), which predominantly determine the conduction process. First, by limitation to a one-dimensional case, one can derive directly from Eq. (VII.5.10) the equation

$$v = \frac{1}{\hbar}\cdot\frac{dE}{dk} > \frac{1}{\hbar}\frac{\Delta E}{\Delta k}$$

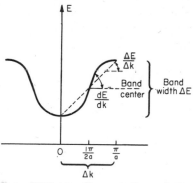

Fig. VIII.4.3. Computation of the electron velocity in the band center.

in which one can substitute for ΔE a band width of the order[2] of 10 ev $= 1.6 \cdot 10^{-11}$ cm^2 g-sec^{-2} and for Δk a quantity of the order of $\pi/a \approx 1 \cdot 10^{+8}$ cm^{-1}. Thus one obtains the value

$$v \approx \frac{1}{1\cdot 10^{-27}\text{ cm}^2\text{ g-sec}^{-1}}\cdot\frac{1.6\cdot 10^{-11}\text{ cm}^2\text{ g-sec}^{-2}}{1\cdot 10^{+8}\text{ cm}^{-1}} = 1.6 \cdot 10^8 \text{ cm-sec}^{-1}$$

which, according to Fig. VIII.4.3, is somewhat too low. The alterna-

[1] Owing to this temperature independence, the approximation (A.II.3) is *not* sufficient where the specific heat of the electron gas is concerned.

[2] See, e.g., F. Herman, *Phys. Rev.*, **88:** 1210 (1952), where a width of **22** ev is computed for the valence band of diamond.

tive method consists of using the approximation (VIII.4.02) in the equation $v = \dfrac{1}{\hbar} \dfrac{dE}{dk}$ with the result

$$v = \frac{\hbar}{m_{\text{eff}}} \cdot k$$

If we now use for m_{eff} the electron mass $9 \cdot 10^{-28}$ g and for k the value $\frac{1}{2}\pi/a \approx \frac{1}{2} \cdot 10^{8}$ cm^{-1} in the center of the band, we obtain

$$v = \frac{1 \cdot 10^{-27} \text{ cm}^2 \text{ g-sec}^{-1}}{9 \cdot 10^{-28} \text{ g}} \cdot \frac{1}{2} \cdot 10^{+8} \text{ cm}^{-1} \approx \frac{1}{2} 10^{+8} \text{ cm-sec}^{-1}$$

In other words, all three estimations result in the same order of magnitude.

c. The Band Model of the Insulator and of the Intrinsic Semiconductor[1] at Temperatures $T > 0$

It can be seen from Fig. VIII.4.2 that at temperatures $> 0°$K valence band II below conduction band III is no longer fully occupied.[2] Since at all temperatures the *total* number of electrons in the crystal must be the same to maintain neutrality, the number of electrons in the conduction band must equal the number of vacancies or "holes" in valence band II below the conduction band.[3]   In the case of Fig. VIII.4.2 it is therefore no longer permissible to consider only the conduction band and the number of electrons therein.   The number of electrons is now no longer the same at all temperatures but varies greatly with temperature.   The simplified procedure which in the case of Fig. VIII.4.1, previously described, consisted of ignoring bands I and II and of considering only band III has in the case of Fig. VIII.4.2 to be modified so that only band I is ignored.   The discussion must cover bands II and III and all the electrons which have to be accommodated in these two bands and whose number may again with fair accuracy be regarded as temperature independent.

The significance of the following discussion would be greatly reduced if explicit expressions were used for the density of states in the whole valence band II below the conduction band.   Fortunately, an expedient relieves us from this necessity.   This expedient consists of con-

---

[1] See pages 16 to 20 concerning this term.

[2] In principle, this was true in the case of Fig. VIII.4.1 just considered.   However, there the number of vacancies or "holes" in valence band II is practically negligible as compared with the number of electrons in conduction band III.

[3] Strictly speaking, the holes in the electron occupancy of band I should also be considered.   However, their number is again negligibly small.

sidering, instead of the distribution of *electrons* over the states of valence band II, the distribution of the *vacancies* or "holes" or "defect electrons."[1]   If the probability of an electron level E being occupied by an electron is, according to (VII.10.01),

$$f(E) = \frac{1}{e^{\frac{E-E_F}{kT}} + 1} \qquad \text{(VII.10.01)}$$

then the probability that this energy level E is *not* occupied is

$$1 - f(E) = \frac{e^{\frac{E-E_F}{kT}} + 1 - 1}{e^{\frac{E-E_F}{kT}} + 1} = \frac{1}{1 + e^{\frac{E_F-E}{kT}}} \qquad \text{(VIII.4.10)}$$

On the other hand, for the computation of the density of states $D(E)$, one makes the *assumption*, in accordance with Eq. (VIII.4.02), that

$$E = E_V - \frac{\hbar^2}{2m_p} |\mathbf{k} - \mathbf{k}_V|^2 \qquad \text{(VIII.4.11)}$$

(m_p = absolute value of the effective mass of the electrons at the upper edge of the valence band[2]) from which it follows that

$$|\mathbf{k} - \mathbf{k}_V| = \frac{\sqrt{2m_p}}{\hbar} (E_V - E)^{1/2}$$

Comparison with (VIII.1.02) shows that we have to carry out the substitutions

$$E - E_{\text{pot}} \to E_V - E \qquad m \to m_p \qquad \text{and} \qquad \mathbf{k} \to \mathbf{k} - \mathbf{k}_V$$

and that hence we have now for the number of electron places in the energy interval $[E, E + dE]$ the expression[3]

$$2D(E)\, dE = V \cdot N_V \cdot \frac{2}{\sqrt{\pi}} \left(\frac{E_V - E}{kT}\right)^{1/2} d\left(\frac{E}{kT}\right) \qquad \text{(VIII.4.12)}$$

Here N_V is the effective density of states in the valence band

$$N_V = 2 \left(\frac{2\pi m_p kT}{h^2}\right)^{3/2} = 2.5 \cdot 10^{19} \left(\frac{m_p}{m}\right)^{3/2} \left(\frac{T}{300°K}\right)^{3/2} \text{cm}^{-3} \qquad \text{(VIII.4.13)}$$

[1] This procedure is not limited to intrinsic semiconductors. The equations derived below are, therefore, of general validity for semiconductors—with the exception of (VIII.4.24), (VIII.4.25), and (VIII.4.26) where the relation $n = p$ (VIII.4.24), which defines the intrinsic semiconductor, enters decisively.

[2] The effective mass of the electrons at the upper edge of the valence band is negative, i.e., $-m_p$.

[3] Here the density of states $D(E)$ is of course zero at the upper band edge $E = E_V$.   See also footnote 1, p. 298.

If we introduce the number P or the concentration $p = P/V$ of the vacancies or holes in the almost complete electron occupancy at the upper edge of the valence band, we obtain[1] for P

$$P = V \cdot p = 2 \int_{E=-\infty}^{E=E_V} D(E) \cdot (1 - f(E))\, dE$$

$$= V N_V \frac{2}{\sqrt{\pi}} \int_{E=-\infty}^{E=E_V} \left(\frac{E_V - E}{kT}\right)^{1/2} \frac{1}{e^{\frac{E_F - E}{kT}} + 1} \cdot d\left(\frac{E}{kT}\right)$$

or, with

$$\frac{E_V - E}{kT} = \eta$$

as integration variable

$$\frac{2}{\sqrt{\pi}} \int_{\eta=0}^{\eta=\infty} \frac{1}{e^{\eta - \frac{E_V - E_F}{kT}} + 1} \cdot \sqrt{\eta} \cdot d\eta = \frac{p}{N_V} \qquad \text{(VIII.4.14)}$$

By comparison with the defining equation (A.II.1) of the function ζ, one can again derive

$$E_F = E_V - \zeta\left(\frac{p}{N_V}\right) \qquad \text{(VIII.4.15)}$$

With regard to the electron concentration n in the conduction band, we obtain in the present case of the insulator, as with a metal, in accordance with (VIII.4.06),

$$E_F = E_C + \zeta\left(\frac{n}{N_C}\right) \qquad \text{(VIII.4.16)}$$

where in the definition of the effective density of states N_C in the conduction band

$$N_C = 2 \left(\frac{2\pi m_n kT}{h^2}\right)^{3/2} = 2.5 \cdot 10^{19} \left(\frac{m_n}{m}\right)^{3/2} \left(\frac{T}{300°K}\right)^{3/2} \text{cm}^{-3} \qquad \text{(VIII.4.17)}$$

we now call the effective mass of the conduction electrons m_n in order to achieve complete analogy with (VIII.4.13).

In Eqs. (VIII.4.15) and (VIII.4.16) E_F can be eliminated and one can see that the equation

$$\zeta\left(\frac{n}{N_C}\right) + \zeta\left(\frac{p}{N_V}\right) = E_V - E_C(<0) \qquad \text{(VIII.4.18)}$$

[1] The lower integration limit $E = -\infty$ is unimportant because according to (VIII.4.10) $1 - f(E)$ approaches zero very quickly as $E \to -\infty$ and no further important contributions to the integral arise.

must always hold, independent of the position E_F of the Fermi level. This equation will now be shown to represent the generalization of the law of mass action (see Eq. I.3.03) $np = n_i^2$ between electrons and holes, valid even in the case of degeneracy.

We can assume that at the edges of the conduction and of the valence band the effective masses m_n and m_p of the electrons will not differ in order of magnitude from the mass m of the free electron. Hence, as long as the temperature is not excessively low, N_C and N_V represent very high concentrations and we have[1]

$$p \ll N_V \quad \text{and} \quad n \ll N_C \qquad \text{(VIII.4.19)}$$

Now the logarithmic limiting expression (A.II.2) for ζ can be used in (VIII.4.15), (VIII.4.16), and (VIII.4.18) and we obtain

$$E_F = E_V - kT \ln \frac{p}{N_V} \qquad \text{(VIII.4.20)}$$

$$E_F = E_C + kT \ln \frac{n}{N_C} \qquad \text{(VIII.4.21)}$$

and
$$kT \ln \frac{n}{N_C} + kT \ln \frac{p}{N_V} = -(E_C - E_V)$$

or
$$n \cdot p = N_C \cdot N_V \cdot e^{-\frac{E_C - E_V}{kT}} \qquad \text{(VIII.4.22)}$$

This is—as just mentioned—the important law of mass action

$$n \cdot p = n_i^2 \qquad \text{(I.3.03)}$$

between electrons and holes. By comparison with (VIII.4.22), one obtains for the "inversion density n_i" (see page 26)

$$n_i = \sqrt{N_C N_V} \, e^{-\frac{1}{2} \frac{E_C - E_V}{kT}}$$

$$= 2.5 \cdot 10^{19} \, \text{cm}^{-3} \left(\frac{m_n}{m}\right)^{\frac{3}{4}} \left(\frac{m_p}{m}\right)^{\frac{3}{4}} \left(\frac{T}{300° \text{K}}\right)^{\frac{3}{2}} \cdot e^{-\frac{1}{2} \frac{E_C - E_V}{kT}} \qquad \text{(VIII.4.23)}$$

In the present case of the insulator we have already noted (page 302) that the number of all electrons in valence and conduction band taken

[1] If one bears in mind that in the first approximation $m_n \approx m_p$ and hence $N_C \approx N_V$, one can see that the later result VIII.4.25 confirms these assumptions for low temperatures as well. In other words, in the case of the intrinsic semiconductor with which we are dealing here, the concentrations n and p decrease much faster with temperature than N_C and N_V.

However, as in footnote 1, p. 303, it should be emphasized once again that Eqs. (VIII.4.20) to (VIII.4.23) do not hold only for intrinsic semiconductors but also for impurity semiconductors in which the assumption (VIII.4.19) of non-degeneracy is fulfilled as long as the doping is not excessive. Only the assumption (VIII.4.24) effects the limitation to the case of intrinsic conductors.

together must be temperature-independent and we have concluded from this that the concentration of the conduction electrons in the conduction band must be equal to the concentration of the holes in the valence band:

$$n = p \tag{VIII.4.24}$$

From the combination of (VIII.4.22) and (VIII. 4.24) follows

$$n = p = n_i = \sqrt{N_C N_V}\, e^{-\frac{1}{2}\frac{E_c - E_v}{kT}} \tag{VIII.4.25}$$

With the aid of these expressions the energetic position E_F of the Fermi level can be computed from (VIII.4.20) and (VIII.4.21):

$$E_F = \frac{1}{2}(E_C + E_V) + \frac{3}{4}kT \ln \frac{m_p}{m_n} \tag{VIII.4.26}$$

In this equation the definitions (VIII.4.13) and (VIII.4.17) for the state densities N_V and N_C have been used. Thus one can see that *in an insulator the Fermi level E_F lies practically halfway between the lower edge E_C of the conduction band and the upper edge E_V of the valence band. This result is independent of the temperature T*, apart from a small correction that may be required to allow for any differences in the effective masses m_n and m_p.

This result could have been obtained, even without calculation, from the symmetry of the distribution functions $f(E)$ and $1 - f(E)$ around the Fermi level E_F (see Fig. VII.10.1). Owing to this symmetry, the condition "concentration n of the electrons = concentration p of vacancies or holes" is just fulfilled if the Fermi level E_F lies halfway between E_C and E_V.

Thus the complete picture for the insulator at temperatures $T > 0$ encompasses an electron gas in the conduction band and a gas consisting of "holes" or "defect electrons" in the valence band. Stated more precisely, the assumptions (VIII.4.02) and (VIII.4.11) lead to the conclusion that the electron gas has an apparent potential energy E_C (lower edge of the conduction band) and the hole gas has an apparent potential energy E_V (upper edge of the valence band). Within these potential wells of depth E_C and E_V, respectively, the electron and hole gases, respectively, are "quasi-free."[1] Both gases have very low concentration and behave completely like Maxwell gases. Hence the thermal velocity v_{th} of the electrons can be computed from the equation[2]

---

[1] An influence of the lattice beyond these apparent potential energies E_C and E_V is expressed in the substitutions $m \to m_n$ and $m \to m_p$.

[2] Mean energy per degree of freedom = $\frac{1}{2}kT$ (principle of equipartition).   See

$$\frac{m_{\text{eff}}}{2} v_{\text{th}}^2 = \frac{3}{2} kT$$

to be $\quad v_{\text{th}} = \sqrt{\dfrac{3kT}{m_{\text{eff}}}} = 1.168 \cdot 10^7 \text{ cm sec}^{-1} \cdot \sqrt{\dfrac{T}{300°\text{K}}} \sqrt{\dfrac{m}{m_{\text{eff}}}}$ (VIII.4.27)

Therefore, v_{th} in insulators (and semiconductors) is of the order of magnitude 10^{-7} cm-sec^{-1} (at $300°$K).

§5. Fermi Statistics in Semiconductors

In §3 of Chap. I we have seen that at temperature $T = 0$ a semiconductor is an insulator because it does not contain any free charge carriers. These are created only if the temperature is raised. First, electrons are then supplied by donor impurities (n-type conduction). Secondly, electrons are pulled out of valence bands by temperature excitation and captured by acceptor impurities. The vacancies in the totality of valence electrons are then available as "defect electrons" for the transport of current (p-type or hole conduction). Finally, at high enough temperatures, electrons are raised directly from the valence band into the conduction band, and the current is then carried by equal numbers of excess electrons in the conduction band and of holes in the valence band.

We intend to calculate the position of the Fermi level E_F, first in an n-type semiconductor, then in a p-type semiconductor, and finally in a semiconductor with donors *and* acceptors. From the point of view of Fermi statistics, we are concerned (for example, in an n-type semiconductor) with the distribution of a certain total number of electrons among the donor levels and the levels of the conduction band. In Chap. II the same problems have been considered from the point of view of impurity reactions and the laws of mass action. Where we spoke before, for instance, of a "neutral donor $D^\times$," we shall now describe the same situation as an "electron at a donor level." At the end of §5, we shall return to the earlier point of view and derive an expression for the mass-action constant. This will form a transition to Chap. IX in which the law of mass action will be considered again, this time from the dynamic point of view. This will also be an opportunity to indicate the treatment of the inertia of impurity reactions, whereas in Chap. II and also here thermal equilibrium between the impurities and the electrons and holes is always assumed.

G. Joos, "Theoretical Physics," 2d ed., p. 587, Hafner Publishing Company, New York, 1950.

a. Semiconductors with Donors: n-Type Semiconductors

In analogy to the previous discussion of metals and insulators where we did not have to consider the electrons in the lower bands explicitly, we can now again ignore the lower bands, including the valence band, and need deal only with the conduction band and the donor levels

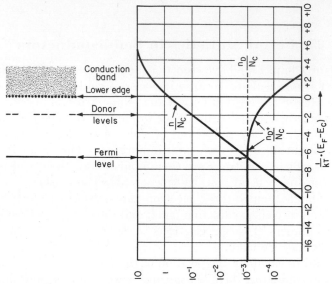

Fig. VIII.5.1. Position of the Fermi level E_F in the band model; n-type conductor; impurity saturation.

Fig. VIII.5.2. Graphic determination of the Fermi level E_F in n-type conductors; impurity saturation; $E_C - E_D = 2\mathrm{k}T$; $n_D = 10^{-3}\ N_C$.

below it (see Fig. VIII.5.1).   For the density of states in the conduction band we use again the expression (VIII.4.03) based on the assumption (VIII.4.02) and obtain, as previously for metals and insulators,

$$E_F = E_C + \zeta \left(\frac{n}{N_C} \right) \qquad \text{(VIII.4.06)}$$

i.e., a functional correlation $E_F(n)$ or $n(E_F)$, respectively, between the Fermi level E_F and the concentration n of the electrons in the conduction band. n as a function of E_F provides one of the two curves of Fig. VIII.5.2.

According to the principles of Fermi statistics, the probability with which a donor level E_D is occupied by an electron is[1]

----

[1] See Appendix III.

$$f(E_D) = \frac{1}{\frac{1}{2} e^{+\frac{1}{kT}(E_D - E_F)} + 1} \tag{VIII.5.01}$$

Hence if we have in unit volume n_D donors at the energy level E_D, the fraction $n_D \cdot f(E_D)$ is occupied by an electron[1] and is therefore neutral:

$$n_{D^\times} = n_D \frac{1}{\frac{1}{2} e^{+\frac{1}{kT}(E_D - E_F)} + 1} \tag{VIII.5.02}$$

Hence the concentration of the positively charged donors is

$$n_{D^+} = n_D - n_{D^\times} = n_D \left(1 - \frac{1}{\frac{1}{2} e^{+\frac{1}{kT}(E_D - E_F)} + 1} \right)$$

$$n_{D^+} = n_D \frac{1}{1 + 2 e^{+\frac{1}{kT}(E_F - E_D)}} \tag{VIII.5.03}$$

The functional dependence of this positive charge density n_{D^+} on E_F provides the second curve in Fig. VIII.5.2. To preserve the neutrality of the semiconductor as a whole, the concentration n of the negative electrons must be equal to the density n_{D^+} of the positive donors that remain. The resulting value E_F of the Fermi level, the *solution* of the equation

$$n(E_F) = n_{D^+}(E_F) \tag{VIII.5.04}$$

is determined by the intersection of the two curves in Fig. VIII.5.2. With the assumed values for $E_C - E_D$ and n_D, a situation arises in which

$$n = n_{D^+} \approx n_D \tag{VIII.5.05}$$

i.e., in which almost all donors are dissociated. In this state of "donor saturation,"[2] the Fermi level lies *below* the donor level ($E_F < E_D$), and just for this reason the majority of the donor levels are not occupied. For the ($E_C - E_D$) values assumed in Figs. VIII.5.3 and VIII.5.4, on the other hand, we have an "impurity reserve"

$$n = n_{D^+} \ll n_D \tag{VIII.5.06}$$

---

[1] If the Fermi level E_F is several kT below the donor level E_D, the number of electrons in the donor level is consequently

$$2n_D e^{+\frac{1}{kT}(E_F - E_D)}$$

This observation will be needed for footnote 1, p. 318.

[2] See Chap. II, §6, particularly p. 50.

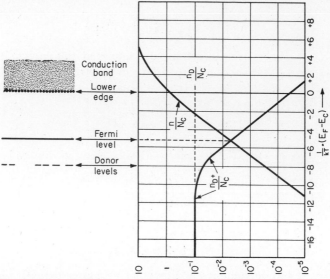

FIG. VIII.5.3. Position of the Fermi level E_F in the band model; n-type conductor; impurity reserve.

FIG. VIII.5.4. Graphic determination of the Fermi level E_F in n-type conductors; impurity reserve; $E_C - E_D = 8kT$; $n_D = 10^{-1} N_C$.

The Fermi level lies *above* the donor level ($E_F > E_D$), and therefore most of the donor levels are occupied.

b. Semiconductors with Acceptors: p-Type Semiconductors

Here we have to investigate the distribution of the electrons among the valence band and the acceptor levels above it (see Fig. VIII.5.5). With the assumption (VIII.4.11) and the resulting density of states (VIII.4.12) in the valence band, we obtain the following functional correlation between the hole concentration p in the valence band and the Fermi level E_F

$$E_F = E_V - \zeta \left(\frac{p}{N_V} \right) \qquad \text{(VIII.4.15)}$$

With the aid of this equation, the curve $p(E_F)$ in Fig. VIII.5.6 can be drawn. Of the n_A acceptors in unit volume, the fraction $f(E_A)$ is occupied by an electron and therefore negatively charged:

$$n_{A^-} = n_A \frac{1}{2 \, e^{+\frac{1}{kT}(E_A - E_F)} + 1} \qquad \text{(VIII.5.07)}$$

This supplies the curve $n_{A^-}(E_F)$ in Fig. VIII.5.6. To maintain

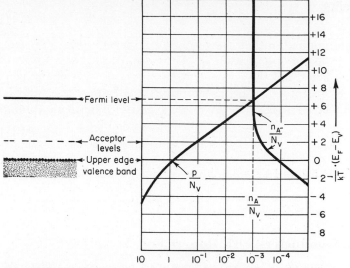

FIG. VIII.5.5. Position of the Fermi level E_F in the band model; p-type conductor; impurity saturation.

FIG. VIII.5.6. Graphic determination of the Fermi level E_F in p-type conductors; impurity saturation; $E_A - E_V = 2kT$; $n_A = 10^{-3} \cdot N_V$.

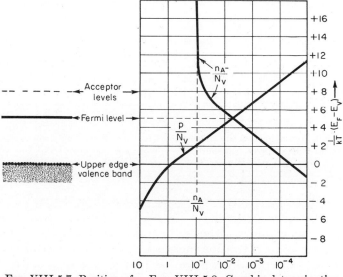

FIG. VIII.5.7. Position of the Fermi level E_F in the band model; p-type conductor; impurity reserve.

FIG. VIII.5.8. Graphic determination of the Fermi level E_F in p-type conductors; impurity reserve $E_A - E_V = 8kT$; $n_A = 10^{-1} N_V$.

neutrality

$$p(E_F) = n_A\text{-}(E_F) \qquad\qquad \text{(VIII.5.08)}$$

is again required so that the actual Fermi level in Fig. VIII.5.6 can be found from the intersection of the concentration curve $p(E_F)$ of the positive holes and the concentration curve $n_A\text{-}(E_F)$ of the negatively charged acceptors. The assumptions made in Figs. VIII.5.5 and VIII.5.6 concerning $E_A - E_V$ and n_A lead to impurity *saturation*

$$n_{A^-} \approx n_A \qquad\qquad \text{(VIII.5.09)}$$
$$E_F > E_A$$

Figs. VIII.5.7 and VIII.5.8, however, lead to an impurity *reserve:*

$$n_{A^-} \ll n_A \qquad\qquad \text{(VIII.5.10)}$$
$$E_F < E_A$$

c Semiconductors with Donors *and* Acceptors

The poisoning of an n-type conductor by added acceptors and of a p-type conductor by added donors. If the donor concentration in an n-type conductor is increased (see Fig. VIII.5.9), the intersection of

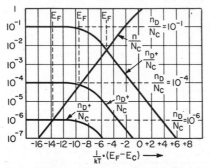 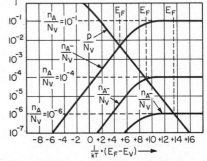

FIG. VIII.5.9. Variation of the Fermi level E_F and the electron concentration n with the donor concentration $n_D(E_C - E_D = 8kT)$.

FIG. VIII.5.10. Variation of the Fermi level E_F and the hole concentration p with the acceptor concentration $n_A(E_A - E_V = 8kT)$.

the n_{D^+} and of the n curve moves upward and to the right, i.e., the Fermi level E_F and particularly the electron concentration n assume higher and higher values. Hence the n-type conductivity of the semiconductor under consideration increases with the donor concentration n_D, at first proportionally with n_D as long as one does not leave the range of saturation. In the reserve range it increases[1] with $n_D^{1/2}$ [see

---

[1] A further attenuation of the increase occurs when the electron concentration exceeds the value N_C and degeneracy sets in.

Eqs. (II.6.15) and (II.6.17)]. Correspondingly, addition of acceptors to a p-type conductor increases the hole concentration and thereby the hole conduction (see Fig. VIII.5.10).

These results are not at all surprising. It is the donor content that makes a semiconductor into an n-type conductor; hence it seems obvious that an increase in the number of donors enhances the n-type conductivity. However, this argument might lead one to expect that addition of acceptors to an n-type conductor causes side by side with the n-type conduction additional p-type conduction, thus improving the total conductivity. In fact, however, the reverse effect takes place. The total conductivity decreases because the n-type conduction is poisoned by the added acceptors and additional p-type conduction is not produced.

This effect is easy to understand if one remembers that the acceptors have a tendency to capture electrons. By capturing ("trapping") of conduction electrons, the number of free carriers is reduced. Alternatively, one can say that the introduction of neutral acceptors produces additional deep electron levels without a corresponding increase of the total number of electrons which have to be accommodated. Hence it is certain that the Fermi level is lowered, with the result that the occupation of the states in the conduction band is reduced, i.e., that the concentration of conduction electrons is reduced.

Again, a complete understanding can be provided only by a quantitative treatment; therefore, in Figs. VIII.5.11 and VIII.5.12, and VIII.5.13 and VIII.5.14 the situations are shown which arise when acceptors are introduced into the impurity semiconductors of Figs. VIII.5.1 to VIII.5.4, the concentration of the acceptors in both cases being half an order of magnitude below that of the donor concentration. The condition for neutrality is then expressed by

$$n_{A^-} + n = n_{D^+} + p \qquad\qquad \text{(VIII.5.11)}$$

From Figs. VIII.5.12 and VIII.5.14 one can see that in both cases the hole concentration p is of no practical importance. The Fermi level E_F lies *so* high above the states of the valence band that these are all filled, with the exception of a negligible number (see Figs. VIII.5.11 and VIII.5.13). The same applies to the acceptors so that for all E_F values of interest the term n_{A^-} in the charge balance (VIII.5.11) is constant.

If the same applies for the donors, i.e., if there exists, even in the absence of acceptors, *saturation* of donors

$$n = n_{D^+} \approx n_D \qquad \text{and} \qquad E_F < E_D \qquad \text{(VIII.5.05)}$$

(Figs. VIII.5.1 and VIII.5.2, and VIII.5.11 and VIII.5.12), the poisoning effect of the acceptors is readily understood quantitatively. The addition of acceptors creates additional *deep* levels and thereby produces a lowering of the Fermi level and thus, if anything, enhances

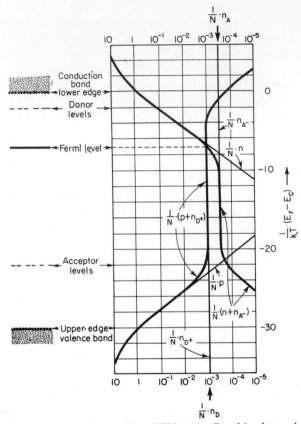

Fig. VIII.5.11. Position of the Fermi level E_F in the band model; semiconductor with donors and acceptors.

Fig. VIII.5.12. Graphic determination of the Fermi level E_F in a semiconductor with donors and acceptors: $E_C - E_D = 2kT$; $E_C - E_A = 22kT$; $E_C - E_V = 30kT$; $n_D = 10^{-3}$ N; $n_A = 3 \cdot 10^{-4}$ N; $N = N_C = N_V$.

the donor saturation (VIII.5.05). In the charge balance (VIII.5.11) the two terms n_{A^-} and n_{D^+} are then practically independent of the position of the Fermi level E_F, and the term p becomes negligible. Hence simply

$$n = n_{D^+} - n_{A^-}$$
$$n \approx n_D - n_A \qquad \text{(VIII.5.12)}$$

Figures VIII.5.13 and VIII.5.14 show the more complicated case where a donor *reserve* existed before the introduction of acceptors. Into the impurity semiconductor of Figs. VIII.5.3 and VIII.5.4, an acceptor concentration is introduced whose value is again one third

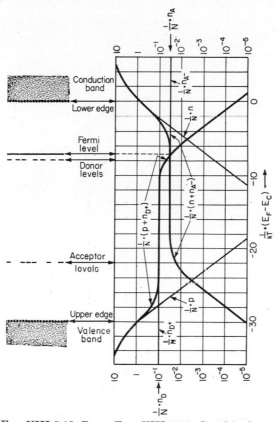

FIG. VIII.5.13. Position of the Fermi level E_F in the band model; semiconductor with donors and acceptors.

FIG. VIII.5.14. Graphic determination of the Fermi level E_F in a semiconductor with donors and acceptors: $E_C - E_D = 8kT$; $E_C - E_A = 22kT$; $E_C - E_V = 30kT$; $n_D = 10^{-1}N$; $n_A = 3 \cdot 10^{-2}N$; $N_V = N_C = N$.

of the donor concentration. A comparison of Figs. VIII.5.4 and VIII.5.14 shows that the electron concentration is reduced by about a factor 10 while in the preceding case the factor was only about $\frac{3}{2}$.

The temperature T enters into the graphic determination of the Fermi level, e.g., in Fig. VIII.5.12, first, in the scale unit kT of abscissas, but also, secondly, in the scale unit of the ordinates

$$N = 2 \left(\frac{2\pi m \mathrm{k} T}{h^2}\right)^{3/2}$$

To determine the temperature dependence of the Fermi level E_F and thereby of the electron concentration in the different levels, the graphic construction has to be carried out for a number of temperatures. Figure VIII.5.15 shows the result[1] for assumptions which apply

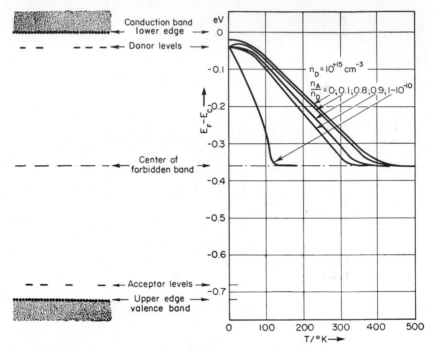

FIG. VIII.5.15. Temperature dependence of the Fermi level E_F. Germanium with 10^{15} donors per cm³ and varying acceptor concentration.

approximately to the case of germanium. Essentially, the Fermi level E_F is lowered with increasing temperature. Hence, with increasing temperature the donors are all dissociated. At higher temperatures, the Fermi level lies in the center of the band, independent of the impurity concentrations n_D and n_A. This corresponds to the state

[1] For similar investigations, see H. Mueser, Z. Naturforsch., 5A: 18 (1950). K. Seiler, Z. Naturforsch., 5A: 393 (1950). R. A. Hutner, E. S. Rittner, and F. K. DuPré, Philips Research Repts., 5: 188 (1950). W. Shockley, "Electrons and Holes in Semiconductors," pp. 465ff., D. Van Nostrand Company, Inc., Princeton, N.J., 1950.

of intrinsic conduction which will therefore be reached in every semi-conductor at high enough temperatures, provided that the crystal does not melt first [see Eq. (VIII.4.25) and the discussion on page 25].

We now refer again to the fact that with known position of the Fermi level E_F the electron concentrations in the various levels are given by the equations (VIII.5.02), (VIII.5.07) and (VIII.4.06), (VIII.4.15). In the case of nondegeneracy

$$n \ll N_C \qquad\qquad\qquad \text{(VIII.5.13)}$$
$$p \ll N_V \qquad\qquad\qquad \text{(VIII.5.14)}$$

the last two equations can be replaced by (VIII.4.20) and (VIII.4.21). From these follow

$$\ln \frac{n}{N_C} = -\frac{1}{kT}(E_C - E_F) \qquad\qquad \text{(VIII.5.15)}$$

$$\ln \frac{p}{N_V} = -\frac{1}{kT}(E_F - E_V) \qquad\qquad \text{(VIII.5.16)}$$

Hence the distances $E_C - E_F$ and $E_F - E_V$ between Fermi level E_F and the band edges E_C and E_V, respectively, measured in units of kT, are a logarithmic measure of the concentrations n and p, respectively. However, if the Fermi level does not lie in the forbidden zone but, for instance, in the valence band, then (VIII.5.16) would lead to a hole concentration $p \gtrless N_V$ and the assumption (VIII.5.14) is no longer valid, i.e., degeneracy has set in. Therefore the equations (VIII.4.20), (VIII.4.21) and (VIII.5.15), (VIII.5.16), respectively, apply with reasonable accuracy only when the Fermi level is several kT away from the band edges. In this case the results can be translated into the language of the laws of mass action, which has certain advantages.

d. The Law of Mass Action

The computation of the concentration of the conduction electrons and the related problem of the saturation and of the reserve of one type of impurities have been treated in Chap. II, by using the reaction equations and the laws of mass action.

At that time it was noted that the application of the laws of mass action presupposes "sufficient" dilution of the electron gas. However, it could not be stated precisely what degree of dilution was sufficient, nor was it possible to give a reason for the given value of the mass-action constant.

From our new point of view the following can be said concerning these two questions. The dilution of the electron gas is sufficient for the law of mass action to be valid, provided that

$$n \ll N_C \qquad\qquad\qquad \text{(VIII.5.13)}$$

because then we are in the linear part of the $n(E_F)$ curve of Figs. VIII.5.2, VIII.5.4, VIII.5.12, and VIII.5.14. Since in these figures n has been plotted on a logarithmic scale, this means the validity of the approximation (VII.4.21), which by solving for the concentration n of the conduction electrons results in[1]

$$n = N_C \, e^{+\frac{1}{kT}(E_F - E_C)} \qquad \text{(VIII.5.17)}$$

From this, together with Eqs. (VIII.5.02) and (VIII.5.03), we obtain the expression

$$\frac{n_{D^+} \cdot n}{n_{D^\times}} = n_D \, \frac{1}{1 + 2 \, e^{+\frac{1}{kT}(E_F - E_D)}} \cdot N_C \, e^{+\frac{1}{kT}(E_F - E_C)} \, \frac{\tfrac{1}{2} \, e^{+\frac{1}{kT}(E_D - E_F)} + 1}{n_D}$$

$$= \frac{N_C}{2} \, e^{+\frac{1}{kT}(E_F - E_C)} \cdot e^{+\frac{1}{kT}(E_D - E_F)}$$

Hence
$$\frac{n_{D^+} \cdot n}{n_{D^\times}} = \frac{N_C}{2} \, e^{-\frac{1}{kT}E_{CD}} \qquad \text{(VIII.5.18)}$$

where
$$E_{CD} = E_C - E_D \qquad \text{(VIII.5.19)}$$

We can see that the Fermi level E_F which depends on the electron concentration n has been eliminated and that with a constant independent of concentration

$$K_D = \frac{N_C}{2} \, e^{-\frac{1}{kT}E_{CD}} \qquad \text{(VIII.5.20)}$$

the law of mass action

$$n_{D^+} \cdot n = K_D \cdot n_{D^\times} \qquad \text{(VIII.5.21)}$$

is valid.[2] The "internal work function E_{CD} of the donors" occurring in the expression (VIII.5.20) for the mass-action constant K_D is the

---

[1] If we compare (VIII.5.17) with footnote 1, p. 296, we see that the continuum of the available states in the conduction band behaves effectively like N_C states/cm³, with a uniform energy level E_C. For this reason, Shockley chose the term "effective density of states" for N_C. (See Shockley, *op. cit.*, p. 240.) See also footnote 1, p. 285.

[2] In addition to this statistical proof, we have already mentioned a kinetic proof for the law of mass action on p. 46 which we shall discuss in more detail in Chap. IX. Finally, the law of mass action can be derived from the general equilibrium condition of footnote 1, p. 294.

(Electrochemical potential)$_{\text{phase I}}$ = (electrochemical potential)$_{\text{phase II}}$

if we use in this equilibrium condition the expression for the chemical potential of a Maxwell gas as obtained from thermodynamics. However, without the aid of statistics, the constant of the law of mass action remains undefined because the entropy constant in thermodynamics is undefined. See W. Weizel, "Theoretische Physik," pp. 732, 733, and 1237, Springer-Verlag OHG, Berlin, 1949.

activation energy which has to be supplied to an electron to raise it from a donor level into the conduction band (see Fig. VIII.5.16). A corresponding law of mass action applies to the acceptors:

$$n_{A^-} \cdot p = K_A \cdot n_{A\times} \tag{VIII.5.22}$$

with
$$K_A = \frac{N_V}{2} \cdot e^{-\frac{E_{AV}}{kT}} \tag{VIII.5.23}$$

and with
$$E_{AV} = E_A - E_V > 0 \tag{VIII.5.24}$$

if the concentration p of the holes is sufficiently small:

$$p \ll N_V \tag{VIII.5.25}$$

Using the example of the semiconductor with donors *and* acceptors, we want to indicate briefly the treatment of such a somewhat complex

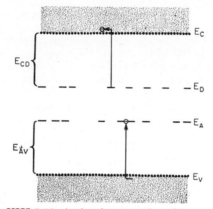

FIG. VIII.5.16. Activation energies of impurities.

problem with the methods of reaction kinetics[1] instead of a purely statistical procedure.

In this case, we have the three laws of mass action:

$$n_{D^+} \cdot n = K_D n_{D\times} \tag{VIII.5.21}$$
$$n_{A^-} \cdot p = K_A n_{A\times} \tag{VIII.5.22}$$
$$n \cdot p = n_i^2 \tag{I.3.03}$$

Furthermore we have two expressions for the impurities

$$n_{D\times} + n_{D^+} = n_D \tag{VIII.5.26}$$
$$n_{A\times} + n_{A^-} = n_A \tag{VIII.5.27}$$

and finally a neutrality condition

$$n_{A^-} + n = n_{D^+} + p \tag{VIII.5.11}$$

[1] See W. Schottky, *Z. Elektrochem.*, **45**: 33 (1939).

These are six equations with the six unknowns n, p, $n_{D^\times}$, n_{D^+}, n_{A^-}, and $n_{A^\times}$ which are thus "determined," i.e., expressed in terms of the material constants K_D, K_A, n_i and the total impurity contents n_D and n_A.

§6. Problems

1. Plot the temperature dependence of the Fermi level for a semiconductor with the following properties: $E_C - E_V = 0.72$ ev, $N_C = \frac{1}{8}N$, $N_V = N$, $E_C - E_D = 0.04$ ev, $n_D - n_A = 10^{16}$ cm^{-3}, $n_A = 0$.

2. Figure VIII.5.15 shows that the Fermi level for $T = 0$ does not lie halfway between the donor level and the conduction band but at the donor level itself if the semiconductor contains acceptors as well as donors. Under what conditions, then, does the Fermi level rise initially with temperature, that is, under what conditions is

$$\frac{dE_F}{dT}\bigg|_{T=0} > 0$$

3. Plot the temperature dependence of the Fermi level for a "partly compensated" semiconductor with a constant donor excess, $n_D - n_A$, of 10^{16} cm^{-3}, but with different donor and acceptor densities. Assume the same numerical values as in Prob. 1, except for the following values of the acceptor density: $n_A = 10^{15}$ cm^{-3}, $3 \cdot 10^{15}$ cm^{-3}, 10^{16} cm^{-3}, and 10^{17} cm^{-3}, and corresponding donor densities. Plot the curves only for the low-temperature range where they differ from the curve obtained in Prob. 1, with $n_A = 0$.

4. Plot the room-temperature Fermi level as a function of the "net" impurity concentration $n_D - n_A$ for a semiconductor whose other properties are given in Prob. 1.

5.* In Eq. (VIII.4.07) a temperature-independent approximation was given for the Fermi level in a metal. This value was obtained by replacing the actual Fermi function for a finite temperature by that for $T = 0$. The value obtained, therefore, holds only for $T = 0$ but is a good approximation otherwise. Calculate the first order deviation of the actual Fermi level from this approximation, that is, calculate the quantity

$$\Delta\zeta = T \cdot \left(\frac{d\zeta}{dT}\right)_{T=0}$$

6.* Determine the room-temperature Fermi level in an intrinsic semiconductor like indium antimonide which has a very narrow forbidden band and a very low effective mass for the electrons. Assume the following numerical values: $E_G = 0.18$ ev, $m_n = 0.03m$, $m_p = m$. *Note:* Make use of the graph of Fig. A.II.1 for the determination of the Fermi level.

CHAPTER IX

The Dynamic Approach to Impurity Equilibria and the Inertia of Impurity Reactions

In the investigation of any semiconducting material, one of the most important tasks is the determination of the number of free charge carriers, e.g., of the concentration of excess electrons in the conduction band. While the experimental methods for this purpose are characterized by the terms "Hall effect" and thermoelectric power, their counterparts in the realm of theory are "Fermi statistics" and "laws of mass action." We have discussed the statistical method in detail in Chap. VII, §10, and in the whole of Chap. VIII. The laws of mass action have been treated in Chap. II, §6, and on pages 317 to 319. It was shown that the statistical method is more comprehensive than the method of the laws of mass action because it is also applicable for large concentrations[1] $n \gg N_C$ and, furthermore, because it supplies the magnitude of the proportionality factors in the laws of mass action which remain undetermined in the thermodynamic treatment.[2] On the other hand, the laws of mass action have the advantage of great simplicity.

These remarks refer in the first place to the treatment of equilibrium states, but they are all the more valid when dynamic processes are under consideration, e.g., the slow rise and decay of luminescence in phosphors or the behavior of rectifying boundary layers at high frequencies.[3]

In the case of dynamic processes the statistical method, just because of its comprehensive and fundamental character, creates a number of very difficult problems.[4] Furthermore, it uses several concepts (life-

[1] N_C = effective density of states in the conduction band. See Eqs. (VIII.1.04) and (VIII.4.04).

[2] See, for instance, W. Weizel, "Lehrbuch der theoretischen Physik," pp. 732–733, Springer-Verlag OHG, Berlin, 1949.

[3] W. Schottky, Z. Physik, **132**: 261 (1952).

[4] W. Schottky, Ann. Physik, **6**: 193 (1949).

time, formation rate) which are introduced and defined more easily
on the basis of the laws of mass action than within the scope of the
statistical method itself. For this purpose, however, the laws of mass
action have to be extended beyond the equilibrium form. This will
be done below. In §1 we shall deal in a *general* way with the definition
of the so-called mean lifetime τ, while the lifetimes of charged and
neutral donors will be discussed specifically in §2 and §3. In §4, Eqs.
(IX.4.02) and (IX.4.03) will give the previously mentioned extension
of the simple law of mass action $n_{D^+} \cdot n = K_D \cdot n_{D^\times}$ for dynamic
processes. In addition, the case of equilibrium will be reviewed once
more from the newly gained point of view. Finally, in §5 a simple
typical example of a nonstationary process will be considered and the
time constant obtained for it will be discussed.

§1. Relaxation Time and Mean Lifetime for a Particular Type of Imperfection

An impurity, e.g., a donor D, which can react according to $D^\times \leftrightharpoons$
$D^+ + \ominus$ is by no means permanently in the charged state D^+; instead,
after a shorter or longer period of time, it will associate with a free
conduction electron and change into a neutral donor $D^\times$. Correspondingly, the state $D^\times$ is not permanent or final, but it too will, after a
shorter or longer period of time, dissociate again by thermal excitation
into $D^+ + \ominus$. In the first process, we have the "death" of a D^+ and
the "birth" of a $D^\times$, in the second process the "death" of a $D^\times$ and
the "birth" of a D^+; extending this nomenclature, we call the period
of time for which the impurity is in the charged (neutral) state its
"lifetime" in the charged (neutral) state. The processes just described
are statistical events, and therefore the time intervals during which the
donors of a given type are neutral or charged are by no means uniformly the same. Hence statements regarding, e.g., the temperature
dependence of these times will primarily refer to mean values, i.e.,
mean lifetimes $\tau_{D^\times}$ or τ_{D^+}. Later on we shall have to discuss the fact
that *different* mean lifetimes can be defined for a given particle. However, before we come to that we introduce a relaxation time τ_{rel} which
is defined as follows:

We consider a group of N_S particles of a given type[1] S. The indi-

---

[1] For the remaining discussions of §1, type S may comprise, in addition to $D^\times$,
D^+, $A^\times$, A^-, the minority carriers, i.e., the holes in an n-type conductor or the
electrons in a p-type conductor. In that case the relaxation time τ_{rel} defined by
(IX.1.01) is the "lifetime τ_p or τ_n" of the holes or the electrons. A detailed treatment of the lifetimes of minority carriers in connection with traps can be found in
W. Shockley and W. T. Read Jr., *Phys., Rev.*, **87**: 835 (1952).

vidual members of this group die one after the other in statistical irregularity.   According to definition, we do not include in the group new particles of type S which were born after the beginning $t = t_0$ of the observation.   Then the number N_S decreases steadily, and a decay or relaxation time τ_{rel} can be defined by the equation

$$dN_S = - \frac{1}{\tau_{\text{rel}}} N_S \, dt \qquad \text{(IX.1.01)}$$

In formulating this defining equation, one thinks in the first place of the case of sufficient dilution in which the fates of individual group members are independent of each other.[1]   Then the probability that a given group member dies during the time from t to $t + dt$ is the same for all group members because it was postulated that they were all identical.   Hence the number $|dN_S| = -dN_S$ of deaths during this time element $(t, t + dt)$ is proportional to the number $N_S(t)$ of the group members still alive at time t.   Further, the expression (IX.1.01) refers to particles whose death is a purely random event which is quite independent of its previous history.[2]   Then the time t cannot enter the number $-dN_S$ of deaths during the time $(t, t + dt)$ explicitly but only by way of the number $N_S(t)$ of the surviving group members at time t.   This, however, presupposes that any physical parameters affecting the place and the environment of the events (such as the temperature) do not vary with time.[3]   Hence τ_{rel} is a constant independent of time and concentration if the three assumptions of "sufficient dilution," "independence of the individual fate from previous history," and "constancy of environment in time" are satisfied.   Integration of (IX.1.01) leads, for this case, to

$$N_S(t) = N_S(t_0) \, e^{-\frac{t - t_0}{\tau_{\text{rel}}}} \qquad \text{(IX.1.02)}$$

Here the relaxation time defined by (IX.1.01) is also related to the initially mentioned mean lifetimes τ because the concentration of a group $N_S(t_0) = \nu(t_0) \, dt_0$ of particles born during the time interval $(t_0, t_0 + dt_0)$ decreases according to (IX.1.02), as expressed by the equation

$$N_S(t) = \nu(t_0) \, e^{-\frac{t - t_0}{\tau_{\text{rel}}}} \, dt_0$$

Hence the number of group members with a lifetime between $\tau = t - t_0$ and $\tau + d\tau = t - t_0 + dt$ is, in accordance with Fig. IX.1.1,

$$|dN_S| = \frac{1}{\tau_{\text{rel}}} \nu(t_0) \, e^{-\frac{t - t_0}{\tau_{\text{rel}}}} \, dt_0 \, dt = \nu(t_0) \, dt_0 \cdot e^{-\frac{\tau}{\tau_{\text{rel}}}} \cdot d\left(\frac{\tau}{\tau_{\text{rel}}}\right)$$

[1] Opposite: Fermi gas!
[2] Opposite: A group of living beings where age affects the future fate decisively.
[3] Opposite: See end of §2, particularly footnote 1, p. 327.

The mean lifetime $\bar{\tau}$ can be computed by ascertaining the mean value only for the members of the group of particles characterized by identical birth date t_0

$$\bar{\tau} = \frac{\displaystyle\int_{\tau=0}^{\tau=\infty} \tau \cdot |dN_S|}{\displaystyle\int_{\tau=0}^{\tau=\infty} |dN_S|} = \frac{\displaystyle\int_{\tau=0}^{\tau=\infty} \nu(t_0)\, dt_0 \int_{\tau=0}^{\tau=\infty} \tau\, e^{-\frac{\tau}{\tau_{\text{rel}}}}\, d\left(\frac{\tau}{\tau_{\text{rel}}}\right)}{\displaystyle\int_{\tau=0}^{\tau=\infty} \nu(t_0)\, dt_0 \int_{\tau=0}^{\tau=\infty} e^{-\frac{\tau}{\tau_{\text{rel}}}}\, d\left(\frac{\tau}{\tau_{\text{rel}}}\right)}$$

If we integrate, we obtain

$$\bar{\tau} = \tau_{\text{rel}}$$

Hence the relaxation time τ_{rel} defined by (IX.1.01) has also significance

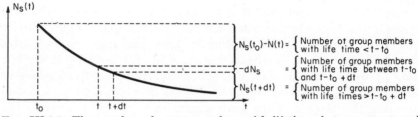

FIG. IX.1.1. The number of group members with lifetimes between $t - t_0$ and $t - t_0 + dt$ is

$$-dN_S = \frac{1}{\tau_{\text{rel}}} \cdot N_S(t_0) \cdot e^{-\frac{t-t_0}{\tau_{\text{rel}}}} dt = \frac{1}{\tau_{\text{rel}}} \cdot \nu(t_0) \cdot e^{-\frac{t-t_0}{\tau_{\text{rel}}}} \cdot dt_0 \cdot dt$$

as a mean value provided that τ_{rel} is time-independent as in the foregoing case.

Incidentally, the demonstrated identity of relaxation time τ_{rel} and mean lifetime of all particles *born* at the same time t_0 is by no means a matter of course. For instance, if we take the mean value $\bar{\bar{\tau}}$ of the lifetimes of all particles existing simultaneously at a given time t_1, we have to compute

$$\bar{\bar{\tau}} = \frac{\displaystyle\int_{t_0=-\infty}^{t_0=t_1} \nu(t_0)\, dt_0 \int_{\tau=t_1-t_0}^{\tau=\infty} \tau\, e^{-\frac{\tau}{\tau_{\text{rel}}}}\, d\left(\frac{\tau}{\tau_{\text{rel}}}\right)}{\displaystyle\int_{t_0=-\infty}^{t_0=t_1} \nu(t_0)\, dt_0 \int_{\tau=t_1-t_0}^{\tau=\infty} e^{-\frac{\tau}{\tau_{\text{rel}}}}\, d\left(\frac{\tau}{\tau_{\text{rel}}}\right)}$$

Assuming, by way of example, that the number of births $\nu(t_0)$ is constant in time we obtain for the thus defined mean lifetime $\bar{\bar{\tau}} = 2\tau_{\text{rel}}$.

Assuming, in another example, that no particles were born at all in the time interval $t_0 = t_1 - 10\tau_{rel}$ to $t_0 = t_1$, then when the mean values are ascertained at the time t_1 there exist only particles with lifetimes $\geqq 10\tau_{rel}$. In this case, the mean value $\bar{\tau}$ must become greater than $10\tau_{rel}$.

Hence we have to be careful with the statement that the relaxation time τ_{rel} defined by (IX.1.01) is equal to the mean lifetime. For instance, the statement is correct if τ_{rel} is time-independent and if the mean value is taken for all simultaneously born particles of the type under consideration. If the mean value is taken for all particles simultaneously alive at a given moment t_1, the statement is not correct because in this total the long lifetimes are favored.

Theoretical deductions frequently refer to Eq. (IX.1.01), and therefore the relaxation time τ_{rel} of the particle type concerned which is defined by this equation is sometimes more important than any mean values of the statistically distributed lifetimes. It is now common practice to talk of τ_{rel} simply as the mean lifetime τ of the particles concerned although, as we have just shown, this identity depends on several assumptions which are often *not* fulfilled. The situation is similar to that concerning the mean collision time of the conduction electrons (see page 253). Here, too, in the continued development of the theory, the original character of a real mean value has given way to that of a relaxation or decay time of a group of particles, while the original name of "mean collision time" has been retained. In the following we, too, shall call the time value defined by Eq. (IX.1.01) simply τ_s = mean lifetime of the particles of type S. In §2 and §3, the particle types S will be represented by the charged donors D^+ and the neutral donors $D^\times$, so that in §2 we have $S = D^+$ and in §3, $S = D^\times$.

§2. Physical Statements about the Lifetime τ_{D^+}

The death of a charged donor D^+ occurs when it associates with a free conduction electron $\ominus$. The frequency of such recombination events will be proportional to the concentrations[1] n_{D^+} and $n_\ominus$, assuming low enough concentrations, i.e., sufficient "dilution" of the two reaction partners D^+ and $\ominus$; hence

$$\frac{\text{Number of association processes}}{\text{(Unit time)} \cdot \text{(unit volume)}} = r_D n_\ominus n_{D^+} \qquad \text{(IX.2.01)}$$

---

[1] As in Chap. II we denote the electron concentration with $n_\ominus$, instead of simply with n as in the rest of this book.

One condition for such recombination events is that the two partners meet in space; then an electron $\ominus$ will be sufficiently close to a given donor D^+ more often if more electrons $\ominus$ are in thermal motion. Therefore the frequency of the association processes is proportional to the electron concentration $n_\ominus$. On the other hand, an electron $\ominus$, during its random thermal motion, will meet a charged donor D^+ more often if more such charged donors D^+ are present, i.e., if n_{D^+} is greater. This is the reason why the number of recombination processes is proportional to n_{D^+}.

The proportionality factor in (IX.2.01) is the so-called recombination coefficient r_D. It is frequently split up into the two factors of effective cross section σ_{D^+} and mean thermal velocity v_{th} of the electrons $\ominus$

$$r_D = \sigma_{D^+} \cdot v_{th} \qquad (IX.2.02)$$

where according to (VIII.4.27)

$$v_{th} = \sqrt{\frac{3kT}{m_{eff}}} = 1.168 \cdot 10^7 \frac{cm}{sec} \sqrt{\frac{T}{300°K}} \cdot \sqrt{\frac{m}{m_{eff}}} \qquad (VIII.4.27)$$

This splitting-up is based on the following consideration. One pictures the stationary donors D^+ as spheres of radius R while the electrons $\ominus$ are supposed to be without spatial extent. Now, if such a point electron passes the center of a donor sphere at a distance smaller than R, a collision occurs (see, however, below). In its zigzag flight with the velocity v_{th}, each one of the $n_\ominus$ electrons therefore sweeps out in unit time a broken cylindrical tube having the volume $\pi R^2 \cdot v_{th}$. This volume contains $n_{D^+} \cdot \pi R^2 v_{th}$ charged donors D^+, and a collision takes place with each one of them (however, see below). Therefore the number of collisions per unit time of *one* point electron $\ominus$ is

$$n_{D^+} \pi R^2 v_{th}$$

and that of $n_\ominus$ point electrons is

$$\pi R^2 v_{th} \cdot n_{D^+} n_\ominus = \sigma_{coll} v_{th} \cdot n_{D^+} \cdot n_\ominus$$

with $\sigma_{coll} = \pi R^2 =$ collision cross section.

Each collision need not necessarily lead to a recombination, and sometimes only a fraction of the collisions is successful. One allows for this by introducing, in place of the cross section σ_{coll}, the

"Effective cross section σ_{D^+} for the recombination $D^+ + \ominus \rightarrow D^\times$"

and obtains

$$\frac{\text{Number of recombination processes}}{\text{(Unit time)} \cdot \text{(unit volume)}} = \sigma_{D^+} \cdot v_{th} \cdot n_{D^+} \cdot n_\ominus \qquad (IX.2.03)$$

Comparison of (IX.2.01) and (IX.2.03) results in Eq. (IX.2.02).

Here it must be emphasized that it is proper to assume the effective cross section σ_{D^+} for the recombination to be smaller than, or at most equal to, the collision cross section. However, there would be no justification at all for equating the collision cross section to the "geometric" cross section of the donors D^+ and assuming it to be $\approx 10^{-15}$ cm². Quantitative statements regarding σ_{coll} can be made only on the basis of a thorough and usually quite difficult analysis of the collision process, quite apart from the fact that the value $(3 \cdot 10^{-8}$ cm)² for the "geometric" cross section is also based on quite arbitrary assumptions.

Now we want to turn to the computation of the lifetime τ_{D^+} of the donors in the charged state. We consider a group of charged donors D^+ at time t whose concentration n_{D^+} decreases during the subsequent time interval dt by

$$-dn_{D^+} = r_D \cdot n_\ominus \cdot n_{D^+}\, dt \qquad (IX.2.04)$$

since each recombination process causes the death of a donor and because according to Eq. (IX.2.01) the number of recombination processes in unit time and unit volume is $r_D n_\ominus n_{D^+}$ and, finally, because, as agreed, charged donors D^+ created by dissociation of neutral donors $D^\times$ during the time interval $(t, t + dt)$ under consideration must not be counted when Eq. (IX.1.01) is used. Next we want to compare Eq. (IX.1.01) with Eq. (IX.2.04), and we obtain for the mean lifetime τ_{D^+} of the charged donors D^+

$$\frac{1}{\tau_{rel}} = \frac{1}{\tau_{D^+}} = r_D n_\ominus \qquad (IX.2.05)$$

The presence of the concentration $n_\ominus$ of the reaction partner $\ominus$ in the expression for τ_{D^+} requires some caution in the use of this lifetime. In dynamic processes, *all* concentrations will usually vary, including $n_\ominus$. In this case, τ_{D^+} is no longer a constant but will vary with time,[1] which must be remembered if integrations have to be carried out.

§3. Physical Statements about $\tau_{D\times}$

This inconvenient though unavoidable difficulty does not arise in the case of the lifetime $\tau_{D\times}$ of donors in the associated and, hence, neutral state. Whether a $D^\times$ dissociates or not can depend only on

[1] Here we have an example of the case mentioned in §1, where a "lifetime" is not constant in time because the "environment" varies with time. This is so because the environment comprises not only the dielectric constant of the fundamental lattice, the temperature of the crystal, etc., but also the concentration of any reaction partners.

the properties of the $D^\times$ and on the available thermal energy, i.e., on the temperature T, but not on any other concentration because no reaction partner is required. The concentration $n_{D^\times}$ itself, too, cannot play any role provided that the dilution is adequate. Therefore in dynamic processes $\tau_{D^\times}$ will not be time-dependent and can be treated as a constant because dynamic processes usually take place too fast for any change of temperature to occur.

The time-independence of $\tau_{D^\times}$ (at constant temperature) will be confirmed when, in §4, we shall derive the following expression for $1/\tau_{D^\times}$ (see page 330):

$$\frac{1}{\tau_{D^\times}} = r_D \cdot \frac{N_C}{2} \cdot e^{-\frac{E_{CD}}{kT}} = \sigma_{D^+} \cdot v_{\text{th}} \cdot \frac{N_C}{2} \cdot e^{-\frac{E_{CD}}{kT}} \qquad \text{(IX.3.01)}$$

Here N_C is the effective density of states in the conduction band[1]

$$N_C = 2 \left(\frac{2\pi m_{\text{eff}} kT}{h^2} \right)^{3/2} = 2.5 \cdot 10^{19} \text{ cm}^{-3} \left(\frac{m_{\text{eff}}}{m} \right)^{3/2} \left(\frac{T}{300°\text{K}} \right)^{3/2}$$
$$\text{(VIII.4.04)}$$

One can see that only the temperature T can cause a time dependence of $\tau_{D^\times}$ because, apart from T, Eq. (IX.3.01) contains only atomic constants e, m, h, k, and the following factors which characterize the type of impurity:

Effective cross section σ_{D^+} and dissociation energy E_{CD}

The presence of the latter is not surprising. At a given temperature T, the more energy is required to remove the electron $\ominus$ from the donor core D^+, the less frequently will the thermal energy kT suffice to cause dissociation and, hence, the larger will be the lifetime $\tau_{D^\times}$.

Apart from this, the number of dissociations in unit time and unit volume is, of course, greater the more associated donors $D^\times$ are present because the probability of dissociation is equally great for each $D^\times$. Therefore we have

$$\frac{\text{Number of dissociation processes}}{\text{(Unit time)} \cdot \text{(unit volume)}} = \frac{1}{\tau_{D^\times}} n_{D^\times} \qquad \text{(IX.3.02)}$$

By appropriate application of (IX.1.01) it follows that the proportionality factor is $1/\tau_{D^\times}$.

§4. The Generalization of the Law of Mass Action for Dynamic Processes

The concentration n_S of an impurity type S and its variation with time dn_S/dt are determined by the opposing actions of birth and death

[1] See Eqs. (VIII.1.04) and (VIII.4.04).

rate:

$$\frac{dn_S}{dt} = + \frac{\text{number of births}}{\text{(unit time)} \cdot \text{(unit volume)}} - \frac{\text{number of deaths}}{\text{(unit time)} \cdot \text{(unit volume)}}$$

(IX.4.01)

For dissociated charged donors D^+, dissociations represent births and associations represent deaths. Equations (IX.3.02) and (IX.2.01) and application of (IX.4.01) to the impurity type $S = D^+$ lead, therefore, to

$$\frac{dn_{D^+}}{dt} = + \frac{1}{\tau_{D^\times}} n_{D^\times} - r_D n_\ominus n_{D^+}$$

(IX.4.02)

In the case of impurity type $S = D^\times$, i.e., of associated neutral donors, we have the reverse situation where dissociations take the role of deaths and associations the role of births:

$$\frac{dn_{D^\times}}{dt} = + r_D n_\ominus n_{D^+} - \frac{1}{\tau_{D^\times}} n_{D^\times}$$

(IX.4.03)

Addition yields

$$\frac{dn_{D^+}}{dt} + \frac{dn_{D^\times}}{dt} = 0$$

The total concentration n_D of all donors ($= n_{D^+} + n_{D^\times}$) remains constant in dynamic processes.[1]

Equations (IX.4.02) and (IX.4.03) are generalizations of the law of mass action which is valid only in the case of equilibrium

$$n_{D^+} \cdot n_\ominus = K_D n_{D^\times} \quad \text{(II.6.04) or (VIII.5.21)}$$

It is worth while to review the case of equilibrium from the newly gained point of view. In the case of equilibrium, the concentrations must be constant in time:

$$\frac{dn_{D^+}}{dt} = - \frac{dn_{D^\times}}{dt} = 0$$

Hence, in accordance with (IX.4.02) or (IX.4.03),

$$n_\ominus \cdot n_{D^+} = \frac{1}{r_D \tau_{D^\times}} n_{D^\times}$$

(IX.4.04)

If we compare this form of the law of mass action with the form in which it is usually written, (II.6.04) or (VIII.5.21), we obtain

$$r_D \tau_{D^\times} K_D = 1$$

(IX.4.05)

Using the expression (VIII.5.20), derived from Fermi statistics, for the mass-action constant K_D and also Eq. (IX.2.02), we obtain the

[1] See also footnote 3, p. 47.

expression previously discussed in §3

$$\frac{1}{\tau_{D_\times}} = r_D \frac{N_C}{2} e^{-\frac{E_{CD}}{kT}} = \sigma_{D^+} \cdot v_{th} \cdot \frac{N_C}{2} \cdot e^{-\frac{E_{CD}}{kT}} \quad \text{(IX.3.01)}$$

which we shall now compare once more with the expression for $1/\tau_{D^+}$ from §2:

$$\frac{1}{\tau_{D^+}} = r_D n_\ominus = \sigma_D v_{th} n_\ominus \quad \text{(IX.2.05)}$$

Both equations have general validity, i.e., not only for the case of equilibrium.[1]

For the special case of equilibrium we obtain from (IX.4.04) by multiplication with r_D

$$r_D n_\ominus \cdot n_{D^+} = \frac{1}{\tau_{D^\times}} n_{D^\times}$$

and further with the aid of (IX.2.05)

$$\frac{1}{\tau_{D^+}} \cdot n_{D^+} = \frac{1}{\tau_{D^\times}} \cdot n_{D^\times} \quad \text{(only valid in the case of equilibrium)}$$
$$\text{(IX.4.06)}$$

and

$$\frac{\tau_{D^\times}}{\tau_{D^+}} = \frac{n_{D^\times}}{n_{D^+}} \quad \text{(only valid in the case of equilibrium)} \quad \text{(IX.4.07)}$$

In the form of (IX.4.06) the condition of equilibrium is again apparent because it says:

Number of deaths of
$$D^+ \ (\equiv \text{number of births of } D^\times) = \text{number of deaths of } D^\times$$
hence
$$\text{Number of births} = \text{number of deaths for } D^\times$$

It can be seen from (IX.4.07) that for the case of *reserve* ($n_{D^+} \ll n_{D^\times}$) we have

$$\tau_{D_+} \ll \tau_{D^\times} \quad \text{(IX.4.08)}$$

The equilibrium in this case of few D^+ is produced by the fact that, while these few D^+ die relatively quickly, an equivalent birth rate is achieved by the dissociation of many $D^\times$ at great time intervals $\tau_{D^\times}$.

In the reverse case of *saturation* ($n_{D^+} \gg n_{D^\times}$) we have

$$\tau_{D^+} \gg \tau_{D^\times} \quad \text{(IX.4.09)}$$

---

[1] Equation (IX.4.05) used for the derivation of (IX.3.01) was obtained by considering the case of equilibrium; however, (IX.4.05) is a relationship between concentration-independent constants so that its limitation to the case of equilibrium is not even possible.

In conclusion, it may be mentioned that a change from a state of stronger association to a state of weaker association ($n_{D^\times}$ decreasing) is obtainable not only by enhanced dissociation. It can also happen that the association falls far below the value required for the preservation of the instantaneous state so that an unchanged or only slightly reduced dissociation is no longer fully compensated. This remark will be of importance at the end of §5.

§5. The Determining Time Constant in Nonstationary Processes

Owing to the finite lifetimes $\tau_{D^\times}$ and τ_{D^+}, the concentrations $n_{D^\times}$ and n_{D^+} cannot, after external interference, adjust themselves instantaneously to their new equilibrium values. The resulting inertia of impurity reactions can be of interest, for instance, for the high-frequency behavior of rectifier boundary layers.[1] The relevant time constant in this case is obtained by integration of the differential equations (IX.4.02) and (IX.4.03).

We carry out the integration in a particularly simple typical case (see Fig. IX.5.1): The electron concentration $n_\ominus$, after having varied in an irregular fashion for some time so that an equilibrium could not be established, retains, beginning at time $t = 0$, a certain value $n_\ominus$ (see Fig. IX.5.1):

$$n_\ominus = \text{const} \qquad \text{for } t > 0 \qquad (\text{IX.5.01})$$

Then, in the course of time, an impurity equilibrium will be established which is determined by the following two conditions:

1. (Death rate of the $D^+ \equiv$) birth rate of the $D^\times$ = death rate of the $D^\times$

$$\frac{1}{\tau_{D^+}} n_{D^+} = \frac{1}{\tau_{D^\times}} n_{D^\times} \qquad (\text{IX.5.02})$$

2. Total number of donors = const

$$n_{D^+} + n_{D^\times} = n_D \qquad (\text{IX.5.03})$$

From the foregoing result the equilibrium concentrations which are reached asymptotically for $t \to \infty$:

$$n_{D^\times}(\infty) = \frac{\tau_{D^\times}}{\tau_{D^+} + \tau_{D^\times}} n_D \qquad (\text{IX.5.04})$$

$$n_{D^+}(\infty) = \frac{\tau_{D^+}}{\tau_{D^+} + \tau_{D^\times}} n_D \qquad (\text{IX.5.05})$$

[1] See W. Schottky, Z. Physik, **132:** 261 (1952).

During the process of adjustment the concentrations $n_{D^\times}$ and n_{D^+} deviate from these equilibrium values by slowly decreasing amounts $\Delta(t)$, one toward higher values, the other toward lower values, so that at any time t the sum of all donors according to (IX.5.03) is equal to n_D:

$$n_{D^\times}(t) = n_{D^\times}(\infty) + \Delta(t) \qquad\qquad \text{(IX.5.06)}$$
$$n_{D^+}(t) = n_{D^+}(\infty) - \Delta(t) \qquad\qquad \text{(IX.5.07)}$$

With the agreed premises, the differential equations (IX.4.02) and (IX.4.03) which govern the process of adjustment are simplified

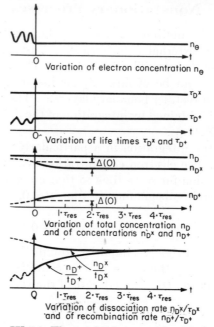

Fɪɢ. IX.5.1. The establishment of equilibrium.

because (IX.5.01) leads to a time-independent[1] $r_D n_\ominus = 1/\tau_{D^+}$ while $1/\tau_{D^\times}$ is time-independent anyway:

$$\frac{dn_{D^\times}}{dt} = -\frac{1}{\tau_{D^\times}} \cdot n_{D^\times}(t) + \frac{1}{\tau_{D^+}} \cdot n_{D^+}(t) \qquad\qquad \text{(IX.5.08)}$$

with $\tau_{D^\times} = \text{const}_1$ and $\tau_{D^+} = \text{const}_2$

$$\frac{dn_{D^+}}{dt} = -\frac{1}{\tau_{D^+}} \cdot n_{D^+}(t) + \frac{1}{\tau_{D^\times}} \cdot n_{D^\times}(t) \qquad\qquad \text{(IX.5.09)}$$

If we now insert (IX.5.06) and (IX.5.07) and bear in mind (IX.5.02),

[1] This eliminates the objections to the use of τ_{D^+} mentioned at the end of §2.

we obtain for the deviation $\Delta(t)$ from (IX.5.08) as well as from (IX.5.09) the same differential equation:

$$\dot{\Delta}(t) = -\left(\frac{1}{\tau_{D\times}} + \frac{1}{\tau_{D+}}\right) \cdot \Delta(t) = -\frac{1}{\tau_{\text{res}}} \Delta(t) \qquad \text{(IX.5.10)}$$

Here τ_{res} is a resultant time constant which according to

$$\frac{1}{\tau_{\text{res}}} = \frac{1}{\tau_{D\times}} + \frac{1}{\tau_{D+}} \qquad \text{(IX.5.11)}$$

is

$$\tau_{\text{res}} = \frac{\tau_{D+} \cdot \tau_{D\times}}{\tau_{D+} + \tau_{D\times}} \qquad \text{(IX.5.12)}$$

Integration of (IX.5.10) gives

$$\Delta(t) = \Delta(0) \cdot e^{-\frac{t}{\tau_{\text{res}}}} \qquad \text{(IX.5.13)}$$

and thus we obtain from (IX.5.06) and (IX.5.07) and using (IX.5.04) and (IX.5.05) finally

$$n_{D\times}(t) = \frac{\tau_{D\times}}{\tau_{D+} + \tau_{D\times}} n_D + \Delta(0) \cdot e^{-\frac{t}{\tau_{\text{res}}}} \qquad \text{(IX.5.14)}$$

$$n_{D+}(t) = \frac{\tau_{D+}}{\tau_{D+} + \tau_{D\times}} n_D - \Delta(0) \cdot e^{-\frac{t}{\tau_{\text{res}}}} \qquad \text{(IX.5.15)}$$

Hence the relevant time constant τ_{res} is given by Eq. (IX.5.11). If, for instance, we have reserve during the whole process ($n_{D+} \ll n_{D\times}$), we have according to (IX.5.02) $\tau_{D+} \ll \tau_{D\times}$ and according to (IX.5.12)

$$\tau_{\text{res}} \approx \tau_{D+} \ll \tau_{D\times} \qquad \text{(IX.5.16)}$$
$$\text{(Reserve } n_{D\times} \gg n_D \text{)}$$

Inversely in the case of saturation

$$\tau_{\text{res}} \approx \tau_{D\times} \ll \tau_{D+} \qquad \text{(IX.5.17)}$$
$$\text{(Saturation } n_{D\times} \ll n_{D+} \text{)}$$

The resultant time constant is, therefore, always practically equal to the *smaller* one of the two time constants τ_{D+} and $\tau_{D\times}$.

This result may look surprising at first, but a physical understanding is obtained if we compute the number of dissociations and associations in unit time and unit volume. From (IX.3.02), (IX.5.06), and (IX.5.13) and from (IX.2.01) and (IX.2.05), (IX.5.07) and (IX.5.13), we obtain

$$\frac{\text{Number of dissociations}}{(\text{Unit time}) \cdot (\text{unit volume})} = \frac{n_{D\times}(t)}{\tau_{D\times}} = \frac{n_{D\times}(\infty)}{\tau_{D\times}} + \frac{\Delta(0)}{\tau_{D\times}} e^{-\frac{t}{\tau_{\text{res}}}} \qquad \text{(IX.5.18)}$$

$$\frac{\text{Number of associations}}{\text{(Unit time)} \cdot \text{(unit volume)}} = \frac{n_{D^+}(t)}{\tau_{D^+}} = \frac{n_{D^+}(\infty)}{\tau_{D^+}} - \frac{\Delta(0)}{\tau_{D^+}} e^{-\frac{t}{\tau_{\text{res}}}}$$

$$\text{(IX.5.19)}$$

According to (IX.5.02), the first time-independent terms $n_{D^\times}(\infty)/\tau_{D^\times}$ and $n_{D^+}(\infty)/\tau_{D^+}$ represent in each case the final equilibrium rates. The final state of equilibrium is reached by the presence and the combined effect of the exponential terms in both equations, the determining exponential term being the one with the greater amplitude. Since the numerators of the amplitudes are equal, only the denominators $\tau_{D^\times}$ and τ_{D^+} are of importance. Therefore the term with the *smaller* time constant has the larger amplitude. This makes it also plausible that this shorter lifetime dominates the course of the whole process (see Fig. IX.5.1).

Finally a word about the orders of magnitude of $\tau_{D^\times}$ and τ_{D^+} with which we have to reckon. Both terms contain the recombination coefficient r_D or the effective cross section σ_{D^+}, respectively. Using $\sigma_{D^+} \approx (3 \cdot 10^{-8} \text{ cm})^2$ (IX.2.02) and (VIII.4.27) would lead to

$$r_D = 10^{+7} \text{ cm-sec}^{-1} \cdot 10^{-15} \text{ cm}^2 = 10^{-8} \text{ cm}^3 \text{ sec}^{-1}$$

With $n_\ominus = 10^{16} \text{ cm}^{-3}$, we would then obtain for $\tau_{D^+} = 1/r_D n_\ominus$

$$\tau_{D^+} = \frac{1}{10^{-8} \text{ cm}^3 \text{ sec}^{-1} \cdot 10^{16} \text{ cm}^{-3}} = 10^{-8} \text{ sec}$$

Assuming, for example, a dissociation energy $E_{CD} = 0.2$ ev for the donors, we obtain

$$\tau_{D^\times} = \frac{2}{r_D N_C e^{-\frac{E_{CD}}{kT}}} = \frac{2}{10^{-8} \text{ cm}^3 \text{ sec}^{-1} \cdot 2.5 \cdot 10^{19} \text{ cm}^{-3}} e^{+8}$$

$$= \frac{2}{2.5 \cdot 10^{11} \text{ sec}^{-1}} 3 \cdot 10^3 \approx 2 \cdot 10^{-8} \text{ sec}$$

However, it has been mentioned on page 327 that the assumption $\sigma_{D^+} = 10^{-15} \text{ cm}^2$ is completely arbitrary. Other authors estimate values for the effective cross section which are several orders of magnitude smaller and lead to a corresponding increase of the lifetimes[1] $\tau_{D^\times}$ and τ_{D^+}.

§6. Problems (Recombination)

The recombination of injected electron-hole pairs is of great importance in semiconductor physics and technology. This recombination may take place by the electron dropping into the valence band across the forbidden band, releasing the energy difference in form of a photon or a phonon. In germanium,

[1] See W. Schottky, *Z. Physik*, **132**: 261 (1952), particularly p. 276.

this process would lead to a carrier lifetime of roughly 1 sec. It cannot, therefore, account for the much smaller observed lifetimes of the order of 10^{-7} to 10^{-3} sec. The recombination is greatly enhanced, however, if the electron first falls into an impurity level within the forbidden band and from there into the valence band.

We assume that the number of electrons falling into the impurity level is proportional to the number of electrons present in the conduction band and to the probability that the impurity levels are empty. Furthermore, the number of electrons returning to the conduction band is assumed to be proportional to the number of states in that band and to the probability that the impurity levels are occupied. If the latter probability is f_T, we therefore have

$$\frac{dn}{dt} = -\frac{n(1 - f_T)}{\tau_n} + \frac{N_c f_T}{\tau_n'} \qquad (IX.6.01)$$

where τ_n and τ_n' are—as yet undetermined—constants with the dimensions of a lifetime. These constants are related to the number of the impurity centers and to their capture cross section.

An equation analogous to (IX.6.01) can be derived for the change of the hole density, introducing two additional constants, τ_p and τ_p':

$$\frac{dp}{dt} = -\frac{p f_T}{\tau_p} + \frac{N_V(1 - f_T)}{\tau_p'} \qquad (XI.6.02)$$

1.* Derive a relationship between τ_n and τ_n' and between τ_p and τ_p', utilizing the fact that in thermal equilibrium no net changes take place. Assuming that the recombination center density is small, so that no carriers can be stored in the recombination centers, eliminate f_T and show that the net recombination rate is given by an expression of the form

$$\frac{dn}{dt} = \frac{dp}{dt} = -\frac{np - n_i^2}{(n + n^*)\tau_p + (p + p^*)\tau_n} \qquad (IX.6.03)$$

What is the meaning of the quantities n^* and p^*?

2. Define from Eqs. (IX.1.01) and (IX.6.03) a lifetime for the excess carriers. Give the limiting values for low and for high injection levels. Under what condition do they coincide?

3. How does the low-level lifetime vary with the position of the recombination level inside the forbidden band, with the simplifying assumption that τ_n and τ_p do not vary with this position? How does this affect the recombination activity of impurity levels close to the band edges, which determine the conductivity, in comparison with levels deep inside the forbidden band which have little influence upon the conductivity?

4. What is the hole lifetime in an n-type germanium crystal with a resistivity of 10 ohm-cm if one assumes a recombination level 0.22 ev above the valence band and the values $\tau_n = 100$ μsec, $\tau_p = 10$ μsec? How does this lifetime depend on temperature if the τ's are temperature-independent?

5. Answer the questions of Prob. 4 for a p-type germanium crystal with a resistivity of 0.1 ohm-cm.

6.* At what conductivity has the low-level lifetime in a semiconductor its maximum, if one assumes that the τ's do not depend on the concentration of conductivity-determining impurities? Give numerical values for germanium, assuming $\tau_n : \tau_p = 10 : 1$, $p^* = 300 n_i$, $n^* = \frac{1}{300} n_i$.

CHAPTER X

Boundary Layers in Semiconductors and the Metal-Semiconductor Contact

§1. The Electrostatic Macropotential and the Energy of an Electron in a Solid

When the potential inside a solid is mentioned, we think nowadays automatically of the periodic potential U in Fig. I.2.2. We have become so accustomed to the atomistic point of view in this connection that we base our thoughts more or less automatically on the microscopic scale and have lost the more primitive viewpoint of a macroscopic continuum.

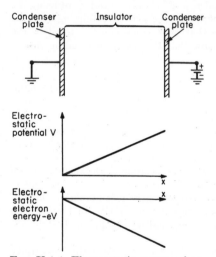

FIG. X.1.1. Electrostatic energy of an electron in the field of a plate condenser.

As long as the conditions in the solid under consideration are macroscopically homogeneous, this atomistic treatment is satisfactory. However, the present chapter is concerned with phenomena at the surfaces and in the boundary layers of semiconductors, and here it is just the deviation from the macroscopic homogeneity, existing inside the solid, which is characteristic. Therefore we have to supplement the results previously obtained, by means of the atomistic treatment, with macroscopic considerations. For this purpose we shall, first of all, consider the energy of an electron within a solid quite simply from this macroscopic viewpoint of a continuum.

Consider an insulator as the dielectric between the plates of a charged plate condenser (Fig. X.1.1). Then, by way of example, we have high potential values on the right side of this insulator and low values on the left. Hence, because of its negative charge, an electron has a low electrostatic energy on the right side and a high one on the left. This statement at first contradicts the position-*in*dependent[1] energy values in the level schemes of Figs. I.3.6 and I.3.8 to I.3.11. The contradiction is caused by the fact that the representation in Chap. I does not concern the total energy of an electron although it was specifically a plot of the sum of kinetic and potential energy.[2] Even so, it would have been incorrect to call these energy values total energies, because only the microscopic aspect of the problem was considered, while macroscopic forces such as the condenser field in the preceding example were neglected.

To describe the previous situation, we could also say that in the level diagrams of Figs. I.3.6 and I.3.8 to I.3.11, only the electron energy E within the lattice was plotted, this energy being the result of the binding forces exerted by the crystal lattice on the electron.[3] To obtain the total energy E of an electron, an electric energy term $-eV$ has to be added to the lattice energy E, this additional energy being due to a macropotential V:

$$\boldsymbol{E} = E - eV \qquad\qquad (\text{X.1.01})$$

The sources of the macropotential V are macroscopic surface or space charges, double layers, etc.[4] The following relationships show the kinetic and potential character,[5] respectively, of the lattice energy

[1] See p. 21 concerning the independence of position of the energy levels of the undisturbed lattice in contrast to the dependence on position of donor and acceptor levels.

[2] See footnote 3, p. 7.

[3] These binding forces are sometimes called chemical binding forces, and correspondingly the lattice energy is called chemical binding energy. These terms are used to emphasize that the chemical characteristics of the solid under consideration affect this component of the energy in particular.

[4] It appears at least doubtful whether in all possible cases such a subdivision of the total energy into electrostatic energy and lattice energy is unique. C. Herring and M. H. Nichols, in *Revs. Mod. Phys.*, **21**: 185–270 (1949), define the electrostatic macropotential by ascertaining the mean value of the electrostatic micropotential. W. Schottky, in *Physik regelmäss. Ber.*, **3**: 17 (1935), particularly in footnote 1, page 19, has introduced a so-called *Leerraumpotential* to define the electrostatic macropotential accurately. We believe that in the boundary layers of semiconductors, to be discussed later, there can be no doubt how one has to formulate the electrostatic energy $-eV$ of the semiconductor electrons and how great their lattice energy E is.

[5] In quantum mechanics, too, a subdivision of the energy according to

$$E = E_{\text{kin}} + E_{\text{pot}}$$

is possible. Here, however, E_{kin} and E_{pot} have to be considered as quantum-

E and of the electrostatic energy portion $-eV$:

$$E = E_{\text{kin}} + \overbrace{E_{\text{pot}}} \tag{X.1.02}$$

$$= \underbrace{E_{\text{kin}} + E'_{\text{pot}}} - eV \tag{X.1.03}$$

$$E = \qquad E \qquad - eV \tag{X.1.04}$$

The lattice energy E has, therefore, partly kinetic[1] and partly potential character,[2] while the electrostatic portion of the energy is solely potential.

It need not worry us that the total energy of an electron is known only apart from an additive constant, i.e., that the zero level of the electron has to be fixed arbitrarily. It is only important, in considering two different solids, such as a metal and a semiconductor, that the total energy of the electrons in both solids be referred to the same zero level. Naturally, nothing can be said about the sign of the electrostatic energy produced by the macropotential. However, the contributions of the lattice energy in the various bands are negative because they have the nature of binding energies. Thus we obtain, by way of example, the energy diagram of Fig. X.1.2[3] for a metal in

---

mechanical mean values, because the operators of the kinetic and of the potential energy are not, as a rule, interchangeable with the Hamilton operator $(E_{\text{kin}} + E_{\text{pot}})_{\text{op}}$. Hence, a ψ function cannot be the eigenfunction of all three operators simultaneously. Usually, one considers a *stationary* solution of the Schrödinger equation, i.e., an eigenfunction of the Hamilton operator $(E_{\text{kin}} + E_{\text{pot}})_{\text{op}}$. Then the electron represented by such a ψ function has only a sharply defined lattice energy E. Kinetic energy E_{kin} and potential energy E_{pot} can be given only as quantum-mechanical mean values.

[1] This applies also to the lowest and the highest states of each band, though in these the ψ function has the character of a standing wave, and one may therefore be tempted, without justification, to assume the kinetic energy to be zero at these band edges. See also p. 206, footnote 1.

[2] At first sight it may seem strange that a chemical binding energy is not purely potential in character but contains also a kinetic portion. Yet, in the case of the single atom, we do not object to equating the binding energy of an electron to the atom core to the ionization energy of the electron concerned. However, if we fix the zero point in the usual way (the separated stationary electron having the energy zero), the binding energy will be equal to the energy of the electron in the appropriate atomic state and therefore has, by way of example, in the ground state of the H atom a potential portion $-Z^2e^2/n^2a_0$ and a kinetic portion $+\frac{1}{2}Z^2e^2/n^2a_0$, Z = atomic number = 1 for the H atom, n = principal quantum number = 1 for the ground state, a_0 = radius of the first Bohr orbit. [See also H. A. Bethe in H. Geiger and K. Scheel, "Handbuch der Physik," 2d ed., vol. XXV, part 1, p. 287, Eq. (3.29), Springer-Verlag OHG, Berlin, 1933.] Thus in this case, too, the chemical binding energy contains a considerable kinetic portion.

[3] In the figures of this chapter, the shading indicates only the presence of a

which, because of the extremely high conductivity, the same macro-potential V prevails throughout.

On the other hand, in a semiconductor the electrostatic macropotential V need not by any means have the same value everywhere. For instance, the electrostatic energy can decrease or increase in layers

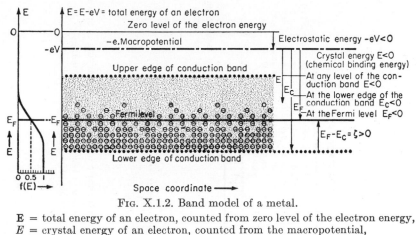

FIG. X.1.2. Band model of a metal.

$\mathbf{E}$ = total energy of an electron, counted from zero level of the electron energy,
E = crystal energy of an electron, counted from the macropotential,
$-eV$ = electrostatic energy of an electron.

several microns in thickness near the surface of a semiconductor.[1]   In fact, this is usually the case, as will be discussed later in §6 and §7. At the moment, we are mainly concerned to prove that such a bending of the potential curve carries along the whole remaining energy diagram.   This is so because the chemical binding forces, being deter-

continuum of states in which electrons can be accommodated, not the density of actual occupancy, in contrast to the figures in Chap. VIII.

An upper edge of the conduction band has been drawn in Fig. X.1.2 mainly for didactic reasons.   The use of the Wigner-Seitz cellular method (see p. 200) has shown that in solids, such as Na, K, etc., the conduction band and the bands above it always overlap so that one cannot speak any longer of an upper edge of the conduction band.   Therefore, an upper edge of the conduction band is omitted in the subsequent figures.

[1] Of course in such a case the additive composition of electrostatic energy $-eV$ and of lattice energy E can possess only the character of an approximation.   The expression

Total potential = periodic lattice potential U + macropotential V

is now no longer entirely periodic.   Hence, we have discarded in principle the basis for the computation of a particular lattice energy.   However, if the local variation of the macropotential V is sufficiently small, the method described represents a good approximation.   A more detailed discussion of this problem will be found in B. Kockel, Z. Naturforsch., 7A: 10–16 (1952).

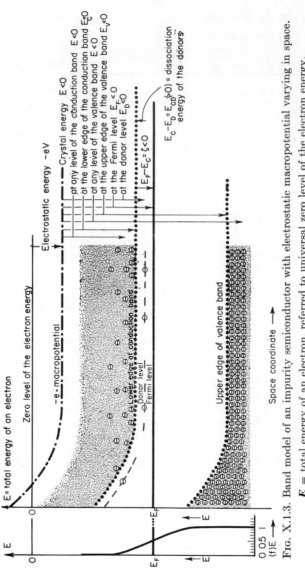

Fig. X.1.3. Band model of an impurity semiconductor with electrostatic macropotential varying in space.

E = total energy of an electron, referred to universal zero level of the electron energy.
$\bar{E}$ = crystal energy of an electron, referred to local value of the macropotential.
$-eV$ = electrostatic energy of an electron.

mined by the crystal lattice itself, have the same effect throughout the semiconductor; thus the binding portion E of each individual lattice level, for instance, E_C for the lower edge of the conduction band, has the same value throughout the semiconductor. The same applies to the upper edge of the valence band and for the impurity levels. Thus we obtain, for instance, Fig. X.1.3.

Finally, no binding forces whatever act in vacuum:

$$E = 0 \qquad (\text{X.1.05})$$

Apart from the electrostatic energy $-eV(x)$ as potential energy and the kinetic energy $1/2m|\mathbf{p}|^2$, no other energy term need be considered

$$E = \frac{1}{2m}\,|\mathbf{p}|^2 - eV(x) \qquad (\text{X.1.06})$$

Comparison with (VIII.1.01)[1] shows that at point x the electron

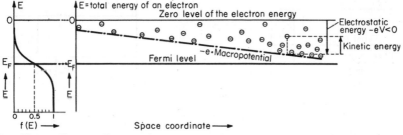

Fig. X.1.4. Energy diagram in vacuum. Linear variation of the electrostatic potential. The concentration of the electron gas is assumed to be so small that the potential curve does not noticeably deviate from a straight line.

gas can be considered as being in a potential well of depth $-eV(x)$, and from (VIII.1.08) we can derive for the Fermi level

$$E_F = \zeta\left(\frac{n(x)}{N}\right) - eV(x) \qquad (\text{X.1.07})$$

Figure X.1.4 shows an (E,x) representation corresponding to Figs. X.1.2 and X.1.3 for the case of a uniform potential rise, or a constant electric field,[2] in the vacuum region under consideration.

[1] In Chap. VIII, §1, the potential well is considered as the simplest model of a solid. Therefore E_{pot} in this case has the character of a chemical binding energy and E is used rather than $\mathbf{E}$. If we wished to include a macropotential V in this simple model, the potential energy of the electrons outside the well would not be zero but would be $-eV$. Correspondingly, the potential energy within the well would not be E_{pot} but $E_{pot} - eV(x)$. However, the consideration of a macropotential $V(x)$ is introduced only in the present Chap. X.

[2] Figures X.2.4 and X.3.1 show an experimental arrangement in which a linear potential variation is achieved at thermal equilibrium.

§2. Thermal Equilibrium between Two Metals.
The Galvani Voltage

In Figs. X.1.2 to X.1.4 the Fermi level is drawn horizontal and the same occupancy function is used in all parts of the volume (hence in all layers in the plane problem under consideration). This is only a special application of the law concerning the thermal equilibrium between different phases which was derived on pp. 288 to 292. The application of this law acquires special significance if we now turn to the consideration of the thermal equilibrium between different solids, for example, between two metals which are in close contact. To begin with, Fig. X.2.1 shows the two metals separated. Thermal

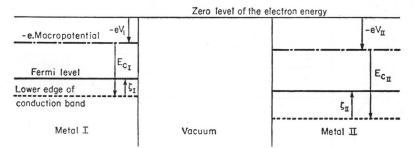

Fig. X.2.1. Two metals, I and II, separated by vacuum. Each metal in equilibrium in itself. Equilibrium between I and II not yet established.

equilibrium exists within each metal, so that the Fermi level is horizontal within each individual metal. We assume that thermal equilibrium has not yet been established between the two metals, and hence the Fermi levels are of different height in the two metals.[1] If the two metals are now brought into intimate contact (Fig. X.2.2), thermal equilibrium is established between them and the Fermi levels must adjust themselves to the same height.

The question arises how this is achieved. The distances $E_{C\mathrm{I}}$ and $E_{C\mathrm{II}}$ between the edges of the conduction bands (drawn as dotted lines) and the dot-dash lines representing the electrostatic energy are chemical binding energies of an electron in the lowest levels of the two conduction bands and are thus fixed by the respective crystal properties. The heights ζ_{I} and ζ_{II} of the Fermi levels, drawn as heavy continuous lines, above the lower edges of the conduction bands, drawn as dotted lines, are fixed by the electron concentrations n_{I} and n_{II} [see Eq.

[1] As a *non*equilibrium state this state is naturally largely dependent on the previous history. Hence the relative position of the Fermi levels in the two metals is essentially arbitrary.

(VIII.4.07)]. None of these values is changed by making contact between the two metals. Hence, only the electrostatic energies are left for the adjustment of the Fermi levels, i.e., the distances $-eV_I$ and $-eV_{II}$, respectively, between the common zero level of the electron energy and the dot-dash lines. Therefore, the macropotentials V_I and V_{II} in the two metals I and II must assume a definite difference relative to each other so that the Fermi level may be at the same height in both metals. The question arises as to what actual physical process brings this about, in other words, what happens when contact is made between the two metals, i.e., during the transition from Fig. X.2.1 to X.2.2. A certain number of electrons from the uppermost atomic layer of one metal passes into the uppermost atomic layer of the other metal. Thus the surface of one metal is charged positive, the surface

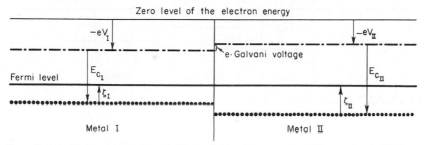

Fig. X.2.2. Two metals, I and II, in intimate contact. Thermal equilibrium. Difference $V_{II} - V_I$ between the two macropotentials = Galvani voltage.

of the other metal is charged negative, and the resulting double layer produces a jump between the two macropotentials, i.e., the two dot-dash lines are displaced relative to each other. This process continues until the resulting potential gradient suffices to establish the Fermi levels at the same height, i.e., until thermal equilibrium is reached. The potential difference between the two internal values of the macropotential, which is characteristic for the two metals, is called the Galvani voltage.

If three or more metals at the same temperature are combined into a closed circuit and if no current flows through this circuit, i.e., if all these metals are in thermal equilibrium (see Fig. X.2.3), the Fermi level, drawn in heavy print, must be at the same height in all metals. The values of the electrostatic energy $-eV_I$, $-eV_{II}$, $-eV_{III}$ are not fixed, but the heights $|E_{CI}| - \zeta_I$, $|E_{CII}| - \zeta_{II}$, $|E_{CIII}| - \zeta_{III}$ of the electrostatic energy, in dot-dash lines, above the Fermi level, in heavy print, are determined by the lattice properties. Therefore, after moving through the circuit from left to right, we return in metal I to the same level of the dot-dash electrostatic energy and we can see that the sum of all Galvani voltages $G_{\text{II I}} + G_{\text{III II}} + G_{\text{I III}}$ in traversing a conducting loop must be exactly zero. We shall use this result below (see page 361).

Finally, it is known that hot metal surfaces emit electrons into the vacuum. We have to assume such an electron emission even for metals at normal temperature although it will be orders of magnitude

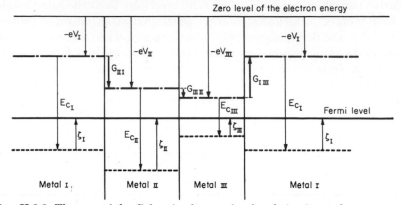

Fig. X.2.3. The sum of the Galvani voltages of a closed circuit equals zero:

$$G_{\text{II I}} + G_{\text{III II}} + G_{\text{I III}} = 0$$

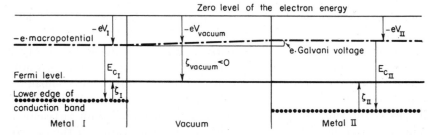

Fig. X.2.4. Two metals, I and II, separated by vacuum. Thermal equilibrium between I and II. No atomic double layers at the surfaces. Galvani voltage = difference of the internal values of the macropotential.

smaller than for hot surfaces. Therefore, even between the spatially separated metals of Fig. X.2.1, electrons will be exchanged, and this exchange will be stronger in one direction than in the other until thermal equilibrium is established, i.e., until the correct potential difference between the macropotentials V_{I} and V_{II} has been established and the Fermi levels have thus been brought to the same height (Fig. X.2.4).[1] Here the positively or negatively charged metal surfaces are

---

[1] In the case of hot surfaces this will occur relatively soon, but with cold surfaces it will take an extremely long time.

not in close proximity but cause an electric field right across the vacuum, corresponding to a linear potential gradient through the vacuum in Fig. X.2.4.

§3. Surface Double Layers. The Volta Potential Difference (Contact Potential)

The situation represented in Fig. X.2.4 by no means corresponds to reality, because at the boundary between each metal and the vacuum we have to assume a spontaneous double layer which can be due to many causes.

1. Within the metal the electrons are in vigorous thermal random motion. The electrons moving toward the surface of the metal, even if their energy is insufficient to leave the metal, will move somewhat beyond the lattice of the fixed positive ions before they turn back. Hence a thin negative skin is formed above a thin positive skin, in brief, a double layer.

2. At the metal-vacuum boundary a lattice exists only on one side, while the other side borders on essentially empty space. Hence the ions of the uppermost atomic layer are, by comparison with the bulk of the metal, subject only from one side to the "proper" forces of a complete lattice, while from the other side the near vacuum exerts practically no, i.e., "wrong," forces. Therefore the ions of the uppermost atomic layers take up displaced positions relative to the configuration in the bulk of the metal. Since quasi-neutrality prevails in the bulk of the metal, charges will result at the surface of the metal. However, neutrality must obtain in the total system, and therefore a double layer results.

3. A further contribution to the spontaneous double layer can be supplied, apart from the ion displacements discussed under 2, by ion deformations, i.e., polarizations of the ion cores which do not occur in the uppermost atomic layers in the same way as in the bulk of the metal because of the "wrong" forces of the vacuum.

4. Finally, we must also recall the well-known phenomena of monatomic impurity layers on metal surfaces. We may mention, by way of example, the problem of surface layers of thorium or cesium or other elements on tungsten which has been investigated in detail by Langmuir and his school. Here the adsorbed foreign atoms are pulled apart to form dipoles, which explains their adhesion as well as their double-layer effect.

Hence, in place of the continuous change of the electrostatic potential at the metal surfaces in Fig. X.2.4, we must assume a potential jump of unknown magnitude arising from spontaneous double layers (Fig. X.3.1). As a result the difference of the surface potentials is no longer identical with the difference of the macropotentials within the two metals as in Fig. X.2.4. Therefore we need a new name for this difference of the surface potentials which is usually different from the Galvani voltage. We call this potential difference Volta potential difference or contact potential.[1]

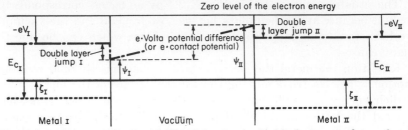

Fig. X.3.1. Two metals, I and II, with atomic double layers at the surfaces. Difference of the external surface potentials = Volta potential difference or contact potential. The figure indicates the validity of the statement: Volta potential difference (or contact potential) = difference of the vacuum work functions.

In contrast to the Galvani voltage, the contact potential can be determined directly by experiment. Here we mention only the case of the vacuum tube where the contact potential between cathode and grid has to be considered in the determination of the effective grid potential.

§4. The Work Function and the Photoelectric Activation Energy of Metals

Whereas the Fermi gas of electrons in metals is degenerate because of the extremely high electron concentration ($\sim 10^{22}$ cm^{-3}), the electron concentrations in vacuum are so low that the Maxwell-Boltzmann special case of Fermi statistics obtains. This, because of $n \ll N$, simplifies Eq. (X.1.07) in accordance with Eq. (A.II.2) to

$$E_F = \zeta - eV \approx kT \ln \frac{n}{N} - eV \qquad (X.4.01)$$

We apply this equation to the situation in the vacuum immediately

---

[1] We doubt whether the name contact potential is a happy choice. Experience has shown that the word "contact" in this name distracts attention from the fact that we deal with a potential difference between two free surfaces which are *not* in contact with each other but are separated by a large distance. The fact that the two solids are in intimate contact somewhere else only ensures thermal equilibrium between them and could in principle be replaced by waiting for a sufficiently long time if the solids were separated.

in front of the surface of metal I, where ζ_I is negative.   We replace this by introducing the positive work function

$$\Psi_I = -\zeta_I = -(E_F + eV_I) = -eV_I - E_F$$

(see Fig. X.3.1) and obtain

$$n_{\text{vacuum}} = N \, e^{-\frac{\Psi_I}{kT}} \tag{X.4.02}$$

Here we have assumed thermal equilibrium.   Hence the number of electrons leaving the metal surface in unit time exactly equals the number of electrons returning to the metal surface in unit time.   A unidirectional thermal current away from the metal surface is just compensated by a unidirectional thermal current in the opposite direction.

Of much greater importance experimentally are two deviations from thermal equilibrium: (1) that in which the electrode facing the metal surface under consideration has a much lower temperature than this surface and hence practically does not emit at all and (2) that in which the electric field between the two metals can be altered arbitrarily with a battery.   In contrast to the case of thermal equilibrium we can now arrange, by applying the proper polarity, that fewer electrons return from the vacuum into the metal than leave the metal surface. In other words, an emission current can be drawn from the hot metal surface.   Now, the larger the value of the suitably directed electric field is made, the smaller will be the number of electrons returning to the metal surface and the larger will be the emission current until beyond a certain field strength all electrons which have left the metal are carried away into the vacuum and no longer return to the metal surface.   By further increase of the field, the emission current cannot, for the time being, be increased any further, i.e., we have saturation current.

Although this state of "complete stationary transport" and the state of thermal equilibrium differ tremendously and must be kept apart conceptually, a more detailed discussion[1] shows that the two cases are intimately related inasmuch as the saturation current, in the case of complete stationary transport, is equal to the unidirectional thermal current in the case of thermal equilibrium:

$i_{\text{sat}} = $ unidirectional thermal current density

$$= e \cdot \int_{v_x=0}^{+\infty} \int_{v_y=-\infty}^{+\infty} \int_{v_z=-\infty}^{+\infty} v_x \cdot n(v_x v_y v_z) \cdot dv_x \, dv_y \, dv_z \tag{X.4.03}$$

[1] W. Schottky, Physik der Glühelektroden, in Wien and Harms, "Handbuch der Experimentalphysik," vol. 13, part 2, particularly pp. 31–42, Akademische Verlagsgesellschaft, Leipzig, 1928.

Since $n_{\text{vacuum}} \ll N$, we must here use the Boltzmann distribution for the distribution function $n(v_x v_y v_z)$. The former is derived from Eq. (VIII.1.12), in the form here required, by the following transformations:

$$N(E)\, dE = N \cdot \frac{2}{\sqrt{\pi}} \left(\frac{E - E_{\text{pot}}}{kT}\right)^{\frac{1}{2}} e^{-\frac{E - E_{\text{pot}}}{kT}}\, d\left(\frac{E - E_{\text{pot}}}{kT}\right)$$

$$= N \cdot 2\pi^{-\frac{1}{2}} \cdot \left(\frac{m}{2kT}\right)^{+\frac{1}{2}} v\, e^{-\frac{mv^2}{2kT}} \frac{m}{2kT} \cdot 2v\, dv$$

$$N(E)\, dE = N \cdot \pi^{-\frac{3}{2}} \left(\frac{m}{2kT}\right)^{+\frac{3}{2}} e^{-\frac{mv^2}{2kT}} \cdot 4\pi v^2\, dv$$

With a transformation of the variables and simultaneous transition from the total numbers N to the densities n, we finally get

$$n(v_x v_y v_z)\, dv_x\, dv_y\, dv_z = n \cdot \pi^{-\frac{3}{2}} \left(\frac{m}{2kT}\right)^{+\frac{3}{2}} \cdot e^{-\frac{m(v_x^2 + v_y^2 + v_z^2)}{2kT}} \cdot dv_x\, dv_y\, dv_z \tag{X.4.04}$$

Using this in (X.4.03) we obtain

$$i_{\text{sat}} = e \cdot n_{\text{vacuum}_{\text{I}}} \cdot \pi^{-\frac{3}{2}} \left(\frac{2kT}{m}\right)^{\frac{1}{2}} \cdot \int\limits_{u_x = 0}^{\infty} e^{-u_x^2} u_x\, du_x \cdot \int\limits_{u_y = -\infty}^{+\infty} e^{-u_y^2}\, du_y$$

$$\cdot \int\limits_{u_z = -\infty}^{+\infty} e^{-u_z^2} du_z$$

$$i_{\text{sat}} = e \cdot n_{\text{vacuum}_{\text{I}}} \cdot \pi^{-\frac{3}{2}} \left(\frac{2kT}{m}\right)^{\frac{1}{2}} \cdot \frac{1}{2} \cdot \sqrt{\pi} \cdot \sqrt{\pi}$$

and with (X.4.02)

$$i_{\text{sat}} = \frac{1}{2} e \left(\frac{2kT}{\pi m}\right)^{\frac{1}{2}} \cdot N \cdot e^{-\frac{\Psi_{\text{I}}}{kT}} \tag{X.4.05}$$

Using (VIII.1.04), we finally obtain

$$i_{\text{sat}} = \frac{4\pi e m k^2}{h^3} T^2\, e^{-\frac{\Psi_{\text{I}}}{kT}} = A T^2\, e^{-\frac{\Psi_{\text{I}}}{kT}} = 120\, \frac{\text{amp}}{\text{cm}^2} \left(\frac{T}{\text{degree K}}\right)^2 e^{-\frac{\Psi_{\text{I}}}{kT}} \tag{X.4.06}$$

This is the well-known Richardson law for the saturation current density from a hot surface.

The decisive term Ψ in the exponent of the Richardson law (X.4.06) is called the thermal metal–vacuum work function. We see from Fig. X.3.1 that in such a representation this thermal metal–vacuum work function appears as the distance between the Fermi level and the electrostatic potential immediately in front of the metal surface. From Fig. X.3.1 we can hence derive the important law:

The difference of the thermal work functions of two metals equals the relative Volta potential difference of these two metals.

Finally, for later application, we mention that according to Fig. X.3.1 we have[1]

$$\Psi = E_{C_{\text{metal}}} - \zeta_{\text{metal}} \pm (\text{double layer})_{\text{metal vacuum}} \quad (X.4.07)$$

Means other than thermal excitation can be used to liberate electrons from the binding forces of the solid and to push them into the vacuum. In particular we must mention here the photoelectric process, where the incident photon has to impart to the electron an increase of energy which is at least equal to the difference between the energy of an electron bound in the solid and the energy of a stationary electron in the vacuum in front of the metal surface. Since the crystal states above the Fermi level are very sparsely occupied by comparison with the states below the Fermi level, the described process will occur with great frequency only if the energy $\hbar\omega$ of the light quantum is sufficient[2] to lift an electron from the Fermi level to the electrostatic surface potential. In the limiting case $T \to 0$ this "red limit"[3] of the photoeffect becomes quite sharp, and this minimum energy required, in the limiting case $T \to 0$, for the liberation of an electron by impact with a light quantum can simply be called *the* photoelectric activation energy. In metals this energy is equal to the thermal work function because it is equal to the difference between the electrostatic surface potential and the Fermi level.

The fact that this equality happens to obtain for metals and the fact that this subject has in the past usually been discussed only in relation to metals have led to a replacement of the somewhat abstract thermodynamic definition of the thermal work function as the decisive term in the exponent of a Richardson law, by the undoubtedly simpler definition of the photoelectric activation energy. However, we shall see in the following paragraph that this is not permissible in the case of semiconductors.

[1] On this occasion we must remember that the several terms in Eq. (X.4.07), and hence also the work function Ψ itself, cannot a priori be considered independent of temperature. As long as the temperature dependence of Ψ is not known exactly, (X.4.06) does not give definite information about the temperature dependence of the saturation current. See W. Schottky and H. Rothe, Physik der Glühelektroden, in Wien and Harms, *op. cit.*, vol. 13, part 2, particularly Chap. 6.

[2] ω = angular frequency = $2\pi f$; $\hbar = (1/2\pi)h = 1.054 \cdot 10^{-27}$ cm^2 g-sec^{-1}.

[3] The condition $\omega > \omega_{\min}$ establishes a low-frequency, or long wavelength (i.e., "red" light), limit to the photoelectrically active spectrum.

§5. The Work Function and the Photoelectric Activation Energy of Semiconductors

If we now consider, instead of two metals, a metal and a semiconductor at a great distance from each other, we obtain Fig. X.5.1 when equilibrium is established.[1]

This means that an equilibrium concentration n of the electrons exists also in front of semiconductor surfaces. Using the separation

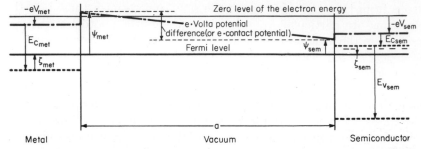

Fig. X.5.1. Metal and semiconductor widely separated by vacuum. Again the statement is valid: Volta potential difference (or contact potential) = difference of the vacuum work functions.

Ψ_{sem} of the Fermi level from the electrostatic potential we obtain, just as before for the metal, the equation

$$n = N\,\mathrm{e}^{-\frac{\Psi_{\mathrm{sem}}}{kT}} \qquad (X.5.01)$$

corresponding to Eq. (X.4.02) whereupon we can then carry out the transition to the Richardson equation, just as in §4:

$$i_{\mathrm{sat}} = \frac{1}{2}\,e\left(\frac{2\mathrm{k}T}{\pi m}\right)^{\frac{1}{2}} N \cdot \mathrm{e}^{-\frac{\Psi_{\mathrm{sem}}}{kT}} = \frac{4\pi emk^2}{h^3}\,T^2\,\mathrm{e}^{-\frac{\Psi_{\mathrm{sem}}}{kT}}$$

$$= 120\,\frac{\mathrm{amp}}{\mathrm{cm}^2}\cdot\left(\frac{T}{\mathrm{degree\ K}}\right)^2\mathrm{e}^{-\frac{\Psi_{\mathrm{sem}}}{kT}} \qquad (X.5.02)$$

From this it can be seen that in the semiconductor, too, the distance Ψ_{sem} between electrostatic surface potential and Fermi level yields the decisive term in the exponent of the Richardson law, i.e., the thermal work function.

---

[1] This may be accomplished by electron emission from both sides into the vacuum and then requires a relatively long time. As an alternative, we can imagine the metal and semiconductor to be bent in ring shape. At the surfaces under consideration they are far apart, but somewhere else they are in direct contact with other parts of their surface. In this way, the equilibrium can be established *quickly*.

In analogy to (X.4.07) one can derive from Fig. X.5.1

$$\Psi_{sem} = |E_{C_{sem}}| + |\zeta_{sem}| \pm (\text{double layer})_{sem\,vac} \qquad (\text{X.5.03})$$

In contrast to metals there is now no longer any relationship between this thermal work function and any significant photoelectric activation energy which is related to some threshold wavelength of the photoelectric effect. In metals the Fermi level is, in the limiting case $T \rightarrow 0$, the highest occupied electron level and therefore the most favorable starting point for an electron which is to be released photoelectrically. In the semiconductor, however, the Fermi level, except in the case of degeneracy, lies in the forbidden zone where, apart from

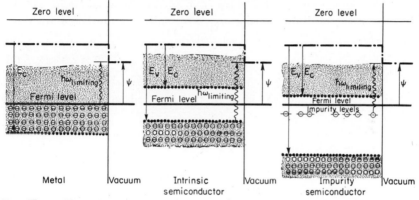

FIG. X.5.2. Photoelectric activation energy $\hbar\omega_{lim}$ and thermionic work function ψ. Limiting case of $T \rightarrow 0$.

the discrete impurity levels, no levels exist which can accommodate electrons. Hence, in the limiting case $T \rightarrow 0$, the photoelectric emission of electrons can originate only from an impurity level or from the fully occupied valence band; for $T > 0$, in addition, from the Maxwell tail in the conduction band. This shows that only in a few well-defined special cases[1] the Fermi level in the semiconductor can be the source of photoemission of an electron. Hence, thermionic work function Ψ_{sem} and photoelectric activation energy are not identical in the semiconductor (see also Fig. X.5.2).

[1] In a semiconductor with a large number of impurities, degeneracy can set in; then the Fermi level lies in the lower part of the conduction band and is therefore occupied by electrons. Another special case is the transition from "saturation" to "reserve," where the Fermi level coincides with the impurity level.

In both these cases, there exist electrons with even higher energy, and therefore, in these special cases, too, the thermionic work function Ψ_{sem}, referred to the Fermi level, does not appear as the photoelectric activation energy which is related to a long wavelength threshold.

In order to retain this identity which is so useful for the understanding of the physical meaning, we might be tempted to change the definition of the work function of semiconductors. For instance, we might choose for it the separation of the electrostatic surface potential and the lower edge of the conduction band:

$$\Psi^*_{\mathrm{sem}} = |E_{C\mathrm{sem}}| \pm (\text{double layer})_{\mathrm{sem\,vac}} \qquad (\mathrm{X.5.04})$$

Comparison with (X.5.03) yields

$$\Psi_{\mathrm{sem}} = \Psi^*_{\mathrm{sem}} + |\zeta_{\mathrm{sem}}| \qquad (\mathrm{X.5.05})$$

At the low electron concentrations n_S in the semiconductor, we usually have the limiting case $n_S \ll N$, and in accordance with Eq. (A.II.2)

$$\zeta_{\mathrm{sem}} = kT \ln \frac{n_S}{N} < 0 \qquad (\mathrm{X.5.06})$$

Using (X.5.05) and (X.5.06) in the Richardson law (X.5.02), we obtain

$$i_{\mathrm{sat}} = \frac{1}{2}\, e \left(\frac{2kT}{\pi m}\right)^{\frac{1}{2}} \cdot N\, e^{-\frac{\Psi_{\mathrm{sem}}^*}{kT}} \cdot e^{-\ln\frac{N}{n_S}}$$

$$i_{\mathrm{sat}} = e \left(\frac{k}{2\pi m}\right)^{\frac{1}{2}} \cdot n_S \cdot T^{\frac{1}{2}} \cdot e^{-\frac{\Psi_{\mathrm{sem}}^*}{kT}} \qquad (\mathrm{X.5.07})$$

The term Ψ^*_{sem} occurring in this form of the emission law can, as previously mentioned, be plausibly defined as the work required to raise an electron from the lower edge of the conduction band to a position at rest in front of the surface. This procedure has the disadvantage that, in contrast to the numerical coefficient $4\pi emk^2/h^3 = 120\ \mathrm{amps/cm^2}$ of form (X.5.02) of the Richardson law, the numerical coefficient $e(k/2\pi m)^{\frac{1}{2}} \cdot n_S$ of Eq. (X.5.07) is no longer a universal quantity because of n_S and will also be strongly temperature dependent in many semiconductors, again because of n_S. Furthermore, the correlation between work function and contact potential is lost. Finally, this whole transformation of the Richardson law is limited to cases where the electron gas in the semiconductor is not degenerate. However, in very highly conducting samples of Si and Ge, degeneracy is quite likely.

For all these reasons, the form (X.5.02) of the Richardson law has been retained in the literature for semiconductors, together with the corresponding definition of the semiconductor work function as referred to the Fermi level.

It must be emphasized that in semiconductors the work function Ψ_{sem} is definitely not temperature independent because of the temperature dependence of the Fermi level.   This requires even more care in the interpretation of an experimental [ln i_{sat} versus $1/T$] plot than in the case of metals.

§6. Semiconductor Boundary Layers.   The Metal-Semiconductor Contact

Figure X.5.1 was based specifically on the case of metal and semiconductor surfaces which are far apart.   The purpose of this assumption was to keep the electric field due to the contact potential sufficiently small.   Strong fields would cause special effects even with metal surfaces, such as lowering of the work function by image forces (Schottky emission) and also by the tunnel effect.   In semiconductor surfaces we have to reckon, in addition, with the fact that charges must be located at the ends of the field lines which are due to the Volta potential difference.   At the surface of a metal, considerable surface charges can be accommodated by slightly increasing or decreasing the large metallic electron density in the uppermost atomic layer. On the other hand, the accommodation of an equal amount of surface charge on the semiconductor surface requires[1] very large increases or decreases of the electron density in a layer up to 1,000 to 10,000 atoms deep because the available electron density is smaller by several orders of magnitude.   We therefore deal no longer with an actual *surface* charge; instead, the field lines penetrate partly up to 10^{-5} or 10^{-4} cm into the semiconductor and end successively at the charges of a *space* charge distributed over distances up to 10^{-4} cm (see Fig. X.6.1).

In a metal, the sudden ending of all field lines at a surface charge causes a break in the potential curve, whereas in a semiconductor the gradual dissipation of the field in a spatially extended space charge causes a curving of the potential variation over some distance.   If the semiconductor had the dielectric constant unity, like vacuum, the absence of surface charge would cause the potential variation to traverse the semiconductor surface with constant slope.   In the general case $\varepsilon > 1$, it is not the field strength $\mathbf{E} = -dV/dx$ that has to be continuous at the surface but the dielectric displacement $\mathbf{D} = -\varepsilon\,dV/dx$. This means that the curved potential variation in the semiconductor starts at the surface with a slope that is smaller by the factor $1/\varepsilon$ than that with which it ends at the vacuum side of the surface.   In any

---

[1] See, however, the later discussion of surface states.

case we can see that, when semiconductor and metal come close together, a space charge will be established in a boundary layer of the semiconductor, resulting in a curvature in the plot of the electrostatic electron energy $-eV$. The strength of the chemical binding, however, does not change because it is determined by the crystal structure. Therefore, the dotted line representing the lower edge E_C of the conduction band must have the same curvature (Fig. X.6.2), while the Fermi level E_F, indicated by a heavy continuous line, will remain horizontal as long as thermal equilibrium obtains. In the boundary layer, therefore, the distance $E_C - E_F$ changes. According

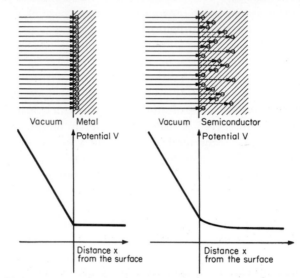

FIG. X.6.1. Vacuum field ending at a metal or semiconductor surface.

to page 317 and Eq. (VIII.5.15) this distance is a logarithmic measure for the electron concentration n:

$$E_C - E_F \approx kT \ln \frac{N_C}{n} > 0 \qquad \text{for } n \ll N_C \qquad (\text{X.6.01})$$

Thus the electron concentration n varies in the boundary layer and, since it deviates from its neutral value n_S, a space charge is created. Atomic double layers on the metal and on the semiconductor which, for greater clarity, were neglected in the potential representations of Fig. X.6.1, have been taken into consideration in Fig. X.6.2.

When the metal and semiconductor surfaces (see Fig. X.6.2) come infinitely close together, the dot-dash line indicating the electrostatic energy term $-eV$ has, in the end, to be raised so much that the whole

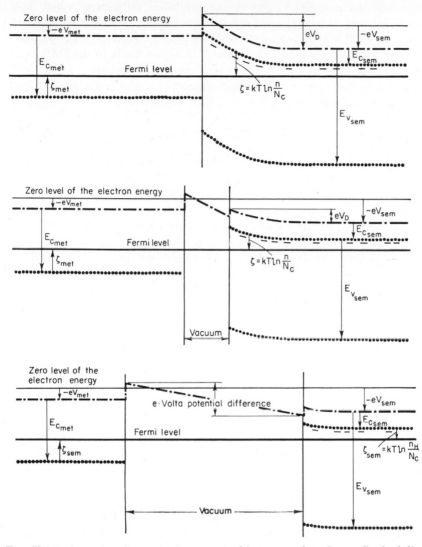

F<small>IG.</small> X.6.2. A semiconductor surface approaching a metal surface.   Gradual distortion of the bands in the semiconductor by an amount equal to the diffusion voltage V_D.   Hence the limiting condition of continuous transition of dielectric displacement εE at the semiconductor surface is fulfilled; a space-charge boundary layer is created.

potential difference, i.e., the Volta potential difference, which was previously in the vacuum, occurs now within the semiconductor. Since we call the potential difference within the boundary the diffusion voltage V_D (see page 76), the above discussion leads to the statement that the diffusion voltage V_D in a semiconductor boundary layer must be equal to the Volta potential difference between the electrode metal and the semiconductor:

$$V_D = \Psi_{\text{met vac}} - \Psi_{\text{sem vac}} \qquad \text{(X.6.02)}$$

We have to make many reservations with regard to this statement. To begin with, a quantitative discussion of the process of bringing the surfaces together, which is only qualitatively represented in Fig. X.6.2, shows that the deviations of the diffusion voltage V_D from the Volta potential difference are very considerable,[1] even for an approach within atomic distances, and would become zero only when the distance between the two surfaces disappears completely. It may be doubted, however, whether the assumption of the two surfaces approaching each other within subatomic distances is meaningful. Further, it was assumed in Fig. X.6.2 that the values of the potential jumps at the surfaces remain constant while they come closer together. However, during the approach the field between the two surfaces increases, and a polarizing effect of this field on the surface double layers can, of course, not be excluded. In this case the equality of diffusion voltage and Volta potential difference, derived for the two surfaces at a great distance, is no longer valid. Finally, just because of the existence of such surface double layers, it is awkward to talk of the Volta potential difference between the electrode metal and the semiconductor. One can expect a value characteristic of the two materials only with perfectly clean surfaces. Yet it has been shown more and more clearly during the last few years how difficult it is to prepare really clean surfaces. While it is difficult enough to measure a Volta potential difference between the separated metal and semiconductor surfaces without obtaining wrong results due to impurity layers, it is an even greater problem to avoid all contamination during the process of making contact. In fact, experiments to prove a relationship between diffusion voltage and Volta potential difference have been only partially successful.[2]

---

[1] This is particularly true in a semiconductor with very many impurities where even a small rise in potential, and the small deviations from neutrality linked with it, releases strong space charges.

[2] See, for instance, S. Poganski, Z. *Physik*, **134**: 469 (1953), particularly Fig. 3.

§7. Semiconductor Boundary Layers. The Metal-Semiconductor Work Function and the Diffusion Voltage V_D

The method of representation used so far dominates the literature in English, in which, therefore, the term diffusion voltage is not introduced as a special name for the curving of the potential plot in the semiconductor, but where it is simply stated that the potential plot in the semiconductor has to be raised or lowered by the value of the contact potential in order to compensate for the contact potential.

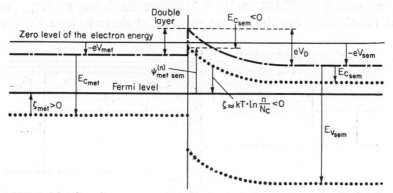

Fig. X.7.1. Metal and n-type semiconductor in intimate contact. Definition of work function $\psi^{(n)}_{\text{met-sem}}$. Note that this work function is *not* identical with the diffusion voltage V_D. Case of depletion boundary layer.

However, at the end of the previous paragraph we saw that the relationship

Diffusion voltage V_D = Volta potential difference

has only approximate validity. Therefore it may be useful, following the ideas of W. Schottky,[1] to regard the diffusion voltage V_D, after intimate contact has been established between metal and semiconductor, as an independent new term which is identical neither with the Galvani voltage nor with the Volta potential difference ($\equiv$ contact potential), nor with the vacuum work function, nor with the photoelectric activation energies. The question now arises whether, in the description of the intimate contact between metal and semiconductor, it is at all useful to start from the case of widely separated solids. If,

[1] In the publications of Schottky, these matters are treated rather briefly. The author is in the happy position of being able to refer to uncompleted and therefore unpublished manuscripts of Schottky.

instead, we depart directly from the case of intimate contact between metal and semiconductor, we obtain, by way of example, Fig. X.7.1 or X.7.2. In thermal equilibrium an electron concentration n_B is established[1] in the semiconductor at the boundary with the metal. Applying Eq. (X.6.01) to the semiconductor boundary, we obtain in the case of degeneracy

$$n_B = N_C\, e^{-\frac{\Psi^{(n)}_{\text{met sem}}}{kT}} \qquad (\text{X.7.01})$$

Here $\Psi^{(n)}_{\text{met sem}} = (E_C - E_F)_{\text{bound}}$ is the distance, measured at the boundary, of the conduction band from the Fermi level, drawn as a heavy continuous line.

In analogy to (X.4.02) and (X.5.01), we can interpret $\Psi^{(n)}_{\text{met sem}}$ as a thermionic work function for the emission of electrons from the metal

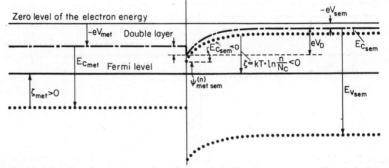

FIG. X.7.2. Metal and n-type semiconductor in intimate contact. Case of accumulation boundary layer.

into the semiconductor. The main justification for such an interpretation is the fact that this term is independent of the impurity content of the semiconductor and of the position of the Fermi level which is, so to speak, accidental. Thus we have, according to Fig. X.7.1,

$$\Psi^{(n)}_{\text{met sem}} = |E_{C_{\text{met}}}| - \zeta_{\text{met}} + (\text{double layer})_{\text{met sem}} - |E_{C_{\text{sem}}}| \qquad (\text{X.7.02})$$

Compared with the thermionic work function for the emission of electrons into vacuum [see Eq. (X.4.07)], we have only one new term, the binding energy $E_{C_{\text{sem}}}$, i.e., a characteristic of the undisturbed semiconductor lattice.

Therefore the chemical binding of the electrons in the metal lattice ($E_{C_{\text{met}}}$), the number of the electrons therein (ζ_{met}), the surface conditions at the boundary metal semiconductor (double layer), and the chemical binding of the electrons in the semiconductor ($E_{C_{\text{sem}}}$) determine a work

---

[1] The subscript B indicates the semiconductor boundary.

function $\Psi^{(n)}_{\text{met sem}}$ for the emission of electrons from the metal into the semiconductor and thereby, at least in thermal equilibrium, a boundary concentration n_B of the electrons quite independent of the impurity content of the semiconductor and of the position of the Fermi level in the semiconductor. Conversely, the electron concentration deep within the semiconductor is decisively influenced by the impurity content of the semiconductor because this impurity content enters, here, into the quasi-neutrality condition which, in turn, determines a value n_S of the electron concentration. Therefore a boundary layer must be formed in which a gradual transition takes place from the boundary value n_B to the semiconductor value[1] n_S. We have a depletion layer or an accumulation layer according to whether $n_B < n_S$ (Fig. X.7.1) or $n_B > n_S$ (Fig. X.7.2). Therefore, in this transition zone, i.e., in the boundary layer, electron concentrations prevail which deviate from the neutral value n_S. Consequently, we have here, instead of the quasi-neutrality *within* the semiconductor, a space charge of the density $\rho(x)$. In accordance with the Poisson equation

$$\frac{d^2V}{dx^2} = -\frac{4\pi}{\varepsilon}\rho(x) \qquad (\text{X.7.03})$$

this space charge causes a curvature in the plot of the electrostatic energy $-eV$, represented by dot-dash lines in our figures. This is the cause of the diffusion voltage V_D between the semiconductor boundary and the inside of the semiconductor. The name is explained by the fact that the field current generated by the diffusion voltage V_D balances out the diffusion current generated by the concentration gradient from n_S to n_B so that the zero current of thermal equilibrium is established. This has already been discussed on pages 76ff., together with the difficulties involved in visualizing the existence of an electrostatic potential difference within a conductor with zero current.

We want to discuss these difficulties once more from the newly gained point of view and note, to begin with, that the objections arise from an assumption that there is a law to the effect that the potential in a conductor is constant in the absence of a current. This law is incorrect if we mean by the potential the electrostatic potential represented by dot-dash lines in our figures. All the same, the law contains a core of truth, because in the thermodynamics of electric systems it is proved that this law is correct if we mean by the potential the electro*chemical* potential.[2] The electrochemical potential is the sum of electrostatic

---

[1] The subscript S indicates the value for the semiconductor.

[2] See, for instance, W. Schottky and H. Rothe, Physik der Glühelektroden, in Wien and Harms, *op. cit.*, vol. 13, part 2, chap. III, in particular Eq. (5), p. 18.

energy per particle and chemical potential ($\equiv$ free energy per particle). The electrostatic energy per electron is $-eV$. The other term of the sum can be computed, with the usual assumptions of solid-state physics, as chemical potential of a Fermi gas which is not free but has a potential energy equal to the total energy $E_C < 0$ of the lower edge of the conduction band (see pages 300 and 306). The chemical potential of a *free* Fermi gas with the concentration n is equal[1] to $\zeta(n)$. According to pages 300 and 306, the conduction electrons can be treated, under certain assumptions, not as a free gas, but as a gas in a potential well of depth E_C. Their chemical potential is, therefore, expressed by $E_C + \zeta(n)$ and their electrochemical potential by $-eV + E_C + \zeta(n)$. The law of the constancy of the electrochemical potential in a conductor in thermal equilibrium, i.e., with zero current, requires therefore that

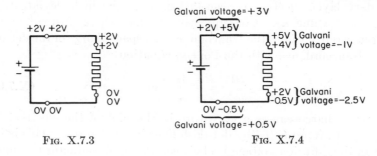

Fig. X.7.3   Fig. X.7.4

the sum $-eV + E_C + \zeta$ be constant. This, however, is just the distance of the Fermi level (in heavy type) from the zero level of the electron energy. Thus we have again a proof, from the thermodynamic point of view, that the Fermi level must be horizontal throughout all conductors and parts of conductors, provided that thermal equilibrium obtains.

Incidentally, it is this electrochemical potential which we use, without ever worrying about the thermodynamics of electric systems, in the usual considerations concerning potential distributions in electric circuits in everyday work. To take a simple example, in the circuit of Fig. X.7.3 we would use the indicated potential values without troubling about the fact that the different parts of the conductors are made of different metals. The point is that we deal here with values of the

[1] See L. Brillouin, "Die Quantenstatistik," Springer-Verlag OHG, Berlin, 1931, Eq. (32a) on p. 141 in connection with Eq. (28) on p. 139. A very simple and elegant proof, unfortunately based on incorrect arguments, is given in H. Fröhlich, "Elektronentheorie der Metalle," p. 64, Springer-Verlag OHG, Berlin, 1936, and by A. Sommerfeld in Geiger and Scheel, *op. cit.*, vol. 24, part 2, p. 342. However, the derivation in the latter can be corrected by elementary mathematical means.

electrochemical potential, whereas indicating the electrostatic macro-potentials might lead to Fig. X.7.4. Since the Galvani potential jumps summed over the complete circuit add up exactly to zero (see page 344 and Fig. X.2.3), we obtain by this procedure the same value of 2 volts for the terminal voltage as previously when we used the electrochemical potential.[1]

In other words, the initial difficulty in understanding the existence of electrostatic potential differences within a semiconductor with zero current may be due to a confusion between terminal voltage and a difference of electro*static* potentials, whereas in reality the terminal voltage which disappears in the case of zero current is equal to the

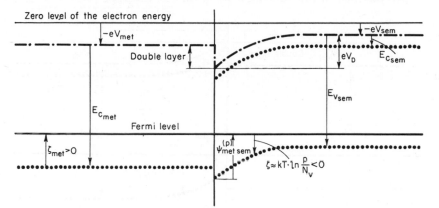

FIG. X.7.5. Metal and p-type semiconductor in intimate contact. Case of depletion boundary layer.

difference of the electro*chemical* potentials. The latter are, in fact, commonly used in everyday work, probably quite intuitively.

Figures X.7.5 and X.7.6 show a depletion and an accumulation layer in a p-type semiconductor. Here a work function $\Psi_{\text{met sem}}^{(p)}$ for the emission of holes from the metal into the semiconductor is shown. At first sight, this term may appear somewhat strange. But we have shown in Chap. III that one can always describe the totality of electrons in a band also as a totality of holes (see pages 65 to 66) and that, correspondingly, one can interpret the transition of a number of valence electrons into a neighboring metal electrode as the escape of a number of holes from the metal into the valence band. We also recall

[1] Here it may be recalled that, just because of the existence of Volta potential differences and the resulting vacuum fields, one has to take care in electrostatic measurements of terminal potentials that the two poles or knife edges or plates of the electrostatic instrument be made of the same material. This precaution is, of course, superfluous if the terminal voltage is measured galvanometrically.

that the distance $E_F - E_V$ of the Fermi level E_F from the upper edge E_V of the valence band usually equals $-\zeta(p/N_V)$ [see Eq. (VIII.4.15)] and, in the Maxwell-Boltzmann case, becomes equal to $kT \ln N_V/p$ [see Eq. (VIII.5.16)]. Accordingly, this distance is a logarithmic measure of the concentration p of the holes (see page 317). Using this relationship for the semiconductor boundary, we obtain for the boundary density p_B of the holes

$$p_B = N_V \, e^{-\frac{\Psi^{(p)}_{\text{met sem}}}{kT}} \tag{X.7.04}$$

The analogy to Eqs. (X.4.02), (X.5.01), and (X.7.01) shows that we are justified in introducing a work function $\Psi^{(p)}_{\text{met sem}}$ for holes.

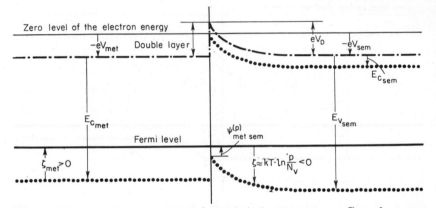

Fig. X.7.6. Metal and p-type semiconductor in intimate contact. Case of accumulation boundary layer.

Since we have defined $(E_C - E_F)_{\text{bound}} = \Psi^{(n)}_{\text{met sem}}$ and

$$(E_F - E_V)_{\text{bound}} = \Psi^{(p)}_{\text{met sem}}$$

we obtain by addition the expression

$$\Psi^{(n)}_{\text{met sem}} + \Psi^{(p)}_{\text{met sem}} = E_C - E_V \tag{X.7.05}$$

The sum of electron and hole work functions in a metal-semiconductor combination is independent of the metal and of any surface double layers and is equal to the width $E_C - E_V$ of the forbidden gap in the semiconductor.

We can summarize as follows: In §6 and §7 we have compared two different descriptions for the situation prevailing at the boundary of a metal and of a semiconductor. The second treatment, originated by Schottky, considers at once the intimate contact between metal and semiconductor. It starts with the concept of the thermionic work function $\Psi^{(n)}_{\text{met sem}}$ for the emission of electrons from the metal into the semiconductor, then points out the difference in electron concentrations n within the semiconductor (n_S) and at the boundary (n_B) and thus arrives at the decisive diffusion voltage V_D. The semiconductor density n_S is determined by the impurity content and the neutrality condition, the boundary density n_B, on the other hand, by the work function $\Psi_{\mathrm{met\ sem}}^{(n)}$.

The first treatment, used mainly in the literature in English, describes the intimate contact of semiconductor and metal as the limiting case of the two solids separated by finite distances a, assuming that the solids are in thermal equilibrium even in the state of spatial separation. This treatment is unobjectionable as long as the possibility is recognized that the surface double layers on the metal and on the semiconductor can be polarized during the process of approach. However, the relationship resulting from this treatment:

Diffusion voltage = contact potential of the widely separated solids
                  = difference of the thermionic vacuum work functions

is valid only if the surface double layers do not change during the process of approach. Otherwise, the relationship has only approximate validity.

§8. Experimental Results for the Work Function of Semiconductors and the Metal-Semiconductor Contact

In the course of the last few years, it has been finally realized that in commercial selenium rectifiers and in point detectors we do not deal with semiconductor-metal contacts but with disguised p-n rectifiers.[1] Prior to that, however, many experiments were carried out to obtain evidence for the behavior of semiconductor-metal contacts in accordance with the Schottky theory. In the first place we have to mention H. Schweickert[2] who produced contacts between selenium and a number of different metals and who found a connection between the blocking resistance and the work function of the metal with which the contact is made.

---

[1] S. Poganski, Z. Physik, 134: 469 (1953).   A. Hoffmann and F. Rose, Z. Physik, 136: 152 (1953).   R. Thedieck, Physik. Verhandl., 3: 31 (1952); 3: 212 (1952); Z. angew. Phys., 5: 165 (1953).   L. B. Valdes, Proc. IRE, 40: 445 (1952).

[2] H. Schweickert, Verhandl. deut. physik. Ges., 3: 99 (1939).   The results of Schweickert are also reproduced in W. Schottky, Z. tech. Physik, 21: 322 (1940).

From Eqs. (IV.4.23) and (IV.4.24) for the characteristics, one obtains for the zero resistance[1]

$$R_0 = \frac{\mathbf{V}}{e\mu_n n_B \mathbf{E}_B} \quad \text{with} \quad \mathbf{V} = \frac{kT}{e} = 25.9 \cdot \left(\frac{T}{300°K}\right) \cdot 10^{-3} \text{ volt}$$

and with the aid of (X.7.01)

$$R_0 = \frac{\mathbf{V}}{e\mu_n N_C \mathbf{E}_B} e^{+\frac{\Psi^{(n)}_{\text{met sem}}}{kT}} \tag{X.8.01}$$

We have already noted on page 358 that the vacuum work function $\Psi^{(n)}_{\text{met vac}}$ and the semiconductor work function $\Psi^{(n)}_{\text{met sem}}$ of a metal contain

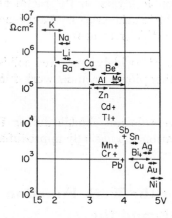

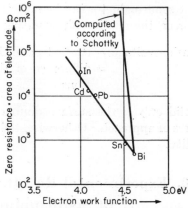

FIG. X.8.1. Work function and resistance of selenium rectifiers [from H. Schweickert, *Verhandl. deut. physik. Ges.* **3**, 99 (1939)].

FIG. X.8.2. Selenium rectifier without barrier layer. Dependence of the zero resistance upon the electron work function of the metal of the blocking electrode. [From S. Poganski, *Z. Physik,* **134**, 476 (1953)].

a number of identical terms. If we make contact between the same semiconductor, selenium, and a variety of metals we would therefore expect that the $\Psi^{(n)}_{\text{met sem}}$ vary in the same way as the $\Psi^{(n)}_{\text{met vac}}$ and that therefore, in view of (X.8.01), we would find that the resistance R_0 varies strongly with the vacuum work function of the metal with which contact is made. The measurements of Schweickert which are reproduced in Fig. X.8.1 show, in fact, such an effect. At first it may

---

[1] H. Schweickert plots in his diagram the maximum blocking resistances of the semiconductor-metal contacts under consideration. However, the maximum blocking resistance is outside the scope of the boundary-layer theory. Therefore, we use the differential resistance at zero bias voltage, the so-called zero resistance, to demonstrate the relationships to be expected from the boundary-layer theory.

seem surprising that with increasing work function the resistance R_0 decreases rather than increases. The explanation is the fact that selenium is a p-type conductor and that instead of (X.8.01) one has to use the expression

$$R_0 = \frac{V}{e\mu_p N_V \mathbf{E}_B}\, e^{+\frac{\Psi^{(p)}_{met\ sem}}{kT}} \qquad (X.8.02)$$

From this one obtains with the aid of (X.7.05)

$$R_0 = \frac{V}{e\mu_p N_V \mathbf{E}_B}\, e^{+\frac{Ec - Ev}{kT}}\, e^{-\frac{\Psi^{(n)}_{met\ sem}}{kT}} \sim e^{-\frac{\Psi^{(n)}_{met\ sem}}{kT}} \qquad (X.8.03)$$

and thus the decrease of the contact resistance with the vacuum work function of the contact-forming metal which has, in fact, been observed by Schweickert.

Other authors[1] obtain only in part results similar to those of Schweickert. It has become more and more apparent that it is extremely difficult to obtain a real metal-semiconductor contact without intermediate layers of reaction products and to clean the surfaces sufficiently before making the contact. S. Poganski[2] has probably carried out the neatest comparison between measurements on metal-semiconductor contacts and the boundary-layer theory, with very good qualitative agreement. Quantitatively, however, the variation of blocking characteristics with the work function of the electrode material is much too small (see Fig. X.8.2).

In the course of the quoted investigations, a large number of Volta potential differences and work functions have been determined. The methods used will be described below, partly because they are of considerable intrinsic interest, but also because they represent excellent material for getting familiar with the use of the terms introduced in §1 to §6, such as photoelectric activation energy, Galvani voltage, etc.

a. Methods for Measuring Volta Potential Difference and Work Function

The experimental arrangement (see Fig. X.8.3) shows two parallel plane surfaces of the two solids to be investigated, facing each other. These are not in thermal equilibrium, but a current of electrons flows across the vacuum from surface I to surface II. The energy for this

---

[1] Unpublished work by Brattain and Shive at Bell Telephone Laboratories, 1940; see J. Bardeen, *Phys. Rev.*, **71**: 2 (1947). A. V. Joffe, *J. Phys. U.S.S.R.*, **10**: 49 (1946). W. E. Meyerhof, *Phys. Rev.*, **71**: 727 (1947). S. Benzer, *J. Appl. Phys.*, **20**: 804 (1949).

[2] S. Poganski, *Z. Physik*, **134**: 469 (1953).

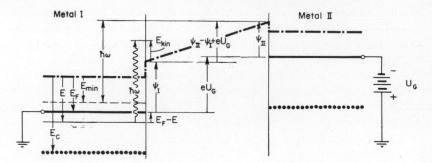

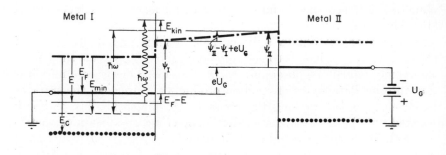

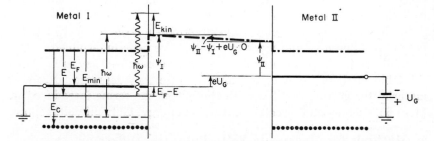

FIG. X.8.3. The decrease of U_G lowers the whole level diagram of metal II during the transition from the top via the intermediate to the lower figure. Within the metal I, E_{min} joins this downward trend, at least to begin with. In the top figure ($E_{min} < E_F$) no electrons at all reach metal II owing to excessive retarding potential U_G ($I = 0$). Electrons reach metal II in the intermediate figure ($E_{min} > E_F$) so that $I \neq 0$ (retarding field current). On transition from the intermediate to the lower figure, however, the upper end of the double arrow $\hbar\omega$ which defines the E_{min} level gets "stuck" at the upper edge of the double layer of metal I and E_{min} no longer takes part in the downward movement. The current I is no longer dependent upon U_G (saturation).

current flow is supplied either by heating or by illumination of solid I. The polarity of the battery in the diagram is such that it provides a retarding potential so that the current can be partially or completely cut off.[1]

As a first case we consider the *photoelectric* emission of electrons. In Fig. X.8.3 it is assumed that both solids I and II are metals. As a simplification it is also assumed that both metals are at temperature $T = 0$.

We now consider an electron on the lattice energy level E. Let a photon transfer its total energy[2] $\hbar\omega$ to this electron. If the electron obtains a velocity component in the direction of the surface, it can leave the metal I, provided that $\hbar\omega$ is large enough, i.e., $\hbar\omega > \Psi_I + (E_F - E)$. In this process it will first lose the energy $E_F - E$ up to the Fermi level and then the work function Ψ_I so that in vacuum, right in front of the surface I, it has the kinetic energy

$$E_{kin} = \hbar\omega - \Psi_I - (E_F - E) \qquad (X.8.04)$$

The electron has to overcome the electrostatic potential difference $(1/e)(\Psi_{II} - \Psi_I) + U_G$ with this kinetic energy, to reach the metal II and thus to contribute to the current J from I and II.

This requires at least[3]

$$E_{kin} = \hbar\omega - \Psi_I - (E_F - E) \geq \Psi_{II} - \Psi_I + eU_G \qquad (X.8.05)$$

Hence only the electrons in the levels above

$$E_{min} = E_F - [\hbar\omega - \Psi_{II} - eU_G] \qquad (X.8.06)$$

contribute to the current J from I to II.

If the retarding potential U_G is too large, the term in parenthesis in Eq. (X.8.06) becomes negative and E_{min} is above the Fermi level E_F. However, at $T = 0$ the levels above E_F are not occupied by electrons so that the energy $\hbar\omega$ of the photons is not large enough to raise a single electron from I to II and the current J is zero (see Fig. X.8.3). The limit $U_G^{(0)}$, where an electron transition from I to II is just possible in the most favorable case, is reached when the term in parenthesis in (X.8.06) becomes zero:

$$U_G^{(0)} = \frac{1}{e}(\hbar\omega - \Psi_{II}) \qquad (X.8.07)$$

---

[1] In the actual performance of such measurements, cylindrical or spherically symmetrical arrangements are preferable because of the reduced edge distortions.

[2] ω = angular frequency = $2\pi f$; $\hbar = \frac{1}{2\pi} h = 1.054 \cdot 10^{-27}$ cm^2 g sec^{-1}.

[3] A part of E_{kin} is likely to be associated with lateral velocity components which are of no use in overcoming the electrostatic potential difference.

It is surprising that this limit depends only on the work function Ψ_{II} of the anode, while the work function Ψ_I of the cathode from which the electrons are released has dropped out. With decreasing retarding potential $U_G < U_G^{(0)}$, more and more lattice energy levels $E < E_F$ can contribute to the current J and therefore J increases (see Fig. X.8.4).

However, this increase is not unlimited. When the retarding potential U_G has become so small that no rise of the electrostatic potential has to be overcome in the vacuum (see Fig. X.8.3, bottom), then condition (X.8.05) has to be replaced by the condition

$$E_{\mathrm{kin}} = \hbar\omega - \Psi_I - (E_F - E) \geqq 0 \qquad (\text{X.8.08})$$

According to (X.8.08) the levels from

$$E = E_F - (\hbar\omega - \Psi_I) \qquad \text{to} \qquad E = E_F \qquad (\text{X.8.09})$$

now contribute to the current J, independent of the magnitude of the

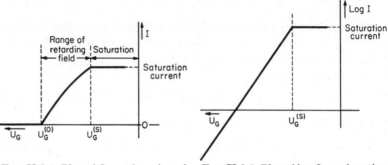

FIG. X.8.4. Plot of I as a function of U_G in photoelectric emission (diagrammatic).

FIG. X.8.5. Plot of log I as a function of U_G in thermionic emission (diagrammatic).

retarding potential U_G. Thus the current J is saturated at a retarding potential U_G for which we obtain from (X.8.08) and (X.8.05)

$$U_G^{(s)} = \frac{1}{e}(\Psi_I - \Psi_{II}) \qquad (\text{X.8.10})$$

(see Fig. X.8.4). Therefore, plotting a current-voltage characteristic, with an arrangement according to Fig. X.8.3, provides information concerning the work function Ψ_{II} of the anode through measurement of the limiting voltage $U_G^{(0)}$ according to (X.8.07) and concerning the Volta potential difference $(1/e)(\Psi_I - \Psi_{II})$ between cathode I and anode II through measurement of the saturation voltage $U_G^{(s)}$ according to (X.8.10). Hence $U_G^{(s)}$ and $U_G^{(0)}$, between them, also provide information concerning the work function Ψ_I of the cathode.

Nothing is changed in the foregoing considerations if the anode II is not a metal but a semiconductor. But the situation is quite different when a metal is replaced by a semiconductor in the cathode I. As is emphasized in Fig. X.5.2, we now have to bear in mind that the Fermi level E_F of a semiconductor is not occupied by electrons. Further, the situation for $T = 0°K$ differs now in some respects *basically* from that for $T > 0°K$. We have to refer the interested reader to specialized papers,[1] also with regard to the conclusions that can be drawn from the shape of the current rise between $U_G^{(0)}$ and $U_G^{(s)}$ in Fig. X.8.4 concerning the distribution $N(E)\,dE$ of the electron levels E below the Fermi level E_F.

We can now deal more briefly with the *thermionic* emission current J from I to II. Here we need modify only the computation of the emission current density of §4 in so far as we have to integrate over the x component v_x of the velocity, not from 0 to ∞, but from the value[2] $\sqrt{(2/m)(\Psi_{II} - \Psi_{I} + eU_G)}$, required to overcome the electrostatic potential difference $(1/e)(\Psi_{II} - \Psi_I) + U_G$, to ∞. Thus we obtain an expression for the retarding-field current

$$i = AT^2\,e^{-\frac{1}{kT}(eU_G + \Psi_{II})} \tag{X.8.11}$$

Of course, the retarding-field current cannot exceed the saturation value (X.4.05), and so we obtain again the Volta potential difference

$$U_G^{(s)} = \frac{1}{e}\,(\Psi_I - \Psi_{II}) \tag{X.8.12}$$

as saturation value of the retarding potential U_G (see Fig. X.8.5).

Thus, for thermionic emission of the current J from I to II, the work function Ψ_{II} of the anode can be determined[3] by measuring the retarding-field current and the variation of i/AT^2 with temperature at a constant retarding voltage U_G, while the transition into the saturation range indicates the Volta potential difference.

Condition (X.8.10) and (X.8.12) for the onset of saturation mean that the plot of the electrostatic potential in vacuum is horizontal (see Fig. X.8.6). However, this disappearance of the vacuum field between the two surfaces I and II also necessitates the disappearance of charges

---

[1] L. Apker, E. Taft, and J. Dickey, *Phys. Rev.*, **73**: 46 (1948); **74**: 1462 (1948); **76**: 270 (1949). E. Taft and L. Apker, *Phys. Rev.*, **75**: 344 (1949). See also J. A. Becker, *Elec. Eng.*, **68**: 937 (1949).

[2] This is the immediate result of (X.8.05) with $E_{kin} = (m/2)v_x^2$.

[3] See, for instance, S. Sano, *Elec. J. Tokyo*, **5**: 75 (1941); and H. Benda, *Frequenz*, **7**: 226–232 (1953).

on the two surfaces. The condition "surface charge zero" can be tested experimentally, for example, by moving the two surfaces relative to each other. If the surfaces are not charged, no current can flow through a wire connecting the two solids I and II. These considerations indicate another method[1] for measuring the Volta potential difference. One varies the voltage U_G between the two surfaces until no current flows through a connecting wire when the surfaces are moved relative to each other (see Fig. X.8.7).

This method has also been used by W. E. Meyerhof[2] when he tried to measure the Volta potential difference between strongly n-type and strongly p-type silicon. We mention this particular example because it shows again clearly that two solids can, from the viewpoint of semiconductor physics, be entirely different materials although they differ only by impurities in the order of 10^{-3} and are therefore both

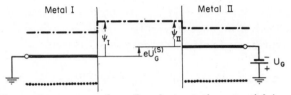

Fig. X.8.6. Saturation occurs when the electrostatic potential in vacuum is a straight horizontal line

$$U_G^{(s)} = \frac{1}{e}(\psi_I - \psi_{II})$$

"silicon" in ordinary chemical language. In strongly n-type silicon, the Fermi level is close to the lower edge E_C of the conduction band; in strongly p-type silicon, on the other hand, close to the upper edge E_V of the valence band. Hence, according to Fig. X.8.8, a Volta potential difference of almost 1.2 volts must be generated between the two surfaces, corresponding to the width of the forbidden zone in silicon. It must be mentioned that in Fig. X.8.8 the surface double layers on the n-type and on the p-type silicon are assumed to produce jumps of the same magnitude. This is an improbable assumption in the presence of accidental impurities in the surface layers, and hence it is not surprising that the expected potential difference of 1.2 volts has not been measured without special precautions in the cleaning process. The cleaning methods that were used led Meyerhof to a value of only 0.3 volt and W. H. Brattain and W. Shockley[3] to a value of only 0.6 volt.

[1] This is the original method of A. Volta, *Ann. chim. et phys.*, **40**: 225 (1801).
[2] W. E. Meyerhof, *Phys. Rev.*, **71**: 727 (1947).
[3] W. H. Brattain and W. Shockley, *Phys. Rev.*, **72**: 345 (1947).

potential difference $= \frac{1}{e}(\psi_{II} - \psi_I) + U_G$ independent of distance a.

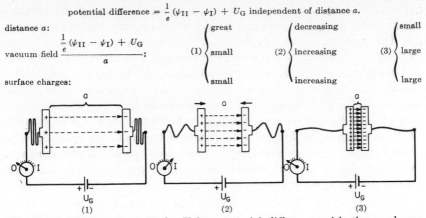

FIG. X.8.7. Measurement of the Volta potential difference with the condenser method. With suitable choice of U_G, namely $U_G = \frac{1}{e}(\psi_I - \psi_{II}) =$ Volta potential difference$_{I\ II}$, the vacuum field vanishes (see Fig. X.8.6). In this case the surface charges vanish too for all values of the distance a. Hence on displacing the plates no current will flow in the connecting wire.

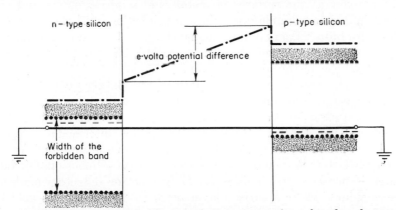

FIG. X.8.8. Volta potential difference between strongly n-doped and strongly p-doped silicon. In this case the Volta potential difference is almost equal to the width of the forbidden band, at least as long as one can assume the *same* double layer on both the n-type and the p-type silicon.

b. Surface States

These experiments and other facts led J. Bardeen[1] to discuss the presence and the effect of so-called surface states in semiconductors. In the undisturbed periodic field within the crystal, the energy values between the conduction and the valence band cannot be occupied

[1] J. Bardeen, *Phys. Rev.*, **71**: 717 (1947).

under stationary conditions.   However, at the surface of the crystal, the periodic potential is radically disturbed because the continuation into the vacuum is not periodic.   I. Tamm[1] and a number of other workers after him have discussed the problem as to whether these disturbances create additional energy states in the forbidden zone.   We also have to reckon with impurity atoms and lattice vacancies at the semiconductor surface which can produce additional localized energy levels in the forbidden zone similar to their effect within the crystal. Without committing himself to any one of these causes for additional energy states, Bardeen assumes that at a semiconductor surface there can exist surface states whose number can be comparable with the number of the surface atoms.

According to the degree to which these surface levels are occupied, the surface is assumed to have a greater or smaller negative charge which, in turn, generates a positive space-charge layer in the semiconductor.   In this way boundary layers are produced, even in free surfaces of semiconductors without a contact, and the whole represents something halfway between the previously mentioned two-dimensional double layers at the surfaces of metals and semiconductors and the three-dimensional double layers in a p-n junction.   In the case considered by Bardeen, a two-dimensional charge is located on the surface while the charge of opposite sign is spatially distributed through a boundary layer of the semiconductor.

With such "spontaneous" boundary layers, Bardeen explained the independence of the contact potential observed for most commercial rectifiers, this independence being incompatible with the Schottky boundary-layer theory.   However, the actual intermediate layers which are produced by chemical reaction are several hundred atomic layers thick so that even here the concept of a two-dimensional surface charge is not correct.   This is certainly true for detectors made of n germanium, where a surface layer of 20 to 30 μ thickness may be converted into p germanium by forming.

All the same, in the discussion of boundary-layer problems in solid-state physics one has always to bear in mind the possibility, emphasized by Bardeen, that the surface charges up and induces next to it a three-dimensional space-charge boundary layer of opposite polarity.[2]

[1] I. Tamm, *Physik. Z. Sowjetunion*, **1**: 733 (1932).   R. H. Fowler, *Proc. Roy. Soc. (London)*, **A141**: 56 (1933).   S. Rijanow, *Z. Physik*, **89**: 806 (1934).   A. W. Maue, *Z. Physik*, **94**: 717 (1935).   E. T. Goodwin, *Proc. Cambridge Phil. Soc.*, **35**: 205, 221, 232 (1939).   W. G. Pollard, *Phys. Rev.*, **56**: 324 (1939).   W. Shockley, *Phys. Rev.*, **56**: 317 (1939).   H. Statz, *Z. Naturforsch*,. **5A**: 534 (1950).   K. Artmann, *Z. Physik*, **131**: 244 (1952).

[2] See W. H. Brattain and J. Bardeen, *Bell System Tech. J.*, **32**: 1 (1953).

§9. The Electrochemical Potentials $E_F^{(n)}$ and $E_F^{(p)}$ of Electrons and Holes

In §6 and §7 we have shown how in the boundary layer of a semi-conductor-metal contact the whole band diagram of the semiconductor is deformed by the action of the metal while the Fermi level, alone, remains horizontal throughout the boundary layer. However, this applies only in thermal equilibrium, i.e., in the case of zero current. Yet, in Chap. VIII, §3, we have shown that the Fermi level, being identical with the electrochemical potential, retains its significance even in nonequilibrium cases. We now show in Fig. X.9.1 the no longer horizontal Fermi level in a boundary layer, both in the forward and in the blocking direction. The representation is based on the same assumptions as in Fig. IV.5.1. From the plot of the concentration $n(x)$ in this figure, we obtain the plot of $E_F^{(n)}(x)$ with the aid of the defining equation[1]

$$E_F^{(n)} = -eV(x) + E_C + \varsigma\left(\frac{n(x)}{N_C}\right) \approx -eV(x) + E_C + kT \ln \frac{n(x)}{N_C}$$
$$(X.9.01)$$

Comparison of Figs. IV.5.1 and X.9.1 shows that in the so called Boltzmann zone the Fermi level is almost horizontal. This must be so because in the Boltzmann zone we approach compensation of diffusion current and field current, i.e., we approach thermal equilibrium. The slope of the Fermi level is related to the total current by Eq. (VIII.3.05) so that we obtain for the current density of the particles, owing to the negative charge of the electrons,

$$\left(\frac{1}{-e} i_{tot}\right) = s_n = -\mu_n n \frac{d}{dx}\left(\frac{1}{e} E_F^{(n)}\right) \qquad (X.9.02)$$

In other words, the electrons roll down the slope of their Fermi level $E_F^{(n)}$, in agreement with their tendency in the energy-band diagrams to fall downward of their own accord and to be raised upward only by thermal excitation, by an incident photon, or by a similar external interference.

---

[1] For the derivation of this defining equation, see pp. 359 ff. We shall soon introduce an electrochemical potential of holes, and therefore we now call the electrochemical potential of the negative electrons $E_F^{(n)}$. For the evaluation of (X.9.01) we need, in addition to the concentration $n(x)$, also the plot of the potential $V(x)$. See E. Spenke, *Z. Physik*, **126**: 67 (1949).

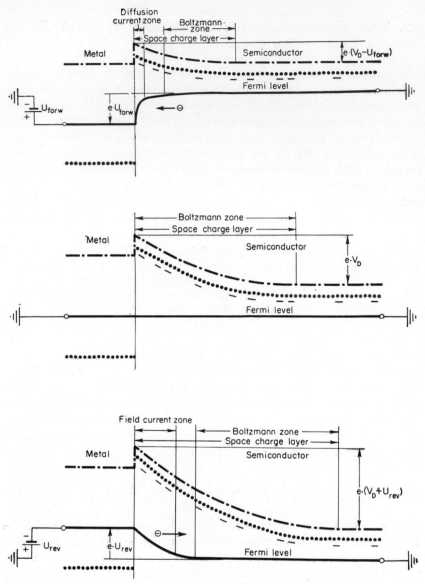

FIG. X.9.1. Plot of the Fermi level in the depletion boundary layer of an n-type semiconductor.   Top: case of current flow, direction of current: $\leftarrow \ominus$.   Middle: case of no current flow.   Bottom: case of blocking, direction of current: $\ominus \rightarrow$.

Exactly the opposite applies to the holes. Let us consider, for example, the recombination of a hole $\oplus$ with a negative acceptor A^-, which is accompanied by a loss of energy[1] and therefore takes place spontaneously. If we, further, remember that this is represented in the energy-band diagram by the rise of a hole from the valence band into an acceptor level above it, we can see that the holes, like air bubbles in water, have an urge to rise upward in the energy-band diagram and that only external effects, such as thermal or optical excitation, can push them down. If we now wish to define the electrochemical potential or the Fermi level $E_F^{(p)}$ of holes, we have to expect that the holes climb up the slope of this Fermi level and that, accordingly, the current density of the particles is given by the equation

$$s_p = +\mu_p p \frac{d}{dx}\left(\frac{1}{e} E_F^{(p)}\right) \tag{X.9.03}$$

If this is, in fact, to be correct, we have to define

$$E_F^{(p)} = E_V - eV(x) - \zeta\left(\frac{p(x)}{N_V}\right) \approx E_V - eV(x) - kT \ln \frac{p(x)}{N_V} \tag{X.9.04}$$

because then we obtain

$$\frac{dE_F^{(p)}}{dx} = + e(-V'(x)) - \frac{d\zeta(p)}{dp} p'(x) \approx + e(-V'(x)) - kT \frac{1}{p} p'(x)$$

or

$$+\mu_p \cdot p \cdot \frac{d}{dx}\left(\frac{1}{e} E_F^{(p)}\right) = +\mu_p p E(x) + \frac{\mu_p}{e} \frac{d\zeta(p)}{d \ln p}(- p'(x))$$

$$\approx \mu_p p E(x) + \mu_p \frac{kT}{e}\cdot(-p'(x))$$

and with the aid of the Nernst-Townsend-Einstein relation (VIII.3.10) and its generalization (VIII.3.08) we obtain in fact

$$+\mu_p p \frac{d}{dx}\left(\frac{1}{e} E_F^{(p)}\right) = s_{\text{field}} + s_{\text{diff}} = s_p$$

The signs have been chosen accordingly in the diagrams of **Fig. X.9.2**, in which the depletion boundary layer of an n-type semiconductor for the cases of forward, back, and zero current is shown. We need not go into further details, but we want to mention that the choice of signs for the definition of the Fermi level $E_F^{(p)}$ of holes has the additional advantage that in thermal equilibrium we obtain

$$E_F^{(p)} \equiv E_F^{(n)} \equiv E_F \tag{X.9.05}$$

[1] In this process the hole loses energy while the lattice (for example) gains energy.

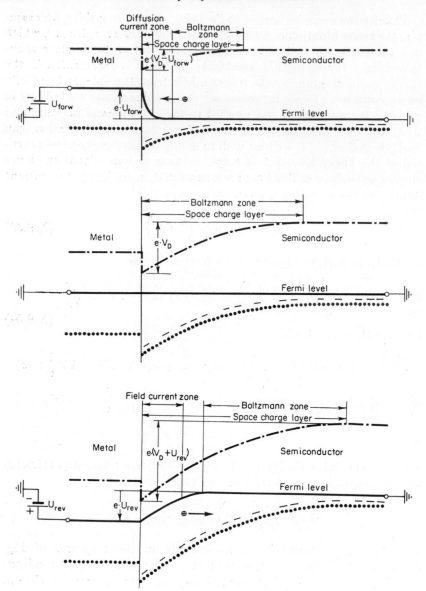

Fig. X.9.2. Plot of the Fermi level in the depletion boundary layer of a p-type semiconductor. Top: case of current flow, direction of current: $\leftarrow \oplus$. Middle: case of no current flow. Bottom: case of blocking, direction of current: $\oplus \rightarrow$.

For thermal equilibrium, we can use in the defining equation (X.9.04) the generalized law of mass action (VIII.4.18), and we can write

$$E_F^{(p)} = E_V - eV(x) - \zeta\left(\frac{p}{N_V}\right) = E_V - eV(x) - \left(E_V - E_C - \zeta\left(\frac{n}{N_C}\right)\right)$$

Hence
$$E_F^{(p)} = E_C - eV(x) + \zeta\left(\frac{n}{N_C}\right)$$

and with (X.9.01)
$$E_F^{(p)} = E_F^{(n)}$$

Thus by the chosen definition we have achieved that in thermal equilibrium the electrochemical potentials $E_F^{(n)}$ and $E_F^{(p)}$ of electrons and holes coincide in the common horizontal Fermi level E_F. If current flows, i.e., in nonequilibrium, the two Fermi levels $E_F^{(n)}$ and $E_F^{(p)}$ separate. They also are no longer horizontal; instead their slopes represent the forces acting on the two current densities of particles s_n and s_p, which can also be computed from (X.9.02) and (X.9.03). This means that the electrons "voluntarily" fall down along their Fermi level $E_F^{(n)}$ while the holes "voluntarily" climb up their Fermi level $E_F^{(p)}$.

Using these principles, we now draw in Fig. X.9.3 band diagrams of a p-n junction for forward current, reverse current, and thermal equilibrium. We use as a basis the special case of low recombination according to Shockley. Then we have still approximately Boltzmann equilibrium (see page 100) in the junction zone, and therefore the Fermi levels in this zone have to be drawn approximately horizontal. From this we obtain for the separation of $E_F^{(n)}$ and $E_F^{(p)}$ in the junction zone the values eU_{forw} and eU_{rev}. Hence we get for the concentrations at the beginning of the diffusion tails the values

$$n_p\, e^{+\frac{e}{kT}U_{\text{forw}}} \text{ (or } n_p\, e^{-\frac{e}{kT}U_{\text{rev}}}) \quad \text{and} \quad p_n\, e^{+\frac{e}{kT}U_{\text{forw}}} \text{ (or } p_n\, e^{-\frac{e}{kT}U_{\text{rev}}})$$

This is so because the distance of the Fermi level $E_F^{(n)}$ from the lower edge $-eV + E_C$ of the conduction band, i.e., the term $(-eV + E_C) - E_F^{(n)}$, is, according to Eq. (X.9.01), a logarithmic measure of the electron concentration n in the Maxwell-Boltzmann case. Corresponding considerations apply to the hole concentration according to Eq. (X.9.04).

On page 100, these results were explained by the identity of the logarithmically plotted concentration curve with the potential curve $V(x)$ in the case of exact or approximate Boltzmann equilibrium.

Finally, we have to mention that the case

$$E_F^{(n)} > E_F^{(p)}$$

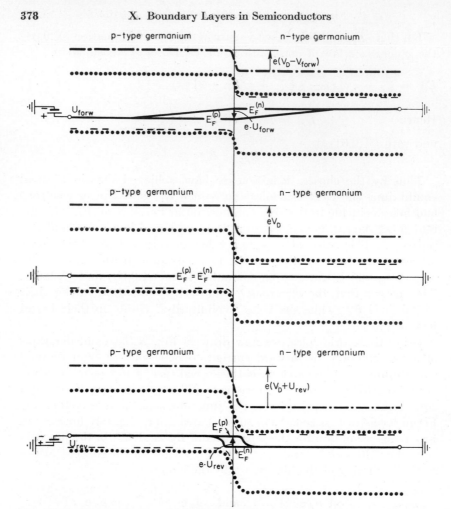

FIG. X.9.3. Plot of the Fermi levels $E_F{}^{(n)}$ and $E_F{}^{(p)}$ in a p-n junction. Top: case of current flow: $\oplus \rightarrow \leftarrow \ominus$. Middle: case of no current flow. Bottom: case of blocking, direction of current: $\leftarrow \oplus \ominus \rightarrow$.

leads, according to the defining equations (X.9.01) and (X.9.04), to

$$E_C - E_V > kT \ln \frac{N_C N_V}{np}$$

and with the aid of (VIII.4.23) to

$$np > n_i^2$$

and thus, according to page 26, signifies that recombination outweighs dissociation. According to Fig. X.9.3, top, the junction zone of a

p-n junction is such a region if it is polarized in the forward direction (see page 94).

Correspondingly, $E_F^{(n)} < E_F^{(p)}$ signifies a region where dissociation predominates. An example, according to Fig. X.9.3, bottom, is the junction zone of a p-n junction which is polarized in the reverse direction.

§10. Problems

1. A parallel-plate condenser of 1 cm^2 area has two plates made of different metals. The condenser plates are connected by a wire. Calculate the current in the wire if the two metals have a work function difference of 1 volt, and if the two plates are vibrating against each other at a frequency of 100 cycles/sec such that their separation varies between d_1 and d_2. Assume $d_1 = 0.01$ cm, and calculate the current as a function of d_2. For what value of d_2 does the current attain one-half of its maximum possible value? *Note:* The current will, in general, not be sinusoidal. Use the average of the absolute value $\overline{|i|}$ as a measure.

2. The two plates in a vibrating condenser such as that of Prob. 1 are connected through a battery with a fixed voltage of 1.5 volts. The current is found to be 1.2 ma. If the battery is reversed, a current of 0.7 ma and of opposite phase is obtained. What is the work function difference of the two metals?

3. According to Richardson's law the plot of log (i_S/T^2) versus $1/T$ should be a straight line. The slope of the straight line is determined by the work function while the intercept with the ordinate axis should be the same for all materials.

a. Show that the plot is still a straight line if the work function varies linearly with temperature. What are now the values of the slope of the line and of the intercept?

b. A plot of log (i_S/T^2) vs. $1/T$ for a certain metal is a straight line with a slope corresponding to 6.50 ev while the intercept is 6,500 amp/cm^2/°C^2 rather than 120 amp/cm^2/°C^2. What is the actual work function at 800°C if Richardson's law is assumed to be correct?

4. An electron which is held a short distance from a metal surface induces positive charge on this surface which, in turn, attracts the electron (the so-called "image force"). Calculate the image force and the potential energy of the electron if the potential energy at infinite distance is normalized to zero. At what distance from the metal surface is the image force equal to the force exerted by an electric field of 10^4 volt-cm^{-1} on the electron?

5. * Calculate the total potential energy of an electron under the influence of both the image force and an electric field of a polarity such as to pull electrons out of the metal. As a reference potential energy, choose the potential energy right at the metal surface in the absence of an image force. How much is the work function lowered by an electric field of $5 \cdot 10^4$ volt cm^{-1}?

6. How are the results of Prob. 5 modified if the electron is not in vacuum but in a semi-conductor with a dielectric constant $\varepsilon = 16$?

APPENDIX I

The Integral $\displaystyle\int\limits_{x=-\frac{G}{2}a}^{x=+\frac{G}{2}a} U(x)\, e^{jkx}\, dx$

In the integral over the fundamental domain

$$I_k = \int\limits_{x=-\frac{G}{2}a}^{x=+\frac{G}{2}a} U(x)\, e^{jkx}\, dx \tag{A.I.1}$$

let $U(x)$ be a lattice-periodic function

$$U(x - na) \equiv U(x) \tag{A.I.2}$$

Let the wave number k have the following values, compatible with the requirement of periodicity in the fundamental domain [see Eq. (VII.2.05)]:

$$k = \frac{2\pi}{a} \cdot \frac{n}{G} \qquad n = 0,\ \pm 1,\ \pm 2,\ \ldots,\ \pm\frac{G}{2} \tag{A.I.3}$$

We then maintain that

$$I_k = 0 \qquad \text{except for } k = 0 \tag{A.I.4}$$

To prove this we carry out the integration, step by step, for one lattice cell at a time:

$$I_k = \sum_{n=-\frac{G}{2}}^{n=+\frac{G}{2}-1} \int\limits_{x=na}^{x=(n+1)a} U(x)\, e^{jkx}\, dx \tag{A.I.5}$$

Now we split off in the integrand the phase rotation e^{jkna} which is already present at the beginning of the nth cell and leave under the integral sign only the advance of the phase rotation within the cell $e^{jk(x-na)}$. With the use of (A.I.2) we obtain

$$I_k = \sum_{n=-\frac{G}{2}}^{n=+\frac{G}{2}-1} e^{jkna} \int\limits_{x-na=0}^{x-na=a} U(x - na)\, e^{jk(x-na)}\, dx \tag{A.I.6}$$

381

Introducing the integration variable $x - na = \xi$, we see that the integral is now independent of the summation index and can therefore be placed in front of the sum sign:

$$I_k = \int\limits_{\xi=0}^{\xi=a} U(\xi)\, e^{jk\xi}\, d\xi \cdot \sum_{n=-\frac{G}{2}}^{n=+\frac{G}{2}-1} e^{jkna}$$

$$= \int\limits_{\xi=0}^{\xi=a} U(\xi)\, e^{jk\xi}\, d\xi \cdot e^{-jka\frac{G}{2}} \cdot \sum_{n+\frac{G}{2}=0}^{n+\frac{G}{2}=G-1} e^{jka\left(n+\frac{G}{2}\right)} \tag{A.I.7}$$

The sum is now a simple geometric progression

$$1 + q + q^2 \cdots + q^l = \frac{(1 - q^{l+1})}{(1 - q)}$$

and by carrying out the summation with $q = e^{jkna}$ and $l = G - 1$, i.e., $l + 1 = G$, we obtain for the wanted integral

$$I_k = \int\limits_{\xi=0}^{\xi=a} U(\xi)\, e^{jk\xi}\, d\xi \cdot e^{-jka\frac{G}{2}} \cdot \frac{1 - e^{jka \cdot G}}{1 - e^{jka}} \tag{A.I.8}$$

According to (A.I.3) we have $ka \cdot G = 2\pi n$. Therefore, the last numerator in (A.I.8) becomes $1 - 1 = 0$ and the inegral I_k vanishes, as was stated. The argument fails only when $k = 0$ because then each term of the geometric progression in (A.I.7) will be one to begin with and the summation formula $(1 - q^{l+1})/(1 - q)$ will be unusable because numerator and denominator vanish simultaneously. The result of the summation will then simply be G, and the integral will be

$$I_0 = G \cdot \int\limits_{\xi=0}^{\xi=a} U(\xi)\, d\xi \tag{A.I.9}$$

while we have $\qquad I_k = 0 \qquad$ for $k \neq 0$ $\qquad$ (A.I.10)

Thus the preceding statement is proved in its entirety.

In conclusion, we mention that integrals of the type under consideration occur in the computation of coefficients of a Fourier expansion with the fundamental domain $G \cdot a$ as period. In this context, the proof just given means that in such a Fourier expansion the G Fourier coefficients

$$C_{-\frac{G}{2}}; C_{-\frac{G}{2}+1}; \cdots C_{-1} \qquad C_{+1}; \cdots C_{+\frac{G}{2}-1}; C_{+\frac{G}{2}}$$

vanish if the represented function has, in reality, not the period $G \cdot a$, but the much smaller period a. This is so because in the Fourier expansion of such a function the period a is the greatest wavelength which occurs. However, the coefficients just mentioned are associated with the wavelengths $2\pi/|k|$, i.e., according to Eq. (A.I.3)

$$\frac{G \cdot a}{\dfrac{G}{2}}; \frac{G \cdot a}{\dfrac{G}{2} - 1}; \cdots \frac{G \cdot a}{1} \qquad \frac{G \cdot a}{1}; \cdots \frac{G \cdot a}{\dfrac{G}{2} - 1}; \frac{G \cdot a}{\dfrac{G}{2}}$$

or $\qquad 2a; \dfrac{1}{1 - \dfrac{2}{G}} 2a; \cdots G \cdot a \qquad G \cdot a; \cdots \dfrac{1}{1 - \dfrac{2}{G}} 2a; \qquad 2a$

which are all greater than a.

APPENDIX II

The Function $\zeta(n/N)$

We define a function $\zeta(n/N)$ by the equation

$$\frac{2}{\sqrt{\pi}} \int_{\eta=0}^{\eta=\infty} \frac{1}{e^{\eta - \frac{\zeta}{kT}} + 1} \sqrt{\eta}\, d\eta = \frac{n}{N} \qquad (A.II.1)$$

We want to find out how the quantity ζ depends on n/N.

Since the definition (A.II.1) is solved for the independent variable n/N, we determine, first, the inverse function n/N as a function of ζ. Here we shall discuss in detail only the two limiting cases "ζ strongly negative" and "ζ strongly positive."

1. $\zeta \to -\infty$. In this case the exponential term in the denominator of the integrand is very large compared with 1. Hence we can write as a first approximation

$$\frac{2}{\sqrt{\pi}} \int_{\eta=0}^{\eta=\infty} e^{-\eta + \frac{\zeta}{kT}} \sqrt{\eta}\, d\eta \approx \frac{n}{N}$$

$$e^{+\frac{\zeta}{kT}} \cdot \frac{2}{\sqrt{\pi}} \int_{\eta=0}^{\eta=\infty} e^{-\eta} \sqrt{\eta}\, d\eta = e^{\frac{\zeta}{kT}} \cdot 1 \approx \frac{n}{N}$$

Since we have assumed the term ζ to be strongly negative to obtain this approximation, we have

$$\frac{n}{N} \ll 1 \qquad \text{or} \qquad n \ll N$$

Solving the approximation $e^{\frac{\zeta}{kT}} \approx n/N$ derived for ζ, we obtain the wanted function $\zeta(n/N)$ for the limiting case $n \ll N$:

$$\zeta \approx kT \ln \frac{n}{N} \qquad (A.II.2)$$

2. $\zeta \to +\infty$. In this case the exponential term in the denominator of the integrand is very small compared with 1 as long as $\eta < \zeta/kT$.

384

As soon as $\eta > \zeta/kT$, the exponential term very soon outweighs the term 1 and greatly reduces the value of the integrand. We, therefore, obtain an approximation if in the integration range $0 < \eta < \zeta/kT$ we write 1 for the denominator and in the integration range $\zeta/kT <$

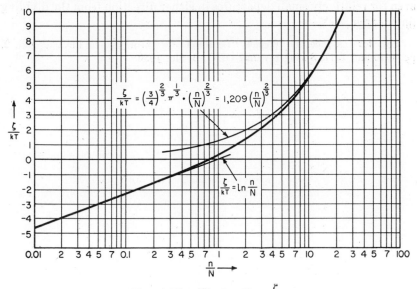

$$\frac{\zeta}{kT} = \left(\frac{3}{4}\right)^{\frac{2}{3}} \pi^{\frac{1}{3}} \cdot \left(\frac{n}{N}\right)^{\frac{2}{3}} = 1{,}209 \left(\frac{n}{N}\right)^{\frac{2}{3}}$$

$$\frac{\zeta}{kT} = \operatorname{Ln} \frac{n}{N}$$

FIG. A.II.1. The function $\dfrac{\zeta}{kT}$.

$\eta < \infty$ the value ∞. Thus we obtain the approximation

$$\frac{2}{\sqrt{\pi}} \int_{\eta=0}^{\eta=\frac{\zeta}{kT}} \sqrt{\eta}\, d\eta \approx \frac{n}{N}$$

$$\frac{2}{\sqrt{\pi}} \cdot \frac{2}{3} \cdot \left(\frac{\zeta}{kT}\right)^{3/2} \approx \frac{n}{N}$$

To obtain this approximation we assumed the term ζ to be strongly positive. Hence we now have

$$\frac{n}{N} \gg 1 \qquad \text{or} \qquad n \gg N$$

If we solve $\dfrac{2}{\sqrt{\pi}} \cdot \dfrac{2}{3} \left(\dfrac{\zeta}{kT}\right)^{3/2} \approx \dfrac{n}{N}$ for ζ, we obtain the wanted function $\zeta(n/N)$ for the limiting case $n \gg N$:

$$\zeta \approx kT \left(\frac{3}{4}\right)^{2/3} \pi^{1/3} \left(\frac{n}{N}\right)^{2/3} \tag{A.II.3}$$

More accurate evaluations of the integral (A.II.1) which go beyond these two limiting cases use expansions of power series.[1] Figure A.II.1 shows ζ/kT as a function of n/N. We can see that the asymptotic variations (A.II.2) and (A.II.3) are valid with great accuracy even for relatively small departures in either direction from the dividing line near $n = N$.

---

[1] See, for instance, W. Weizel, "Lehrbuch der theoretischen Physik," vol. 2, pp. 1416 and 1417, Springer-Verlag OHG, Berlin, 1950.

APPENDIX III

The Occupation Probabilities
f_{don} and f_{acc} of Donors and Acceptors[1]

Let a group of stationary states be characterized by the distribution $D(E)\, dE$ of their energy values E along an energy scale. We now want to know how N electrons are distributed among these states in thermal equilibrium. Using the occupation probability

$$f(E) = \frac{1}{e^{\frac{E - E_F}{kT}} + 1} \tag{A.III.01}$$

Fermi statistics answers this question as follows: The number of electrons with energies between E and $E + dE$ is

$$N(E)\, dE = 2D(E) \cdot f(E) \cdot dE \tag{A.III.02}$$

If now the problem has to be solved how N electrons have to be distributed among the states of the conduction band and among N_D donors, the following seems to be the simple answer: The number

$$N - N_{D^\times} = \int_{E=Ec}^{\infty} 2D(E)f(E)\, dE = 2 \int_{E=Ec}^{\infty} \frac{D(E)}{e^{\frac{E - E_F}{kT}} + 1}\, dE \tag{A.III.03}$$

goes into the conduction band and the number

$$N_{D^\times} = N_D \cdot f(E_D) = N_D \frac{1}{e^{\frac{E_D - E_F}{kT}} + 1} \tag{A.III.04}$$

goes into the N_D donor levels $E = E_D$.

---

[1] See on this subject, N. F. Mott and R. W. Gurney, "Electronic Processes in Ionic Crystals," pp. 157ff., Clarendon Press, Oxford, 1948. W. Shockley, "Electrons and Holes in Semiconductors," p. 248, prob. 1, and p. 475, prob. 2, D. Van Nostrand Company, Inc., Princeton, N.J., 1950. P. T. Landsberg, *Proc. Phys. Soc. (London)*, **65A**: 604 (1952). E. A. Guggenheim, *Proc. Phys. Soc. (London)*, **66A**: 121 (1953). P. T. Landsberg, *Proc. Phys. Soc. (London)*, **66A**: 662 (1953). J. H. Crawford and D. K. Holmes, *Proc. Phys. Soc. (London)*, **67A**: 294 (1954).

   In this solution the N_D donors are considered as N_D available places, but this involves an incorrect assumption. An electron can be attached with *two* different spin directions to an empty donor, in the same way as it can be attached to a hydrogen nucleus. At first sight one might think that the mistake could be eliminated by replacing N_D with $2N_D$. But this procedure ignores the fact that when an electron has been attached to a positive donor core the latter has become electrically neutral so that a second electron with opposite spin no longer encounters a potential trough and thus cannot be attached, for electrostatic reasons. In other words, *before* an electron has been attached the donor core offers *two* places to an electron, but *after* the electron has been attached it offers only *one* place, which is already occupied by the attached electron. This means that N_D donors offer neither N_D available places nor twice that number $2N_D$. Rather, the number of available places depends on the momentary degree of occupation, one might say it changes during the process of occupation. Thus it is apparent that the distribution of N electrons among the conduction band and the N_D donor levels is not the type of problem in which a *fixed* number of available places have to be filled with N electrons.[1] Hence, to solve this problem we have to reconsider the usual arguments, which in normal problems lead to the occupation probability

$$f(E) = \frac{1}{e^{\frac{E - E_F}{kT}} + 1} \qquad \text{(A.III.01)}$$

[1] The "normal" type of problem (occupation of N_P places P with the energy value E_P) still has the same solution

$$N_P \frac{1}{e^{\frac{E_P - E_F}{kT}} + 1}$$

If E_F lies several kT below E_P, this expression takes on the simpler form

$$N_P e^{+\frac{E_F - E_P}{kT}}$$

This remark is relevant for the footnote 1, p. 318.

   The occupation of the conduction band alone is covered by the *normal* type of problem, because the quantum states of the conduction band result from a one-electron problem with fixed potential which has been chosen in such a way that the electrostatic effects of the many electrons which have later to be accommodated in these quantum states have been taken into account (self-consistent potential). Therefore, on pages 285 and 299, the possibility of spin reversal in the states of the conduction band could be allowed for simply by a factor 2 in front of the number of these states.

However, we shall have to refer to the literature[1] for the wave-mechanical basis of the counting rules ("each place can be occupied by only 0 or 1 electron," "the electrons cannot be distinguished from each other").

We subdivide the energy scale into intervals 1, 2, . . . i which are grouped around the values $E_1, E_2, \ldots E_i$ and contain $Z_1, Z_2, \ldots Z_i$ available places. The occupation of the ith interval with N_i electrons can be realized in

$$\frac{Z_i!}{N_i!(Z_i - N_i)!} \tag{A.III.05}$$

different ways. This can be derived as follows: One numbers the Z_i available places of the considered ith interval from 1 to Z and arranges them in this sequence (see Fig. A.III.1, top). Then, starting from the

Places | 1 | 2 | 3 | 4 | 5 | 6 | 7 | 8 | 9 |10|11|12|13|14|15|16|17|18|19|20|21|22|23|24|25| $Z_i = 25$
⊖ ⊖ ⊖ ⊖ ⊖ ⊖ ⊖ ⊖ ⊖ ⊖ $N_i = 10$
                                  $Z_i - N_i = 15$
Places | 2 | 3 | 5 | 7 | 8 |11|13|14|17|24| 1 | 4 | 6 | 9 |10|12|15|16|18|19|20|21|22|23|25| $Z_i!$ permutations
⊖ ⊖ ⊖ ⊖ ⊖ ⊖ ⊖ ⊖ ⊖ ⊖   of all places
Places | 2 | 3 | 5 | 7 | 8 |11|13|14|24|17| 1 | 4 | 6 | 9 |10|12|15|16|18|19|20|21|22|23|25| $N_i!$ permutations
⋒ ⋒ ⋒ ⋒ ⋒ ⋒ ⋒ ⋒ ⋒ ⋒   of the occupied places
Places | 2 | 3 | 5 | 7 | 8 |11|13|14|24|17| 1 | 4 | 6 | 9 |10|12|15|16|18|19|20|21|22|25|23| $(Z_i - N_i)!$ permutations of the unoccupied places
⊖ ⊖ ⊖ ⊖ ⊖ ⊖ ⊖ ⊖ ⊖ ⊖

FIG. A.III.1. Different occupations of $Z_i = 25$ places of the ith energy interval with $N_i = 10$ electrons.

$$\frac{Z_i!}{N_i!(Z_i - N_i)!} \quad \text{different combinations are possible.}$$

left, one fills the N_i first places and leaves the remaining $(Z_i - N_i)$ places unoccupied. The occupation of the ith interval with N_i electrons can be realized in a different way if one arranges the Z_i available places in a different sequence, i.e., in a different permutation, and if one again fills the N_i places on the left while the $(Z_i - N_i)$ places to the right remain empty (see Fig. A.III.1, second line). This procedure can be repeated $Z_i!$ times, but it leads only to a novel possibility if during the permutation at least one unoccupied place is exchanged for a filled one. Permutation of the N_i filled places at the left among themselves (Fig. A.III.1: transition from second to third line) and

---

[1] See, for instance, L. Nordheim in Müller-Pouillet, "Lehrbuch der Physik," vol. IV, part 4, p. 251, Vieweg-Verlag, Brunswick, Germany, 1933; or R. C. Tolman, "The Principles of Statistical Mechanics," pp. 364ff., Oxford University Press, 1938; or W. Weizel, "Lehrbuch der theoretischen Physik," vol. II, pp. 1193 and 1044ff., Springer-Verlag OHG, Berlin, 1950.

permutation of the $(Z_i - N_i)$ unoccupied places at the right (Fig. A.III.1: transition from third to fourth line) do *not* lead to a novel possibility. Therefore the number of possibilities for the occupation of the ith interval with N_i electrons is not $Z!$, but only

$$\frac{Z_i!}{N_i!(Z_i - N_i)!} \qquad \text{(A.III.06)}$$

Occupation of the whole energy range with $N_1, N_2, \ldots N_i$ electrons can therefore be realized in

$$\prod_{i=1}^{\infty} \frac{Z_i!}{N_i!(Z_i - N_i)!} \qquad \text{(A.III.07)}$$

different ways.

We have repeated these well-known arguments, based on the usual Fermi statistics, in such detail because with the aid of the same arguments it can now be stated immediately that $N_{D^\times}$ electrons can be distributed among the N_D donor levels in

$$\frac{N_D!}{N_{D^\times}!(N_D - N_{D^\times})!} \qquad \text{(A.III.08)}$$

different ways, provided that the possibilities are narrowed down by allowing, for instance, only electrons with clockwise spin. In this case the problem is identical with the one just discussed in detail, namely, how N_i electrons can be distributed among the Z_i available places of the ith interval.

However, in the occupation of the donors it is by no means only the electrons with clockwise spin that are allowed. If the spin of only one donor electron, e.g., at the donor farthest to the left, is reversed

$$\frac{N_D!}{N_{D^\times}!(N_D - N_{D^\times})!}$$

new possibilities are created, corresponding to a factor $2 = 2^1$ in front of the number of possibilities. In the same way the spin reversal of all $N_{D^\times}$ accommodated electrons produces a factor 2 for each electron, hence a total factor of $2^{N_{D^\times}}$, so that finally

$$2^{N_{D^\times}} \frac{N_D!}{N_{D^\times}!(N_D - N_{D^\times})!} \qquad \text{(A.III.09)}$$

is the number of possibilities in which the $N_D^\times$ electrons can be accommodated in N_D donor levels.

With the aid of (A.III.09) and (A.III.07) we thus obtain for the distribution, characterized by $N_{D^\times}$, N_1, N_2, . . . N_i of

$$N_{D^\times} + \sum_{i=1}^{\infty} N_i = N \qquad \text{(A.III.10)}$$

electrons among N_D donor levels and the conduction band the following number of possibilities

$$W = 2^{N_{D^\times}} \frac{N_D!}{N_{D^\times}!(N_D - N_{D^\times})!} \prod_{i=1}^{\infty} \frac{Z_i!}{N_i!(Z_i - N_i)!} \qquad \text{(A.III.11)}$$

In equilibrium the distribution with the largest number of realizable possibilities will be established. The occupation numbers $N_{D^\times}$, N_1, N_2, . . . N_i have to be varied until W or

$$\ln W = \begin{cases} N_{D^\times} \ln 2 + \ln N_D! - \ln N_{D^\times}! - \ln (N_D - N_{D^\times})! \\ + \sum_{i=1}^{\infty} \{\ln Z_i! - \ln N_i! - \ln (Z_i - N_i)!\} \end{cases} \qquad \text{(A.III.12)}$$

is a maximum. But it must be remembered that, in addition to the side condition (A.III.10), another side condition must be fulfilled, namely, that the total energy

$$U = N_{D^\times} E_D + \sum_{i=1}^{\infty} N_i E_i \qquad \text{(A.III.13)}$$

must be conserved. We take the side conditions (A.III.10) and (A.III.13) into account, using two Lagrange factors α and β in the conventional way, by differentiating, not $\ln W$, but

$$\ln W + \alpha \left(N - N_{D^\times} - \sum_{i=1}^{\infty} N_i \right) + \beta \left(U - N_{D^\times} E_D - \sum_{i=1}^{\infty} N_i E_i \right)$$

$$= \text{const} + N_{D^\times} \ln 2 - \ln N_{D^\times}! - \ln (N_D - N_{D^\times})!$$

$$- \sum_{i=1}^{\infty} \{\ln N_i! + \ln (Z_i - N_i)!\} + \alpha N + \beta U - \alpha N_{D^\times}$$

$$- \beta N_{D^\times} E_D - \sum_{i=1}^{\infty} \{\alpha N_i + \beta N_i E_i\} \qquad \text{(A.III.14)}$$

for the variables N_1, N_2, . . . , N_i, . . . , $N_{D^\times}$, α, and β and by equating the derivations with zero. In this procedure we use the Stirling formula

$$\ln A! \approx A \ln A - A \qquad \text{(A.III.15)}$$

which leads to the differentiation rule

$$\frac{d}{dA} \ln A! \approx 1 \times \ln A + A \frac{1}{A} - 1 = \ln A \qquad \text{(A.III.16)}$$

By differentiation for each of the variables N_1, N_2, . . . , N_i, . . . we obtain a system of equations

$$- \ln N_i + \ln (Z_i - N_i) - (\alpha + \beta E_i) = 0 \qquad i = 1, 2, \ldots$$

$$\text{(A.III.17)}$$

Differentiating (A.III.14) for $N_{D^\times}$ we obtain

$$+ \ln 2 - \ln N_{D^\times} + \ln (N_D - N_{D^\times}) - (\alpha + \beta E_D) = 0 \quad \text{(A.III.18)}$$

and differentiating for α and β we finally obtain again the side conditions

$$\sum_{i=1}^{\infty} N_i + N_{D^\times} = N \qquad \text{(A.III.10)}$$

$$\sum_{i=1}^{\infty} N_i E_i + N_{D^\times} E_D = U \qquad \text{(A.III.13)}$$

From (A.III.17) we obtain at once the occupation probability

$$\frac{N_i}{Z_i} = \frac{1}{e^{\alpha + \beta E_i} + 1} \qquad \text{(A.III.19)}$$

of the states in the conduction band and from (A.III.18), correspondingly, the occupation probability $N_{D^\times}/N_D$ of the donor levels

$$\frac{N_{D^\times}}{N_D} = \frac{1}{\frac{1}{2} e^{\alpha + \beta E_D} + 1} \qquad \text{(A.III.20)}$$

With these two equations the problem under discussion is already solved, because the occupation probability (A.III.19) of the states 1, 2, . . . in the conduction band must be identical with the Fermi occupation probability (A.III.01). From comparison of the two equations we obtain

$$\beta = \frac{1}{kT} \qquad \text{(A.III.21)}$$

and

$$\alpha = - \frac{E_F}{kT} \qquad \text{(A.III.22)}$$

Hence, using (A.III.20) for the occupation probability of the donor levels E_D, we obtain

$$f_{\text{don}}(E_D) = \frac{N_{D^\times}}{N_D} = \frac{1}{\frac{1}{2}\,e^{\frac{1}{kT}(E_D - E_F)} + 1} \qquad \text{(A.III.23)}$$

instead of the original incorrect equation (A.III.04).

Finally, we want to consider briefly the case where, apart from the conduction band, N_A acceptor levels have to be filled, rather than N_D donor levels. By occupation with an electron a donor level changes from a D^+ to a $D^\times$, and hence the number of electrons accommodated in donor levels is $N_{D^\times}$. Acceptor levels, by occupation with an electron, are changed from $A^\times$ into A^-, and hence the number of electrons accommodated in acceptor levels is N_{A^-}. If we ignore the question of spin reversal, the number W of realization possibilities must, in the acceptor case, follow from Eq. (A.III.11) by replacing $N_{D^\times}$ with N_{A^-} and N_D with N_A. This results in the expression

$$\frac{N_A!}{N_A\text{-}!(N_A - N_A\text{-})!} \times \prod_{i=1}^{\infty} \frac{Z_i!}{N_i!(Z_i - N_i)!}$$

However, in determining the power of 2 in front of this expression, the preceding formal substitutions have to be supplemented by some new considerations. In the case of those donor levels in which an additional electron was accommodated, i.e., in the $D^\times$, the spin of an individual electron could be reversed (see Fig. A.III.2), whereas this did not apply to the empty donor levels D^+. The spin reversal in the $N_{D^\times}$ filled donor levels led in (A.III.11) to the factor $2^{N_{D^\times}}$. On the other hand, in the acceptor levels there is a single electron with reversible spin associated with the "empty" acceptors $A^\times$ and not with the filled levels A^- (see Fig. A.III.2). Hence we must now use the factor

$$2^{N_A^\times} = 2^{(N_A - N_A^-)}$$

and we obtain for the number W of the realization possibilities

$$W = 2^{N_A - N_A^-}\frac{N_A!}{N_A\text{-}!(N_A - N_A\text{-})!} \prod_{i=1}^{\infty} \frac{Z_i!}{N_i!(Z_i - N_i)!} \qquad \text{(A.III.24)}$$

If we apply the same considerations that were used in connection with (A.III.11) to (A.III.24) we obtain, generally speaking, equations derived from the earlier ones by replacing $D^\times$ with A^- and D with A. The only modification is that the changed power of the factor 2 produces the term $(N_A - N_A\text{-})\ln 2$ in the equation corresponding to

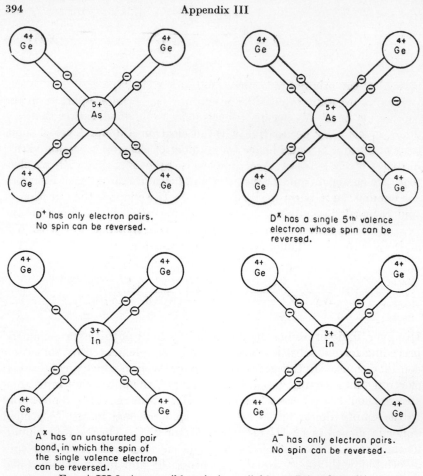

D⁺ has only electron pairs. No spin can be reversed.

Dˣ has a single 5ᵗʰ valence electron whose spin can be reversed.

Aˣ has an unsaturated pair bond, in which the spin of the single valence electron can be reversed.

A⁻ has only electron pairs. No spin can be reversed.

Fig. A.III.2. A reversible spin is available at $D^\times$ and at $A^\times$.

(A.III.12) and after differentiating for N_{A^-}, in the equation corresponding to (A.III.18), it leads to the term $-\ln 2$ instead of $+\ln 2$. Thus, in place of (A.III.23) we finally obtain

$$f_{\text{acc}}(E_A) = \frac{N_{A^-}}{N_A} = \frac{1}{2\,e^{\frac{1}{kT}(E_A - E_F)} + 1} \qquad \text{(A.III.25)}$$

Author Index

395

Subject Index